CONCISE ENCYCLOPEDIA OF
WILDLIFE

RED LEMON PRESS

First published in the UK by:
Weldon Owen
King's Road Publishing
2.07 The Plaza
535 King's Road
Chelsea, London, SW10 0SZ
Weldon Owen Pty Ltd

Much of the text in this book is taken from *The Illustrated Atlas of Wildlife*, originally published by Weldon Owen Pty Ltd in 2009. All the information in this edition has been completely revised and updated.

Authors and Consultants:
Dr. Channa Bambaradeniya
Cinthya Flores
Dr. Joshua Ginsberg
Dwight Holing
Dr. Susan Lumpkin
George McKay
Dr. John Musick
Dr. Patrick Quilty
Dr. Bernard Stonehouse
Dr. Eric J Woehler
Dr. David Woodruff

Project Editor Claudia Martin
Designer Natalie Schmidt
Managing Editor Hazel Eriksson
Publisher Donna Gregory

ISBN 978-1-7834-2337-8

A CIP catalogue for this book is available from the British Library.

Printed and bound in China.

10 9 8 7 6 5 4 3 2 1

Weldon Owen is a division of Bonnier Publishing.

www.bonnierpublishing.com

Zebras on the savanna (right)
The plains zebra is the most widespread species of zebra, ranging across eastern and southern Africa. Each zebra's stripe pattern is unique. Theories for the purpose of the stripes include: camouflage, discouragement of biting insects, and temperature regulation.

CONTENTS

Burchell's sandgrouse (left)

A Burchell's sandgrouse takes flight from a waterhole after drinking and soaking its belly feathers. This desert- dwelling bird flies long distances, returning with water held in its feathers for its chicks to "drink."

Humphead wrasse (far left)

The distinctive humphead wrasse is a common inhabitant of coral reefs but is also found in cooler waters. Easily recognized by the prominent bulge its head, it is among the largest reef fish.

Red-spotted purple butterfly (left)

The red-spotted purple butterfly is common in the eastern United States on aspen and poplar trees. It avoids predation by birds by mimicking the pipevine swallowtail, which is poisonous.

Ring-tailed lemur (left)

Ring-tailed lemurs, natives of Madagascar, spend much of their time on the ground, but early in the day they are likely to be found in the treetops, warming themselves in the sun.

Bobcat (far left)

The secretive, solitary bobcat, an inhabitant of eastern forests in the United States, is an efficient hunter. It remains out of sight by day but seeks its prey—cottontail rabbits and small rodents—at night

FOREWORD

What always surprises me is not the richness of the world's biological heritage, but just how little we know about it. In recent years we have sequenced the human genome, rapidly advanced our understanding of atomic structure, and continued to explore and advance our understanding of the Universe. In contrast, our best estimates suggest that there are 10 to 50 million species on Earth. Whatever the error in this number, we have only described 1.5 million species, at best 10 percent of the world's diversity. Our understanding of ecological communities is, at best, rudimentary.

Study of biodiversity is, increasingly, a time-limited endeavor. Humans are growing in number and in their individual demands for resources. Habitats such as the Amazon, Borneo, and the Congo forests, once thought to be vast, wild, and infinitely resilient, are either highly fragmented and degraded, or under increasing threat from conversion. Some ecosystems, such as the North American sagebrush and grasslands, are represented by a small percentage of their original extent. Europe, dominated by humans for thousands of years, still harbors a remarkable diversity of wildlife, but many species are confined to small islands of their former range, a pattern likely soon to be seen globally. Australia and Oceania have some of the most unusual and unique biological diversity on Earth, but the islands and reefs of the Pacific, initially threatened by habitat conversion, pollution, and a phalanx of introduced species, now face the new threats of climate change, warming oceans, and rising seas. It is not surprising that island species show the highest rate of extinction across all taxa.

However, conservation efforts, while always an uphill battle, show that we can reverse some of the threats to the world's biological heritage, and mitigate others. In the last two decades, the proportion of Earth's surface under formal protection has continued to expand, and efforts now focus on extending protection of coastal and high seas. And because protected areas, while necessary, are not sufficient, new conservation initiatives work with industry, local and indigenous communities, and private landowners to expand conservation beyond park boundaries, to ensure connectivity and freedom for animals to roam.

The *Concise Encyclopedia of Wildlife* helps us better understand both the diversity of life, and the threats that face wildlife and wildlands around the world. In a day and age where seemingly limitless information is on the web, why buy a book? For many of us, the physical act of holding a book, especially one this beautiful and well designed, will never be replaced by a web page and laptop. More importantly, this book is written by experts in their fields and the quality and accuracy of information is remarkable, drawing not just on information widely available, but on some of the most recent scientific research. Finally, this book allows you to learn about the ecoregional structure of the entire world, and of the wildlife that inhabits these diverse environments. Hold it in your hands, and enjoy your global tour.

Dr. Joshua Ginsberg
President of the Cary Institute of Ecosystem Studies
Director of the Ocean Foundation

HOW TO USE THIS BOOK

This book is arranged in two main sections. The first, "Living Earth," provides an overview of how and where natural life occurs on Earth, including pages devoted to different kinds of habitats, the relationship between animals and their environment, and the impact of one animal species on another. The second section is a chapter-by-chapter survey of the world's continents and oceans, and the animal life they support.

Feature box
Special-interest subjects are shown in a feature box, with their own introduction and selected photographs or illustrations.

Locator
These small maps locate the region within its continent.

Climate chart
Accompanying each map is a climate chart, showing average temperature and rainfall in the region.

Regional map
Regional maps are shaded to show the area within the continent that is being described for its animal life.

Conservation watch
At-risk animals are described under this heading. Symbols flag species that are either critically endangered or endangered.

Introduction
Each chapter opens with an overview of the featured continent and its natural life.

Regional overview
Each region covered in the chapter is identified with a map and a captioned wildlife photograph.

Lavish photos
These show the habits and habitats of key species.

Stunning illustrations
Individual species are beautifully illustrated. Habitat scenes show animals in context with each other and their surrounds.

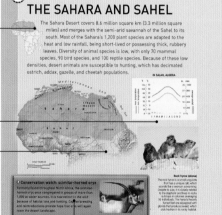

Living Earth

Introductory pages provide an overview of a range of wildlife subjects, including the origins and ecology of animals, the variety of Earth's habitats—from polar to desert and forest to sea—the threats facing many wildlife species, ecological balance, and conservation measures for endangered animals.

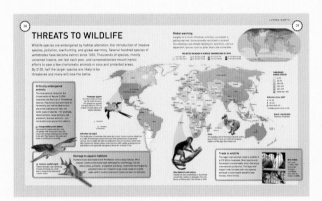

Special subject

Throughout the chapters, special-interest pages take a closer look at a particular animal, or group of animals. In the example below, the cockatoos and parrots of Australia are displayed to show their variety and color, as well as the differences between them in nesting and feeding.

Visual keys

Map legend

The maps in this book contain a variety of labels, symbols, and other graphic devices to provide detailed information such as altitude and ocean floor topography, and the location of mountains, rivers, cities, and country borders.

TOPOGRAPHY

ELEVATION
Feet | Meters

6562 | 2000
4921 | 1500
3281 | 1000
2461 | 750
1640 | 500
1312 | 400
984 | 300
656 | 200
328 | 100
0 | 0

Ice cap

Ice shelf

PHYSICAL FEATURES

⌒ Lake

〜 Major river

⌒ International border

⌒ State/territory border
(Australia, Canada, U.S.A.)

▲ Mountain peak/volcano
Height, feet (meters)

+ Pole

△ Geomagnetic pole

▲ Seamount

▼ Sea trench
Depth, feet (meters)

CAPITAL CITIES OR TOWNS

○ Capital city

○ Major city or town

Conservation icons

The conservation status of endangered and critically endangered animals, as determined by the IUCN Red List of Threatened Species, is indicated by a red or yellow icon.

⚡ Critically endangered   ⚡ Endangered

Charts, tables, and graphs

Additional details about regions, or the animal life found there, are provided in the form of tables, charts, or graphs. This at-a-glance information adds to captions and photographs.

PROPORTIONS OF TOTAL LAND AREA

Forest and woodland
Arable land
Grazing
Other land

31.7%   38.6%
17.2%   12.5%

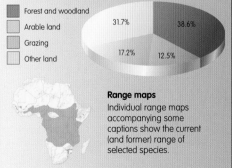

Range maps

Individual range maps accompanying some captions show the current (and former) range of selected species.

Wildebeest migration

Each year at the end of the rainy season, millions of zebra, gazelles, and wildebeest migrate to Kenya from the grassy plains of the Serengeti National Park, Tanzania. In one of Earth's most impressive migrations, masses of wildebeest cross the Mara River into the Masai-Mara Reserve, Kenya. Many drown in the crush to cross.

LIVING EARTH

Life as we know it occurs only on Earth, where it assumes an amazing diversity of forms. Of the millions of animal species, only humans appreciate the role of living organisms in creating a habitable planet. Without microorganisms and plants releasing oxygen into the atmosphere, our planet would be inhospitable. Wildlife depends on the plants, phytoplankton, bacteria, and decomposing fungi that make the biosphere work. Animal species are broadly distributed into eight biogeographic realms.

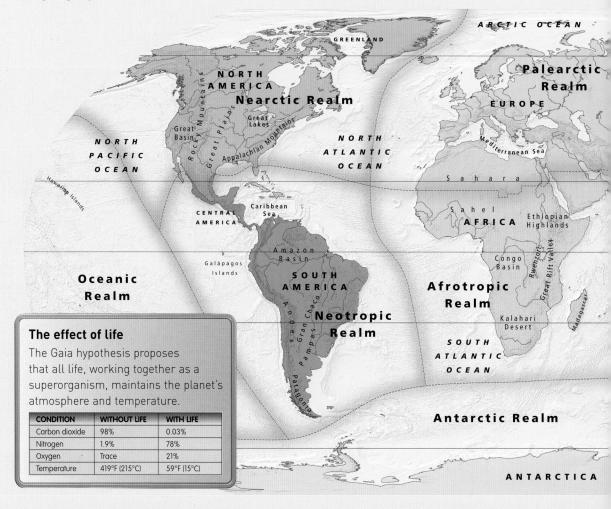

The effect of life

The Gaia hypothesis proposes that all life, working together as a superorganism, maintains the planet's atmosphere and temperature.

CONDITION	WITHOUT LIFE	WITH LIFE
Carbon dioxide	98%	0.03%
Nitrogen	1.9%	78%
Oxygen	Trace	21%
Temperature	419°F (215°C)	59°F (15°C)

Biogeographic realms

Recognizable clusters of species characterize the eight biogeographic realms and tell us much about the geological history of continents and islands, and the evolutionary history of different groups of animals. Life in the oceans is less clearly partitioned because of the homogenizing effects of global currents and the ancient connections of the ocean basins, but there are clear regional differences in the nutrient-based richness of coastal faunas.

SCALE 1:108,000,000
Robinson Projection

Nearctic realm
The species of the Nearctic and Palearctic are so alike that they form a super-realm, the Holarctic. Bald eagles typify North America but related eagles occur in the Palearctic.

Palearctic realm
The Palearctic includes Eurasia and northern Africa. Now hunted to near extinction, wild goats such as the alpine ibex once ranged from Spain to the Himalayas.

Neotropic realm
Encompassing Central and South America, the Neotropic realm includes more tropical rain forest than any other realm. The rich fauna includes the vivid blue poison-dart frog.

Afrotropic realm
The Afrotropic covers all of sub-Saharan Africa and is almost entirely tropical. Its distinctive wildlife includes lions, elephants, giraffes, and baboons and other primates.

Indomalay realm
Extending across most of South and Southeast Asia, the Indomalay contains forests that still harbor a few hundred tigers. Habitat loss and hunting have devastated tiger numbers.

Australasian realm
This realm comprises Australia, New Zealand, New Guinea, and part of Indonesia. On isolated Australia, marsupials such as kangaroos filled niches occupied by placental mammals elsewhere.

Oceanic realm
Islands colonized by species that could swim, float, or fly make up the Oceanic realm. In the absence of competitors, colonists evolved into unique species such as the Fiji banded iguana.

Antarctic realm
Comprising Antarctica and some southern islands, this realm presents great challenges to wildlife. The emperor penguin is one of the few species that survives on the ice cap.

KINGDOMS OF LIFE

Individual organisms are grouped into populations of interbreeding or genetically similar individuals called species. The total number of living species, including animals, plants, fungi, and bacteria, is estimated to be between 10 million and 30 million, with most of these being microscopic lifeforms. There are at least 30 animal groups and about 1.3 million living animal species known.

Species tally

There are estimated to be 10 million animal species. Only 1.3 million of these are known. Vertebrates amount to only 5 percent of all known animal species. There are at least twice as many species of fungi and six times as many species of plants.

Estimated number of animal species
10 million

Known animal species
1.3 million (13%)

Invertebrates 95%

Vertebrates 5%

Fish 48%

Amphibians 9%

Birds 19%

Mammals 9%

Reptiles 15%

Animal groups

The vast majority of animals are invertebrates and include marine sponges, flatworms, corals, segmented worms, mollusks, sea stars, and arthropods such as crustaceans, spiders, and insects. The vertebrates are a minority group that share 400 million years of evolutionary history. These conspicuous consumers of plants and microorganisms dominate most habitats.

Reptiles (above)

Like most of the other 8,000 reptile species, the spotted harlequin snake lays eggs with protective membranes. Turtles, crocodiles, and most lizards possess two pairs of limbs, but snakes have lost these ancestral features. Reptiles breathe air, are cold-blooded, and have impermeable scaly skin.

Birds (below)

The toco toucan and 10,000 other species of living birds share ancestry with the dinosaurs. Defined by their feathered forelimbs (wings), most are superbly adapted for flight.

Mammals (right)

The giraffe is one of about 4,800 living mammal species, all of which have milk glands to nurse their young. Mammals comprise a few egg-laying monotremes, 298 pouched marsupials, and diverse placentals, which nourish their developing young inside their body with a blood-rich organ called a placenta. Mammals usually have body hair and a single bone in the lower jaw.

Invertebrates (below)

Invertebrates have no backbone. Many, such as worms and leeches, are soft-bodied. Most, such as crustaceans, insects, and spiders, have an exoskeleton, or hard external skeleton. Beetles, such as this seven-spotted ladybug, comprise more than 370,000 of the 1 million known species of insects and are the most species-rich animal group.

Bony fish (above left)

Fish are aquatic vertebrates with gills and fins. They are divided between jawless fish (the hagfish and lampreys) and jawed fish, comprising cartilaginous fish and bony fish, named for their bony skeletons. The majority of bony fish are ray-finned, such as these yellowtail scad. The coelacanth and lungfish are lobe-finned fish, which share their ancestry and bony skeletons with ray-finned fish.

Cartilaginous fish (right)

The skeletons of sharks and rays are primarily cartilage. The 960 species include carnivores such as this long-tailed thresher shark, and enormous plankton feeders such as the whale shark.

Amphibians (right)

The 5,500 living amphibian species include frogs, legless burrowing caecilians, and salamanders such as this European fire salamander. Most depend on water for the embryonic and larval phases of life. Amphibians have smooth skin without scales.

The six kingdoms

All life on Earth can be classified into the six broad taxa known as kingdoms. These kingdoms are sometimes grouped into three higher domains: Bacteria (Eubacteria), Archaea (Archaebacteria), and Eukarya (Protista, Fungi, Plantae, and Animalia).

EUBACTERIA

Most known prokaryotes

10,000 species

These microorganisms were the only known prokaryotes, single-celled forms without a nucleus, until the discovery of archaebacteria in the 1970s. Eubacteria recycle nutrients in all Earth's habitats.

ARCHAEBACTERIA

Prokaryotes of extremes

18–23 phyla

Found in or around deep-sea vents, hot springs, and extremely salty water, these ancient lifeforms do not rely on oxygen. They are prokaryotes, but are very different genetically from other bacteria.

PROTISTA

Protists

250,000 species

Like fungi, plants, and animals, protists are eukaryotes, organisms with a cell nucleus. Protists are single-celled, or multicellular without specialized tissues. They include algae, cilia, and slime molds.

FUNGI

Fungi

100,000 species

Fungi include mushrooms, molds, and yeasts. They perform a vital ecological role in decomposing organic matter and recycling nutrients. Unlike plants, fungi cannot make their own food.

PLANTAE

Plants

350,000 species

The vast majority of plants create their own food through the process of photosynthesis and are the primary producers in ecosystems. They include flowering plants, mosses, and ferns.

ANIMALIA

Animals

1,350,000+ species

Animals make up the largest kingdom. It contains about 30 phyla of invertebrates. A single phylum, Chordata, includes all the vertebrates—mammals, birds, reptiles, amphibians, and fish.

HISTORY OF LIVING EARTH

Time, process, and chance are responsible for the incredible diversity of species alive today and all their amazing fossil ancestors. Animal evolution over the past 600 million years is a story of adaptation leading to solutions to life's challenges, played out in an ever-changing ecological theater. Occasional catastrophic change can eliminate even the most apparently successful species.

Continental drift

The slow movement of Earth's surface plates has reconfigured its continents and islands over time, a process known as continental drift. About 200 million years ago, the supercontinent Pangaea started splitting into the northern Laurasia and southern Gondwana landmasses. By 90 million years ago, these, in turn, had begun separating into today's continents. The continents continue to slowly change their positions.

200 million years ago

90 million years ago

Today

Future

KEY
mya Million years ago
● Mass extinction

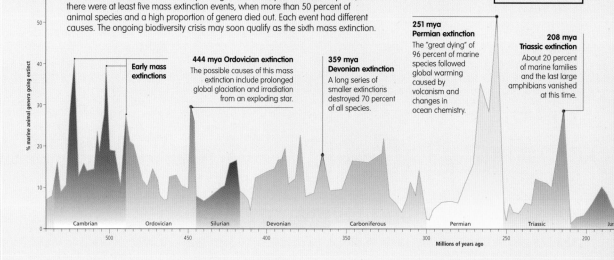

Rate of extinction

Extinctions are not distributed evenly through time. In the past 450 million years, there were at least five mass extinction events, when more than 50 percent of animal species and a high proportion of genera died out. Each event had different causes. The ongoing biodiversity crisis may soon qualify as the sixth mass extinction.

Early mass extinctions

444 mya Ordovician extinction
The possible causes of this mass extinction include prolonged global glaciation and irradiation from an exploding star.

359 mya Devonian extinction
A long series of smaller extinctions destroyed 70 percent of all species.

251 mya Permian extinction
The "great dying" of 96 percent of marine species followed global warming caused by volcanism and changes in ocean chemistry.

208 mya Triassic extinction
About 20 percent of marine families and the last large amphibians vanished at this time.

% marine animal genera going extinct

Cambrian Ordovician Silurian Devonian Carboniferous Permian Triassic Jurassic

Millions of years ago

Our planet's timescale

The vast expanse of time since Earth's formation is represented here by a 12-hour clockface. In this scheme, the first bacteria-like organisms appeared about 9½ hours ago. The first photosynthetic bacteria, which released oxygen into the oceans and atmosphere, appeared roughly seven hours ago. Animals and fungi are latecomers, turning up in the past 90 minutes. Our own species evolved merely a few seconds ago.

KEY
mya Million years ago
bya Billion years ago
● Mass extinction

EVENTS OF THE PAST 535 MILLION YEARS

A. 535–488 mya: Extraordinary diversity of shallow marine invertebrate fossils known as "the Cambrian explosion."
B. 488–444 mya: Trilobites and first fishlike vertebrates. Plants and fungi start slow colonization of land.
C. 444–416 mya: First jawed fish, first land plants, first small land animals.
D. 416–359 mya: Fish diversify, first insects and amphibians, first seed plants and trees.
E. 359–299 mya: First reptiles, first winged insects, first conifers.
F. 299–251 mya: Mammal-like reptiles.
G. 251–208 mya: First dinosaurs.
H. 208–144 mya: Dinosaurs diversify, first true mammals, first birds.
I. 144–65 mya: First flowering plants, first placental mammals and marsupials.
J. 65–59 mya: First large mammals, first primates.
K. 59–34 mya: Early horses, camels, rodents, elephants, monkeys, bats, whales.
L. 10 mya: Mammals, birds, and insects diversify rapidly.
M. 1.8 mya to present: Spread of *Homo erectus* and *Homo sapiens* around the world.

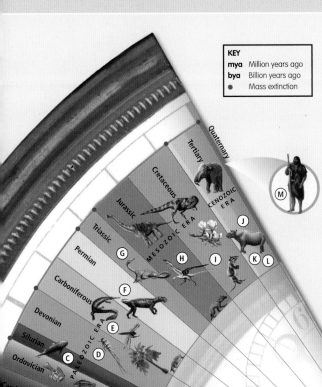

Quaternary
Tertiary
Cretaceous
Jurassic
Triassic
Permian
Carboniferous
Devonian
Silurian
Ordovician
Cambrian

CENOZOIC ERA
MESOZOIC ERA
PALEOZOIC ERA

65 mya
Cretaceous extinction
An asteroid impact and massive volcanism plunged the world into years of "impact winter," finished off the non-avian dinosaurs, and eliminated half of all marine species.

0 to future
Sixth mass extinction?
A dramatic increase in species extinctions began with the disappearance of Pleistocene megafauna and continues today. Cause: humans.

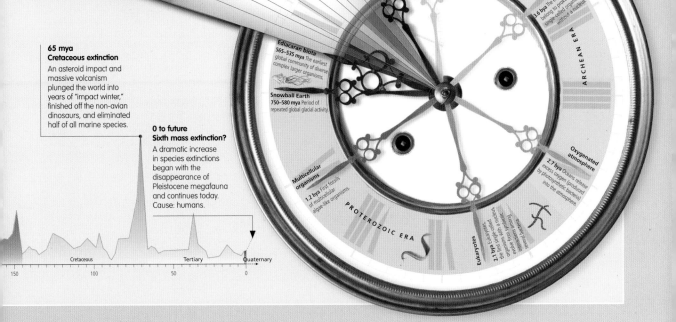

Cretaceous
Tertiary
Quaternary

150   100   50   0

Earth forms
4.6 bya Newly formed planet Earth.

Atmosphere forms
4.3 bya Comet impacts and volcanic eruptions release chemicals that form atmosphere.

Prokaryotes
3.6 bya The earliest fossils belong to prokaryotes, single-celled organisms without a nucleus.

ARCHEAN ERA

Oxygenated atmosphere
2.7 bya Oceans release excess oxygen (produced by photosynthetic bacteria) into the atmosphere.

Eukaryotes
2.1 bya Eukaryotes, the first single-celled organisms with nuclei, evolve from symbiotic associations among several bacteria.

Multicellular organisms
1.2 bya First fossils of multicellular algae-like organisms.

PROTEROZOIC ERA

Snowball Earth
750–580 mya Period of repeated global glacial activity.

Ediacaran biota
565–535 mya The earliest global community of diverse, complex larger organisms.

EVOLUTION

Evolution is life's little secret: a suite of processes that enable populations to change over time. Without the ability to evolve, no species could survive Earth's constant environmental changes. The fundamental process, natural selection, ensures that the individuals best adapted to their environment survive and pass on their genes to the next generation. Other processes, such as mutations and sexual reproduction, ensure the creation of the new genetic variation upon which evolution works.

American vulture (below left)
The turkey vulture is an American scavenger related to storks. Although unrelated to African vultures, it developed similar adaptations, a process called convergent evolution.

Parallel evolution
The brushtail possum of Australia (below left) and the common opossum of South America (below) are both marsupials. Once globally distributed, marsupials were replaced by placental mammals in most places. They survived only on the two southern landmasses of Australia and South America, where they became isolated by continental drift and evolved separately for more than 65 million years.

African vulture (above)
The lappet-faced and other African vultures share looks and behavior with American vultures, but they are unrelated. African vultures are related to eagles.

Charles Darwin

The wildlife of the isolated Galápagos Islands of the Pacific Ocean inspired Charles Darwin's theory of evolution following his visit in 1835. Each of today's 10 surviving subspecies of Galápagos giant tortoise evolved from a single species. Each has a different shell, or carapace, to suit the environment in which it lives. Over many generations, the rainfall and food availability of the island on which each group of tortoises made its home, led to adaptations in shell and body shape.

Saddle-backed shell ventral view   **Domed shell ventral view**

Saddle-backed shell   **Tabletop shell**   **Domed shell**

Giant tortoise shells

Tabletop shells are distinct from the dome shells of tortoises from wetter islands. The shell of the smaller saddle-backed tortoise allows it to extend its head high to feed. Tabletop shells afford more protection than saddle-backs, but domed shells provide the most protection.

Natural selection

A single African species of vanga colonized the island of Madagascar, where it evolved into 14 different species. Through the process of natural selection, the birds developed different bill shapes, for feeding on different insects, and various feather colors. Such adaptive radiations are often found on islands where colonizing species have few competitors. Hawaiian honeycreepers and Galápagos finches have evolved from insect-eating birds to also become seed eaters, nectar feeders, and even vampires.

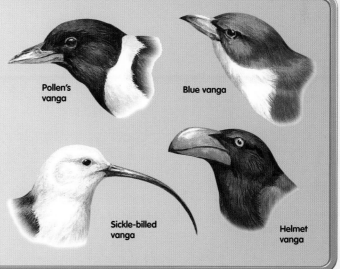

Pollen's vanga

Blue vanga

Sickle-billed vanga

Helmet vanga

EARTH'S HABITATS

Each species has a preferred habitat (its surroundings) and niche (what it does there), which determine its range. Biogeographers study where animals live and how climate, vegetation, and competition affect their distribution.

Water and land habitats

Three-quarters of our "blue" planet is covered with water and ice. The relative sizes of its land habitats are constantly shifting, as more forest is cleared and more desert is created. One species, our own, now uses the equivalent of 40 percent of all the energy fixed by plants.

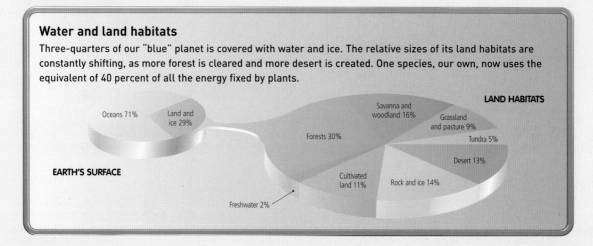

LAND HABITATS

Oceans 71% Land and ice 29%

Savanna and woodland 16%

Grassland and pasture 9%

Forests 30%

Tundra 5%

EARTH'S SURFACE

Desert 13%

Cultivated land 11%

Rock and ice 14%

Freshwater 2%

Today's climate zones

Animals are sensitive to both local day-to-day weather and regional year-round climate. Climates vary by latitude, altitude, and distance from the sea, and are characterized by temperature, rainfall, and seasonality. Human activities, such as the burning of fossil fuels and the clearing of forests, are changing weather and climate on a global scale.

KEY

Wet tropical
Seasonal tropical
Arid
Semiarid
Mediterranean
Subtropical
Continental
Temperate
Cold temperate
Subpolar
Polar
Highland

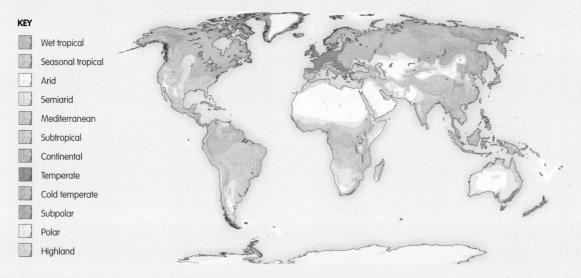

Vegetation zones

This map shows the distribution of major biomes—plant communities and their associated animals—before humans began dramatically changing the planet's surface. Widespread ecological communities can also be recognized in marine and freshwater habitats. Human actions have altered about half of these natural communities, threatening the vital ecological services that they provide.

KEY

- Tropical forest
- Seasonal tropical forest
- Desert
- Tropical grassland and savanna
- Mediterranean forest and scrub
- Midlatitude grassland
- Midlatitude forest
- Boreal forest
- Tundra
- Ice sheet
- Mountain vegetation

Competition between species
The tropical grasslands of east Africa are home to the lion. Lions may stalk and kill their prey but must compete with other species, such as hyenas, for the food. Competition for space and resources is a hallmark of community ecology.

Organization of nature

Within a habitat, plants, animals, and microscopic life, are all dependent on each other. Ecologists recognize five levels of complexity ranging from the individual animal to the entire biosphere. It is clear that no animal can survive without lots of others; it is less clear how many species can be lost and how many communities can be destroyed before the biosphere fails to provide the ecological services we take for granted.

Organism
This level involves the individual, such as the lar gibbon of Asia's rain forests, and its interactions with other members of its own species, other species, and the environment.

Population
A population comprises the members of a species living in one place. Lar gibbons live in family groups. Adult pairs defend a territory and sing to advertise their presence.

Community
All the populations of interdependent species living in one place and their ecological interactions make up a community. The lar gibbon is in the rain-forest canopy community.

Biome
A biome is an association of similar communities distributed over large areas. The major biomes, such as tropical rain forest, are usually named after the dominant vegetation type.

Biosphere
The biosphere is the entire living portion of the planet, from sunlit rain forests to ocean depths, and in the ground wherever there is enough heat and water to permit metabolism.

WHERE ANIMALS LIVE

Biodiversity varies dramatically across the continents and islands. Species numbers tend to be highest in tropical rain forests and coral reefs, and lowest in hot deserts and polar regions. Some places, such as Madagascar, have a high number of endemics—species found nowhere else—and are of special interest to conservationists. Many species are now shifting their ranges because of global warming.

Biodiversity around the world (right)

This map shows the number of vascular plant and vertebrate species—species richness—in each country, as well as which countries have high numbers of endemic vertebrates. Two-thirds of all animal species live in tropical forests, so conservationists are especially active in such biodiversity hotspots.

Vanished mammoth (left)

Ice age woolly mammoths ranged across the northern continents. By 10,000 years ago, they had all but disappeared as a result of climate and vegetation changes and overhunting.

BIODIVERSITY LEVELS

- Highest
- Medium high
- Medium
- Medium low
- Lowest

Feral rabbits (left)

In 1859, European rabbits were introduced into Australia. Their populations exploded in the absence of native predators and competitors. They spread rapidly across the continent, destroying vegetation, soils, and grazing lands.

Endemic lemur (right)

Isolated on the island of Madagascar, lemurs radiated into 40 or so endemic species, including the ring-tailed lemur (right), and ranging from mouse-size lemurs to recently extinct species larger than gorillas. These unique primates are found nowhere else.

Invasive species

Although most animals are found in only one area, a few, such as rats and house sparrows, have worldwide distributions. Humans move such invasive species accidentally or intentionally, and they often become major pests in areas where they have no natural enemies. Controlling introduced species that become pests is an expensive challenge.

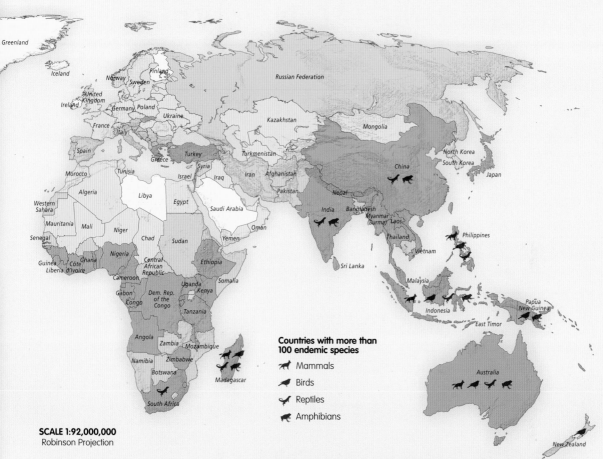

**Countries with more than
100 endemic species**

🐕 Mammals

🐦 Birds

🦎 Reptiles

🐸 Amphibians

SCALE 1:92,000,000
Robinson Projection

Migration

Animals may adapt to seasonal
changes in food supply by migrating.
Some move back and forth seasonally:
caribou migrate annually to escape
winter on the tundra, hummingbirds
follow the flowers, and whales follow
the pulse of life in the oceans. Other
species make a single journey over the
course of many years: salmon migrate
from a mountain stream to the ocean
and back again, a trip European eels
do in reverse.

Wildebeest on the move
Blue wildebeest herds numbering a million animals follow the rains and fresh grass
around East Africa, an annual trek of 1,800 miles (2,900 km).

BALANCING ACT

At first glance, nature seems perfectly organized, with plants to feed the herbivorous animals, predators to hunt the herbivores, and fungi to clean up after them, but this image of nature is too simple. Competition and cooperation are actually more important than the "tooth and claw" of a few fierce animals. Many species are totally dependent on others; most trees, for example, must live symbiotically with microscopic fungi in order to grow and defend themselves. Ecology is the study of all these interactions: the study of our home.

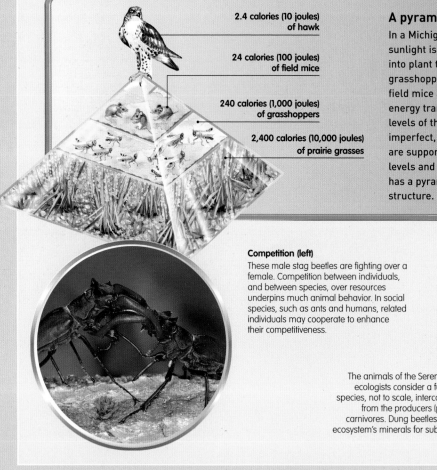

2.4 calories (10 joules) of hawk

24 calories (100 joules) of field mice

240 calories (1,000 joules) of grasshoppers

2,400 calories (10,000 joules) of prairie grasses

A pyramid of energy

In a Michigan field, sunlight is transformed into plant tissue that feeds grasshoppers and, in turn, field mice and hawks. As energy transfer between levels of the food chain is imperfect, fewer animals are supported at higher levels and the community has a pyramid-shaped structure.

Harvester ant

Acacia tree

Impala

Competition (left)

These male stag beetles are fighting over a female. Competition between individuals, and between species, over resources underpins much animal behavior. In social species, such as ants and humans, related individuals may cooperate to enhance their competitiveness.

FOOD WEB ROLES

- Producers
- Decomposers and scavengers
- Herbivores
- Carnivores
- Top carnivores

Savanna food web (above right)

The animals of the Serengeti savanna interact over food in ways that ecologists consider a functional ecosystem. Shown here are typical species, not to scale, interconnected in a food web, with energy flowing from the producers (plants) to the herbivores, carnivores, and top carnivores. Dung beetles, fungi, and soil bacteria recycle much of the ecosystem's minerals for subsequent generations of plants and animals.

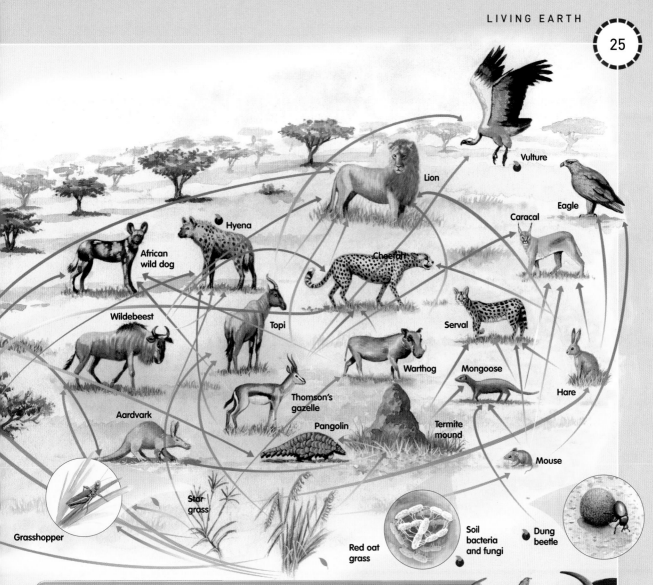

Vulture

Lion

Eagle

Caracal

Hyena

Cheetah

African wild dog

Serval

Wildebeest

Topi

Warthog

Mongoose

Hare

Thomson's gazelle

Aardvark

Pangolin

Termite mound

Mouse

Star grass

Red oat grass

Soil bacteria and fungi

Dung beetle

Grasshopper

Animal interaction

Predation, herbivory, and parasitism are important interactions in which one species is nourished at the expense of another. Although predators usually kill their prey, herbivores and parasites typically do not destroy their source of food. In mutualistic relationships both parties benefit. When the partnership is absolutely essential, the intimate relationship is called symbiotic—literally, "living together." Flowers, for example, depend on bees for pollination and provide bees with nectar.

Parasitism
The white cocoons in this photo belong to parasitic wasp larvae that have eaten the insides of a living sphinx moth caterpillar.

Mutualism
An African buffalo tolerates blood-seeking red-billed oxpeckers because the birds also eat ticks and fly larvae lodged in its skin.

FOREST HABITATS

At least one trillion trees cover 30 percent of the land, and two-thirds of animals are forest-dwellers. From the lush vegetation of the tropics to the snow-covered conifers of the north, forests grow in a wide range of climates. Their three-dimensional structure provides different microhabitats that feed and shelter an extraordinary diversity of wildlife. Through exchanges of energy, water, and carbon dioxide, forests influence climates on a regional and global scale. Much of the world's original forest has been cleared for cropland or pasture.

Forest wildlife

A million species of forest animals show exquisite adaptations to the trees in which they feed, shelter, and reproduce. Just moving around without falling out of the trees can be challenging. Although all forest wildlife is directly or indirectly dependent on trees, few species actually eat the woody trunks and branches; those that appear to, such as termites, rely on bacteria and fungi to break down the wood's indigestible cellulose.

Northern flicker (left)
This North American woodpecker spends more time on the forest floor catching ants than it does drumming on tree trunks for insect larvae.

Northern flying squirrel (right)
This nocturnal rodent can glide from tree to tree using a pair of furry membranes that extend between its front and rear legs.

Carpet python (below)
Arboreal snakes such as the Australian carpet python wait for days to feed on birds and mammals. At night they can detect prey by body temperature.

Red-eyed tree frog (right)
Climbing easily with sucker-padded toes, this amphibian spends most of its life in the trees of the always-humid tropical rain forest.

North American boreal forest

Pacific Northwest temperate rain forest

NORTH AMERICA

California coniferous forest

Eastern deciduous forest

Central American rain forests

Monteverde cloud forest

Amazon rain forest

Brazilian shield seasonal tropical forest

SOUTH AMERICA

Southern temperate rain forest

Boreal forest

The boreal forest, or taiga, is Earth's largest biome. It is dominated by evergreen conifer (needle-leaf) trees such as firs, spruce, and pines. The moose is a year-round resident.

Temperate deciduous forest

A blaze of colors precedes leaf-fall as the forest prepares for winter dormancy. Spring begins with a wildflower show on the forest floor until new leaves provide shade again.

Temperate rain forest

High rainfall, coastal fog, and mild winters characterize these cool wet forests. In North America's Pacific Northwest, tall conifers are festooned with mosses, lichens, and ferns.

Seasonal tropical forest

In seasonal tropical areas, such as Indonesia's Komodo Island, the forest trees lose their leaves during the hot dry season. Komodo dragons stalk prey on the open forest floor.

Tropical rain forest

Ever-wet rain forests are home to more species of animals than any other biome. Scarlet macaws live high in the forest canopy, which is closed 100 feet (30 m) above the ground.

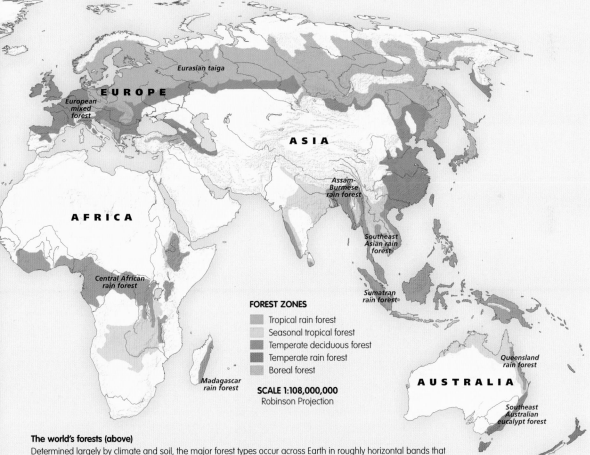

Eurasian taiga

EUROPE

European mixed forest

ASIA

Assam-Burmese rain forest

AFRICA

Southeast Asian rain forest

Central African rain forest

Sumatran rain forest

FOREST ZONES

- Tropical rain forest
- Seasonal tropical forest
- Temperate deciduous forest
- Temperate rain forest
- Boreal forest

Madagascar rain forest

SCALE 1:108,000,000
Robinson Projection

Queensland rain forest

AUSTRALIA

Southeast Australian eucalypt forest

The world's forests (above)

Determined largely by climate and soil, the major forest types occur across Earth in roughly horizontal bands that merge into one another. Year-round warmth and high rainfall near the equator result in lush evergreen rain forests. Farther north and south, trees cope with seasonal temperature and rainfall variation by dropping leaves or becoming dormant. The most northern forest is boreal, where hardy conifers endure bitter winters.

GRASSLAND HABITATS

Earth's grasslands still cover about 10 percent of the land. Most of a grassland community's biomass lies below the ground in a rich, nutrient-storing root-mat, or sod. This enables grasses to quickly recover from frequent drought and fire. Seasonality dominates the ecology. Animals usually feed and reproduce during the rainy season, and switch to survival mode (or migrate) during the hot dry season or cold season. Taking advantage of the fertile soil, humans have converted half the grassland biome for crops, grazing, and urban development.

Fire on the steppe

Wildfire is an essential component of grassland ecology, helping to break down dead matter, recycle nutrients, and prevent shrubs from taking over. In many grassland regions, farmers also deliberately light fires to clear land for agriculture or to regenerate pasture for grazing animals. In the false-color satellite image below, of Central Asia's Kazakhstan steppe, vegetation appears green, burned areas are deep reddish brown, and the red dots represent burning fires.

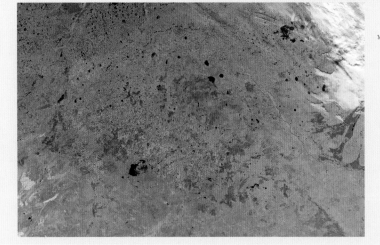

Grassland wildlife

With no trees to hide in, many predators and prey have adopted the burrowing habit and the ability to run fast. The huge standing crop of vegetation is regrown annually and supports large populations of vertebrate and invertebrate herbivores. The large herbivores associated with grasslands include North American bison, South American guanacos, African gazelles, Asian wild horses, and Australian kangaroos. Grasshoppers and their alter-egos, plague locusts, are notorious residents.

Foot patrol (left)
Grassland residents include the tall flightless running birds—ostrich, emu, and rhea—as well as the long-legged African secretary bird, a reptile-eating eagle that patrols the savanna on foot.

Predator and prey (right)
Motionless and hidden in the grass, a lioness can get within pouncing distance of the very wary and fleet-footed Thomson's gazelle.

Outback grazer (right)
Adapted to Australia's driest grasslands, the red kangaroo times its activities to the daily temperature regime, and its reproduction to the sporadic rainfall.

Burrower (above)
Many grassland mammals and birds, such as America's burrowing owl, live underground, where they can hide from predators and escape the heat of summer and the cold of winter.

EUROPE

Central Asian steppe

ASIA

AFRICA

Sahel

Serengeti

GRASSLAND ZONES
- Tropical grassland (savanna)
- Temperate grassland

SCALE 1:108,000,000
Robinson Projection

Great Western Plateau

AUSTRALIA

African veldt

Grazing herds (above)
The grasses themselves depend on grazing, and without large numbers of herbivores, the vegetation changes to scrub or thorny woodland. Large grazing herds once characterized most grasslands but they survive only in parts of Africa, where zebras, wildebeest, and gazelles feed sequentially to reduce competition.

The world's grasslands (above)
Known as savannas, or llanos in South America, the grasslands bordering the tropics often include scattered trees. They are warm year-round but have a pronounced dry season. The temperate grasslands are treeless plains with hot dry summers and cold winters. They are called prairies in North America, pampas in South America, veldt in South Africa, and steppe in Eurasia.

DRY HABITATS

Animals face special challenges when they inhabit areas of little rain and extreme temperatures. In cold deserts, water may be frozen and unavailable. In hot deserts, daytime temperatures regularly exceed 100°F (38°C). Under such conditions, there is little vegetation and limited animal life. During the day, most animals shelter beneath the sand or in whatever shade is available. Desert animals often have coats and scales that resist desiccation, and many use evaporative heat-loss mechanisms such as panting and sweating. A few animals become dormant and estivate for months or years. Rain brings about a transformation as desert plants bloom briefly and animals reproduce.

Western scrub jay (right)
In summer in its chaparral or semidesert habitat, this bird gets all its water from its food, seeks shade at midday, and sheds heat from its unfeathered feet.

Greater roadrunner (right)
Roadrunners sun themselves in the morning to warm up without burning food calories. Later they stand in the shade, spread their wings, and pant to stay cool.

Chuckwallah (right)
The chuckwallah spends its mornings basking and its afternoons foraging. If it is cool, hot, or threatened, the lizard retreats to a rock crevice. If a predator approaches, it puffs up its body so it cannot be dislodged.

Fog-basking beetle (right)
This Namibian beetle emerges from the sand at night and climbs a dune to bask head-down in the passing fog, gathering water that then trickles to its mouth.

NORTH AMERICA

Great Basin

Mojave Desert

Californian chaparral

Sonoran Desert

Chihuahuan Desert

SOUTH AMERICA

Peruvian Desert

Atacama Desert

Chilean mattoral

Patagonian Desert

Deserts and semideserts (left and below left)

Semidesert regions receive less than 10 inches (250 mm) of rain annually. In the Namaqualand semidesert region of South Africa (pictured left, with oryx) wildflowers bloom in the normally barren landscape following the winter rains. True deserts receive less than 2 inches (50 mm) of rain annually and support few plants, and years or decades may pass between rains. The Namib Desert's sidewinding adder (pictured below left) hides during the day with only its eyes and nostrils above the sand.

Bactrian camel (below)

Gobi desert camels have broad feet, long eyelashes, and closeable nostrils to deal with sand. Two fatty humps provide metabolic water.

Indian wild asses (below)

These wild asses can survive in the barren desert of northwest India as long as they live within a couple of miles of a waterhole.

EUROPE

ASIA

AFRICA

Mediterranean maquis

Sahara Desert

Arabian Desert

Karakum Desert

Iranian Desert

Lut Desert

Thar Desert

Taklimakan Desert

Gobi Desert

The world's dry zones (left)

Drylands circle the globe in two bands 20 to 30 degrees north and south of the equator. Deserts cover about 13 percent of Earth's land, but up to one-third of the land can be called arid or semiarid. Desert and semidesert biomes merge into grasslands, thornwoods, and coastal scrub (Mediterranean-type vegetation such as maquis, chaparral, fynbos, and mallee).

DRY ZONES

- Desert
- Semidesert
- Coastal scrub
- ✹ Hot desert
- ☼ Cold desert

SCALE 1:108,000,000
Robinson Projection

Namib Desert

Kalahari Desert

South African fynbos

AUSTRALIA

Great Sandy Desert

Simpson Desert

Great Victoria Desert

Southern Australian mallee

Burchell's sandgrouse (left)

This desert bird has the habit of "belly wetting" when it drinks at a pool just after sunrise; it then carries the water to its chicks.

Central bearded dragon (right)

This lizard's display scares away predators. The color of its scales can slightly lighten or darken to optimize its temperature regulation.

FROZEN HABITATS

The last ice age ended 18,000 years ago, and many cold-adapted species from that time survive around the polar ice caps and on polar and alpine tundra. Animals require special adaptations to survive in frozen habitats year-round. Many species are migratory and walk, swim, or fly toward the equator to escape the winter. Some that stay, such as polar bears, shelter in snow caves and live off their body fat; others, such as lemmings, burrow beneath the snow, where they nibble on remaining vegetation.

The world's ice and tundra habitats (right)

The three major ice caps cover all the Antarctic continent and Greenland. The treeless polar tundra is underlain by frozen soil known as permafrost, and characterized by a short cool summer and a long dark winter. In the southern hemisphere, tundra occurs on subantarctic islands. Alpine tundra is found in mountainous areas. Alpine tundra differs from polar tundra in that it lacks permafrost and does not experience great seasonal changes in day length.

Latitude and altitude (below)

A traveler moving from equator to pole encounters the same sequence of biomes that a climber finds ascending a mountain: rain forest, deciduous forest, coniferous forest, tundra. Very roughly, a 500-mile (800-km) change in latitude is equivalent to nearly 3,300 feet (1,000 m) in elevation.

Ice and/or snow

Tundra

Coniferous forest

Deciduous forest

Rain forest

INCREASING
ALTITUDE
11,500 feet
(3,500 m)

INCREASING
LATITUDE
North pole

Sea level   Equator

Ellesmere
Island

Greenland
ice cap

Brooks Range

Victoria
Island

Baffin
Island

Alaskan
tundra

Canadian
tundra

Mt McKinley
20,321ft (6194m)

Rocky Mountains

NORTH
AMERICA

SOUTH
AMERICA

Andes

Mt Aconcagua
22,835ft (6960m)

Antarctic
Peninsula

West Antarctic
ice sheet

Vinson Massif
16,050ft (4892m)

Wildlife in ice and snow

Ice caps and glaciers are inhospitable places. In contrast, the polar tundra teems with wildlife for at least a few months each year when plants and algae produce enough food for birds and mammals. In contrast, alpine tundra does not experience great seasonal variations. "Cold-blooded" reptiles and amphibians are absent from these habitats.

Mountain goat (left)
This agile Rocky Mountain goat has a thick fur undercoat beneath its long white outercoat to provide extra insulation.

Arctic gyrfalcon (right)
Although 100 bird species breed on the Arctic tundra in the summer, most leave before the winter. Gyrfalcons remain, hunting ptarmigan and small mammals.

Willow ptarmigan (above)
The willow ptarmigan, or willow grouse, remains cleverly camouflaged on the tundra year-round: in summer it is mottled (left), but in winter it turns pure white to match the snow.

Antarctic fur seals (below)
Of the six Antarctic seal species, fur seals are the least adapted to extreme cold and ice. They breed on subantarctic islands, and the females delay development of their pups so they are born in spring.

EUROPE

Mont Blanc
15,771ft (4807m)

ASIA

Kola
Peninsula
tundra

Siberian tundra

Chuckchi
Peninsula
tundra

Elbrus
18,510ft (5642m)

Mt Ararat
16,854ft (5137m)

Himalaya

Mt Everest
29,029ft (8848m)

Atlas
Mountains

AFRICA

Kilimanjaro
19,331ft (5892m)

Gunung Kinabalu
13,435ft (4095m)

Puncak Jaya
16,024ft (4884m)

AUSTRALIA

Mt Kosciuszko
7310ft (2228m)

Mt Cook
12,316ft (3754m)

FROZEN ZONES

Artic tundra

Alpine tundra

Polar ice

SCALE 1:96,000,000
Robinson Projection

East Antarctic
ice sheet

Transantarctic
Mountains

ANTARCTICA

AQUATIC HABITATS

Aquatic habitats span a greater range of physical conditions than are found on land, so life in water is even more diverse. Coral reefs rival rain forests in terms of complexity, and salt marshes are among the most productive ecosystems on the planet. Tiny planktonic algae in sunlit ocean water, and not land plants, are responsible for producing most of the oxygen that land animals depend on.

Aquatic animals

Aquatic animals all need to obtain oxygen and food, and to avoid predators in order to reproduce. Bottom dwellers (benthos) take advantage of the "rain" of food from above, but they may live in total darkness. Open-water animals must swim (nekton) or float (plankton), or they will sink to their deaths. Life around the water's edge (littoral or intertidal zone) is richest, but the risks of predation are higher. Animals in aquatic habitats may be either permanent residents or visitors with adaptations to both land and water. Many more types of animals are found in salt water than in fresh, as oceans are the ancestral habitat of all lifeforms and are easier to live in metabolically.

Blue-ringed octopus (right)
This small tide-pool octopus is usually well-camouflaged, but quickly flashes its bright colors when disturbed, a warning that its venomous bite is deadly.

Sockeye salmon (above)
Sockeye hatchlings migrate from their mountain-stream birthplace to the ocean, where they feed for years before returning to the same stream to reproduce and die.

Mudpuppy (left)
This bottom-feeding carnivore spends its life in ponds and lakes. Although it develops legs, it never loses its gills like other adult salamanders do.

Sail-tailed water lizard (right)
When threatened by a predator, this Central American lizard can make a quick escape. Fringed toes give its feet enough area to run across the surface of streams.

Beaufort Sea
Baffin Bay
Great Bear Lake
Great Slave Lake
Mackenzie
peace
Hudson Bay
Labrador Sea
Gulf of Alaska
Missouri
Great Lakes
St Lawrence
NORTH AMERICA
Mississippi
Great Dismal Swamp
North Atlantic Ocean
North Pacific Ocean
Rio Grande
Gulf of Mexico
Everglades
Hawaii
Caribbean Sea
Llanos
Polynesia
Amazon
SOUTH AMERICA
Pantanal
Paraguay
South Pacific Ocean
River Plate

Ponds and lakes

Living between worlds, painted turtles must warm up in the sun before feeding in cool water. But when the water freezes in winter, turtles hibernate in the pond's muddy bottom.

Wetlands

Wetlands and the rivers that feed them are highly productive habitats that support many invertebrates, fish, and birds. Roseate spoonbills hunt crustaceans and fish in shallow water.

Oceans

Oceanic fish tend to specialize as bottom-, surface-, or mid-water feeders. The head of the great hammerhead shark has sensory organs that guide it to buried stingrays.

Mangroves

Mangroves receive nutrients from both land and sea and support great numbers of algae, plants, invertebrates, and fish, as well as birds such as this black-crowned night heron.

Coral reefs

Corals grow in warm, clear, nutrient-poor seas, but a symbiosis between the coral animals and algae fuels their great productivity. A reef's structure provides niches for many animals.

Deep-sea vents

About 8,000 feet (2,400 m) below the sea's surface, hydrothermal vent communities feature giant tube worms (shown) and depend on bacteria that use sulfide-rich water for energy.

The world's waters (left)

The great rivers, lakes, and wetlands are treasure troves of freshwater life that harbor thousands of fish species, amphibians, and aquatic turtles, snakes, birds, and mammals. Salt marshes and mangroves anchor the coastlines, serve as fish nurseries, and sustain millions of birds. Ocean habitats themselves are partitioned according to water temperature, light, depth, and nutrients (concentrated in upwelling zones). Coral reefs are the fragile crown jewels of the aquatic world.

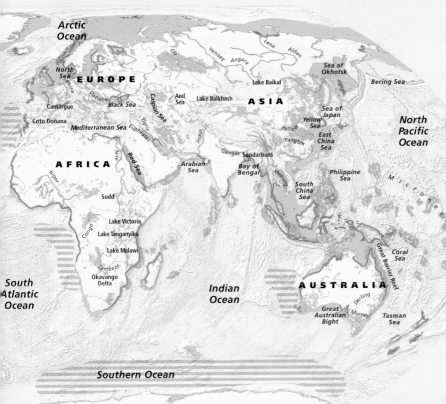

Arctic Ocean

North Sea

EUROPE

Camargue

Coto Doñana

Mediterranean Sea

AFRICA

Niger

Nile

Red Sea

Sudd

Congo

Lake Victoria

Lake Tanganyika

Lake Malawi

Zambezi

Okavango Delta

South Atlantic Ocean

Black Sea

Danube

Caspian Sea

Aral Sea

Lake Balkhash

Tigris

Euphrates

Indus

Ganges

Arabian Sea

Bay of Bengal

Sundarbans

Mekong

Ob'

Yenisey

Angara

Lena

Aldan

Lake Baikal

ASIA

Yellow

Yangtze

Yellow Sea

East China Sea

Sea of Japan

Sea of Okhotsk

Bering Sea

North Pacific Ocean

South China Sea

Philippine Sea

Micronesia

Coral Sea

Great Barrier Reef

AUSTRALIA

Indian Ocean

Great Australian Bight

Darling

Murray

Tasman Sea

Southern Ocean

ANTARCTICA

SCALE 1:104,000,000
Robinson Projection

AQUATIC HABITATS

- Major river
- Lake
- Wetland
- Salt marsh
- Mangrove
- Coral reef
- Deep-sea coral
- Continental shelf
- Upwelling zone
- Open ocean

HUMAN HABITATS

Humans have co-opted nearly half of Earth's surface. Our complicated relationship with wild animals plays out in these human-dominated rural and urban environments. On the one hand, our agricultural practices have disturbed ecosystems and replaced natural vegetation with monocultures, opening the door for invasive species and allowing some animals to become pests. On the other hand, a growing number of people are feeding birds and mammals in gardens and parks. The movement of people from rural areas to cities reduces pressure on remaining wildlife habitats. If urbanization continues and we manage rural areas in more sustainable ways, wildlife will have a future.

Eastern gray squirrel (left)
This tree squirrel has learned to live with humans and their dogs in urban parks in its native America and in Europe.

European starling (left)
Insectivorous European starlings have become pests in North America and Australia, where their flocks damage orchards and displace native birds.

Migratory locusts (right)
Warm, wet weather may cause grasshoppers to transform en masse into plague locusts. The resulting swarm of billions of insects severely damages crops.

Peregrine falcon (left)
This peregrine falcon occupies a wide range of habitats, including many urban areas. In cities its main prey is rock or feral pigeons, as well as other common city birds, such as common starlings and blackbirds.

Urban environments

City life appeals to some animals. Urban areas are warmer in winter and have dependable food supplies. They offer microhabitats such as predator-safe ledges on buildings, waste dumps full of food, and lights that attract insects at night. Unfortunately, urban habitats are not without problems: cars and domestic cats kill hundreds of millions of wild birds and small mammals annually.

California sea lions
Sea lions are tourist attractions in San Francisco, but the large animals occasionally attack people. They may simply see humans as competitors, but are also sometimes deranged from eating contaminated fish.

Raccoon raid
Northern raccoons are opportunistic omnivores. They have moved from their native North American woodlands into suburban backyards and even city streets, where human and pet food is set out for them every night.

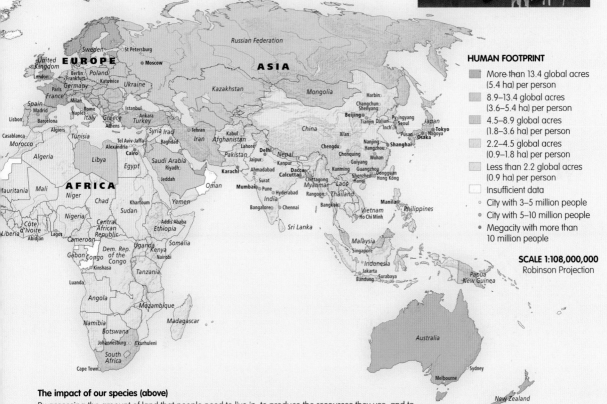

HUMAN FOOTPRINT

- More than 13.4 global acres (5.4 ha) per person
- 8.9–13.4 global acres (3.6–5.4 ha) per person
- 4.5–8.9 global acres (1.8–3.6 ha) per person
- 2.2–4.5 global acres (0.9–1.8 ha) per person
- Less than 2.2 global acres (0.9 ha) per person
- Insufficient data
- City with 3–5 million people
- City with 5–10 million people
- Megacity with more than 10 million people

SCALE 1:108,000,000
Robinson Projection

The impact of our species (above)
By assessing the amount of land that people need to live in, to produce the resources they use, and to absorb their waste, scientists can calculate a human "footprint." In 1987 the global footprint exceeded 1.0 for the first time, which means that our consumption exceeded what our planet could renew. Today, some rich countries have footprints exceeding 4.0 planet-equivalents.

THREATS TO WILDLIFE

Wildlife species are endangered by habitat alteration, the introduction of invasive species, pollution, overhunting, and global warming. Several hundred species of vertebrates have become extinct since 1650. Thousands of species, mostly unnamed insects, are lost each year, and conservationists mount heroic efforts to save a few charismatic animals in zoos and protected areas. By 2100, half the larger species are likely to be threatened and many will lose the battle.

Critically endangered animals

The International Union for the Conservation of Nature (IUCN) maintains the Red List of Threatened Species. Population size and rates of harvesting and habitat destruction are prime indicators of risk, but some types of species—for example, island animals, large animals, top predators, fearless animals—are more extinction-prone than others.

⚡ Orange-bellied parrot (below)

Devastated by habitat alteration and competition with introduced birds, only around 40 orange-bellied parrots remain in the wild. They breed in Tasmania and winter in southeastern Australia.

⚡ Common sawfish (right)

Habitat alteration and overfishing threaten this large ray, which lives in tropical and subtropical coastal waters.

Passenger pigeon

Once the most common bird in North America, this gregarious species became extinct in 1914 as a result of overhunting and habitat alteration.

Extinction risk (right)

The distribution of extinction risk varies by country. Some countries stand out in a tally of threatened species because their governments keep better records, but in reality the risks are highest in tropical countries, which have high biodiversity. Island nations and countries with rapidly growing human populations are especially dangerous places for animals to live.

Damage to aquatic habitats

Humans have destroyed much freshwater and coastal habitat. Most oceanic communities have been damaged by overfishing, habitat destruction, pollution, and global warming. Chemicals discharged by polluted rivers are linked to large dead zones in coastal seas, and to noxious plankton blooms known as red tides.

Canada

236 extinctions
United States of America

Mexico
Cuba
Haiti
Guatemala — Nicaragua
Venezuela — Guyana
Colombia
Peru
Brazil
Bolivia
Paraguay
Chile
Uruguay

Cook Islands

79 extinctions
French Polynesia

Global warming

Largely as a result of human activities, our planet is getting warmer. Some animals restricted to isolated mountaintops are already heading for extinction, and ice-dependent species such as polar bears are vulnerable.

PROJECTED INCREASE IN SURFACE TEMPERATURES BY 2099

- 0–1.8°F (0–1°C)
- 1.8–3.6°F (1–2°C)
- 3.6–5.4°F (2–3°C)
- 5.4–7.2°F (3–4°C)
- 7.2–9°F (4–5°C)
- 9–10.8°F (5–6°C)
- 10.8–12.6°F (6–7°C)
- 12.6–14.4°F (7–8°C)

THREATENED ANIMAL SPECIES

- 0–49
- 50–99
- 100–199
- 200–299
- 300–399
- More than 400

Extinctions since 1600*

- 10–29
- 30–50
- More than 50

* including species extinct in wild

SCALE 1:98,000,000
Robinson Projection

Dodo
This flightless bird of Mauritius became extinct around 1662. It was no match for European sailors and the pigs they introduced.

Miss Waldron's red colobus
Habitat loss and overhunting for bushmeat caused this monkey to disappear from the forests of Ghana and Côte d'Ivoire in 2000.

Trade in wildlife

The legal international trade in wildlife is a US$15 billion business. Most species are harvested unsustainably; only a few enjoy international protection. The legal and illegal trade includes pets and species believed to have health benefits (sea horses, rhino horns).

Bird market
Each year, 5 million wild birds enter the legal and illegal international trade in wildlife.

HABITAT LOSS

Habitat loss is probably the greatest threat to the world's wildlife today. Clearing of habitats for agriculture is the major culprit in habitat destruction, but the myriad other causes of habitat alteration and fragmentation are logging, mining, urban sprawl, water pollution, and noise pollution.

Disappearing forests

The largest cause of species extinction is the loss of 27,000 square miles (70,000 km²) of forest to logging and agriculture each year. Frontier forests are undisturbed areas that are large enough to maintain their biodiversity. Efforts to set aside remaining forests are often frustrated.

⊘ Orangutan
Orangutans are declining rapidly because of deforestation caused by logging and palm oil cultivation. The Sumatran orangutan is critically endangered, with only 6,600 individuals left.

DEFORESTATION
- Original forest extent
- Current forest cover
- Remaining frontier forest

The lost prairies

The great interior plains of the United States were once a sea of grass extending thousands of miles, home to 60 million bison. Between 1830 and 2000, the prairies shrank by two-thirds due to farming and settlement, and the bison were hunted down to about 100 animals. Non-native plants invaded and now account for up to 90 percent of vegetation.

❸ Black footed ferret
Black-footed ferrets were once widespread on the American prairies. Habitat destruction, combined with the decline of prairie dogs (their prey) and disease rendered them almost extinct. The species was saved only by a zoo breeding program.

Warmer poles

The polar regions are warming at three times the rate of the tropics. Life around Antarctica depends on winter sea ice, which is shrinking every year. The algae that shelter beneath the ice provide for the growth of populations of shrimplike krill, which sustain penguins, seals, and whales. The projected loss of Arctic permafrost and ice cover will put new stresses on animals such as caribou and walrus.

ARCTIC WARMING

- Current permafrost area
- Projected permafrost area 2100
- Current sea ice
- Projected sea ice 2070–90

Loss of Arctic permafrost (above)
This map shows the projected impact of global warming on Arctic permafrost and ice cover.

Arctic fox (left)
As the tundra shrinks, the range of the Arctic fox is also shrinking, as bigger and stronger red foxes move northward along with their woodland habitat.

Desertification

Significant areas of grassland are at risk of desertification as a result of global warming and local land-use practices. Desertification occurs at the edges of many drylands.

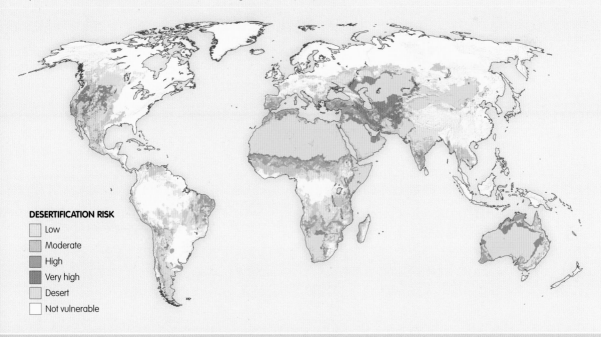

DESERTIFICATION RISK

- Low
- Moderate
- High
- Very high
- Desert
- Not vulnerable

CONSERVATION

The most effective response to the biodiversity crisis is to create the largest possible protected areas. About 10 percent of ice-free lands are now reserved for wildlife. National parks alone are not enough, however, as animals do not recognize reserve boundaries and they are affected by what humans do around each reserve. The attitudes of local people to wildlife are vitally important, so projects that benefit them, such as the development of sustainable tourism, are an essential part of conservation.

Iberian lynx
Habitat conversion, declining wild rabbit populations, and fatal traffic accidents threaten the last hundred of these cats in Spain, even in Doñana National Park.

Resplendent quetzal (above)
Restricted to montane cloud forests and declining in numbers, males still make "joy flights" in Costa Rican national parks.

NORTH AMERICA

California Floristic Province 25%

Madrean Pine-Oak Woodlands 20%

Caribbean Islands 10%

Mesoamerica 20%

Tumbes-Chocó-Magdalena 24%

SOUTH AMERICA

Tropical Andes 25%

Cerrado 22%

Atlantic Forest 8%

Chilean Winter Rainfall-Valdivian Forests 30%

Spectacled bear (right)
The only neotropical bear survives in generally unprotected Andean forests. It is killed for its valuable gall bladder and because it raids crops.

Pygmy hippopotamus (right)
Perhaps 2,000 of these hippos survive in Liberia and nearby countries, but their riverine forest habitat is fast disappearing.

Biodiversity hotspots (right)
More than half the planet's species occur in only 2.3 percent of its land area. Conservation International's 34 global hotspots, indicated on the map, contain an extremely large proportion of the world's biodiversity. Protecting these areas would help conserve many species found nowhere else, including 50 percent of endemic vascular plants and 42 percent of endemic vertebrates. When more widely distributed species are also considered, these small areas contain 77 percent of all terrestrial vertebrate species.

Biodiversity hotspots

% Percentage of original vegetation remaining

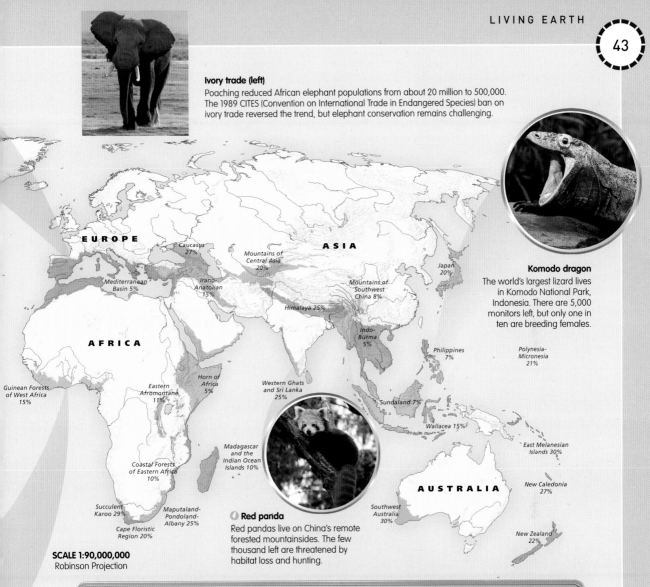

Ivory trade (left)
Poaching reduced African elephant populations from about 20 million to 500,000. The 1989 CITES (Convention on International Trade in Endangered Species) ban on ivory trade reversed the trend, but elephant conservation remains challenging.

EUROPE

ASIA

AFRICA

Caucasus 27%

Mountains of Central Asia 20%

Mediterranean Basin 5%

Irano-Anatolian 15%

Mountains of Southwest China 8%

Japan 20%

Himalaya 25%

Indo-Burma 5%

Guinean Forests of West Africa 15%

Eastern Afromontane 11%

Horn of Africa 5%

Western Ghats and Sri Lanka 25%

Philippines 7%

Polynesia-Micronesia 21%

Sundaland 7%

Madagascar and the Indian Ocean Islands 10%

Wallacea 15%

East Melanesian Islands 30%

AUSTRALIA

New Caledonia 27%

Coastal Forests of Eastern Africa 10%

Succulent Karoo 29%

Maputaland-Pondoland-Albany 25%

Southwest Australia 30%

New Zealand 22%

Cape Floristic Region 20%

SCALE 1:90,000,000
Robinson Projection

Komodo dragon
The world's largest lizard lives in Komodo National Park, Indonesia. There are 5,000 monitors left, but only one in ten are breeding females.

⚡ **Red panda**
Red pandas live on China's remote forested mountainsides. The few thousand left are threatened by habitat loss and hunting.

New roles for zoos

Zoos are reinventing themselves as conservation organizations. They are expensive to run and their traditional focus on entertainment has to be balanced against changing attitudes to animals in captivity. Better zoos now play pivotal roles in public education, with 600 million visitors each year worldwide, and the humane exhibition of species selected for their sustainability and conservation value. Recent successes with Arabian oryx and Californian condors show that zoos can serve as "arks" by providing animals for reintroduction into the wild.

⚡ **Return to the wild**
The Arabian oryx was hunted to extinction in the wild, but captive breeding in North American zoos allowed its reintroduction to the Arabian Peninsula.

CHAPTER TWO

EUROPE

Red deer

Mature red deer stay in single-sex groups for most of the year. During the fall mating season, called the rut, dominant stags collect a harem of females, which they rigorously defend against other males. Red deer are browsers, feeding on grasses, leaves, shoots, and buds. They range across Western Europe.

EUROPE

With an area of 3.9 million square miles (10.2 million km²), Europe makes up less than 7 percent of Earth's land, yet its topography can vary greatly in relatively small areas. Mixed forest once covered much of Europe, but more than half has been lost because of the long-time presence of humans. This has led to widespread disruption of native wildlife—some species have become extinct; others are confined to habitat pockets. The large predatory mammals such as bear, wolf, and lynx have experienced the greatest impact from the spread of urban areas. Herbivores are well represented, along with a diversity of bird species, from large raptors to migratory waterfowl.

Deciduous woodlands
Five vegetation zones layer the broad swath of deciduous woodlands that sweep across Europe, providing many types of habitat for wildlife, such as badgers, to choose from.

River valleys
Dozens of major rivers drain the continent and support the entire spectrum of animal life, from tiny invertebrates to fish, birds, and mammals, such as this river otter.

Coniferous forests of northern Europe
Only wildlife species that are well adapted to the conditions can survive on the limited vegetation, and withstand the severe climate, of the far north coniferous forests.

Mountain ranges
Born from continental collision, Europe boasts some of the steepest and most rugged mountain ranges on the planet, where living relics from the Ice Age still dwell.

Along the shore
The seashore varies dramatically along Europe's relatively long coastline, ranging from rocky tidepools to sandy dunes, and animals take advantage of the selection.

The Mediterranean
A monkey, devil ray, viper, and bone-eating vulture are some of the more unusual animal species found in and around the Mediterranean Sea.

Marshes and wetlands
Every country in Europe boasts a wetland or marsh, and no habitat is more productive in terms of supporting every link in the wildlife food chain.

Climate (left)

Polar winds are largely responsible for the cold winters experienced by northern Europe. More temperate conditions in western Europe are largely because of the Gulf Stream, which carries warm water to Europe's coastline and heats the prevailing westerly winds. More dramatic weather extremes—from bitingly cold winters to scorching summers—are common across the eastern interior. Southern Europe enjoys warm, dry summers and mild, wet winters.

CLIMATE ZONES

	Semiarid		Continental
	Mediterranean		Cold temperate
	Subtropical		Subpolar
	Temperate		Highland

Vegetation (right)

Broadleaf deciduous forests of oak, ash, elm, beech, and birch once covered most of western and central Europe. Large areas of Scandinavia, northwestern Russia, and alpine regions continue to support boreal forests of fir, spruce, and pine. On the tundra of the far north, mosses, small shrubs, and summer wildflowers grow on the permanently frozen soils. Dry areas of eastern Europe are swathed in grasslands.

VEGETATION ZONES

	Midlatitude forest		Tundra
	Boreal forest		Mediterranean forest and scrub
	Mountain vegetation		Ice sheet
	Midlatitude grassland		

Land cover (right)

Urban and industrial areas, roads, and railways cover much of Europe. The surviving forests and woodlands are found mostly in European Russia and Scandinavia, and the highest proportions of arable land and pasture are in Western Europe.

PROPORTIONS OF TOTAL LAND AREA

	Forest and woodland
	Arable land
	Grazing
	Other land

33.6%
21.8%
28.2%
16.4%

DECIDUOUS WOODLANDS

The term "deciduous" describes trees such as the oak, elm, birch, lime, and alder, which lose their leaves in autumn. Much of the broad swath of woodlands that once covered the continent was cleared long ago for agriculture and pastures, towns, and cities.

What remains are pockets of woodland protected within preserves and parks. The five vegetation strata of the woodlands—trees, small trees and saplings, shrubs, herbs, and the ground zone—provide habitats for a variety of wildlife. When flowers are in bloom, numerous delicate butterflies appear.

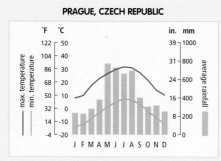

PRAGUE, CZECH REPUBLIC

max. temperature
min. temperature

average rainfall

°F °C
122 — 50
104 — 40
86 — 30
68 — 20
50 — 10
32 — 0
14 — -10
-4 — -20

in. mm
39 — 1000
31 — 800
24 — 600
16 — 400
8 — 200
0 — 0

J F M A M J J A S O N D

REYKJAVÍK

Barents Sea

Norwegian Sea

HELSINKI

OSLO STOCKHOLM TALLINN

North Sea

RĪGA MOSCOW

DUBLIN

COPENHAGEN

VILNIUS

LONDON AMSTERDAM BERLIN

BRUSSELS WARSAW

Bay of Biscay PARIS KIEV

PRAGUE

BERN VIENNA BUDAPEST

BELGRADE BUCHAREST

LISBON MADRID *Black Sea*

ROME

Mediterranean Sea

SCALE 1:32,000,000

0 ———— 500 miles
0 ———— 500 kilometers

Butterflies

Deciduous trees and flowering plants in open glades and meadows provide a plentiful food source for caterpillars and butterflies. Many of Europe's 576 butterfly species are found here.

Map butterfly
Araschnia levana

White letter hairstreak
Satyrium album

Lesser purple emperor
Apatura ilia

Silver-washed fritillary
Argynnis paphia

Red squirrel
Sciurus vulgaris

The deciduous forest

A single tree can support myriad species of wildlife. Red squirrel and black woodpecker nest in cavities in mature trees that also provide an abundant source of seeds and insects. The little owl perches on the high limbs while looking for prey. The soft soil beneath a tree makes digging easier for the badger and European mole.

Little owl
Athene noctua

Fallow deer

Fallow deer are notable for their flattened antlers and long tails. They live in two separate herds, one comprising females and fawns, the other bucks living alone or in bachelor groups.

Black woodpecker
Dryocopus martius

Badger
Meles meles

European mole
Talpa europaea

Clouded yellow butterfly
Colias croceus

Red fox

The red fox has keen senses of sight, smell, and hearing, earning it a reputation for intelligence. A skilled hunter, it is capable of feeding on a wide variety of prey.

Conservation watch: red squirrel

The long tail of the red squirrel helps it balance when jumping from tree to tree. Although the red squirrel is common in many parts of Europe, the introduction of the North American gray squirrel has driven the red species from much of its range in Britain. Conservation efforts are underway.

DECIDUOUS WOODLANDS
THE EUROPEAN BADGER

The badger is an Old World member of the weasel family that also includes the otter and pine marten, and dates back 2.4 million years. There are nine species of badger globally, but only *Meles meles* occurs in the wild in Europe. The badger prefers to live in woodlands and grassy fields. While it resides in burrow systems, often in locations that experience cold winters and snow, it does not hibernate. Animals enter into a state of torpor that can last several weeks, living off fat reserves accumulated during the rest of the year.

Taking to water (above)
While the badger can swim, it prefers walking around ponds and lakes or crossing over streams and canals using fallen trees as bridges. When forced to swim it paddles with its front paws much like a dog.

Badger's diet

A forager rather than hunter, the nocturnal badger spends half its time looking for food, relying on its keen sense of smell and hearing. Though it has carnivorous incisors, its molars are flattened for grinding, making it a true omnivore. Its diet ranges from acorns, fruits, seeds, and mushrooms to earthworms, insects, reptiles, birds, and small mammals. It even eats carrion.

Baby hedgehogs (right)
A hedgehog's spiny fur and its ability to roll into a tight ball are no defense against a hungry badger, which relies on its powerful front claws to pry open its prickly prey.

Worms (right)
Earthworms make up much of the badger's diet, especially in grassy fields on damp nights, when a badger can suck up to 200 wigglers in one sitting.

Sett (right)

The communal burrow, or sett, has numerous entrances, passages, and chambers. It is typically constructed on sloping ground in woodland or on the periphery of a field. Spoil piles of dirt mark its entrances. Setts are often used for decades and continually grow in size and complexity.

Survival

Much of the badger's survival success is because of its highly opportunistic and omnivorous feeding habits, which often bring it into conflict with farmers. Full-grown badgers don't have any natural predators, but cubs are easy prey to bears, wolves, and birds of prey.

Cubs playing (left)

Highly communal badgers live in clans, generally containing up to 12 individuals. Cubs are weaned by six months and will forage with sows, often initiating play with other cubs and adults. Non-breeding sows sometimes serve as babysitters. Badgers use scent and vocalization to recognize clan members.

RIVER VALLEYS

The European continent, Ireland, and Britain are etched with major rivers that form fertile valleys, creating a wide spectrum of ecosystems, from brackish lagoons at the mouth to freshwater springs at the source. River valleys also serve as wildlife corridors, providing anadromous fish such as Atlantic salmon access to freshwater spawning grounds, and migrating waterfowl a road map as well as a resting spot in fall and spring. Farming, industrialization, and the construction of dams have all taken their toll on Europe's river valleys.

WARSAW, POLAND

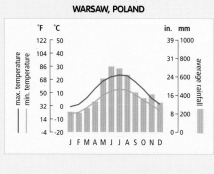

SCALE 1:30,000,000

Fighting wild boar (left)
The wild boar is a highly aggressive omnivore. Adult males sport large tusks that are sharpened by grinding and used as weapons. Females guard their numerous young. The stiff bristles of the boar's fur are used to make hairbrushes.

European kingfisher (above)

The common, or European, kingfisher hunts for fish from an overhanging perch or while hovering above water. Small fish are swallowed immediately, head-first, while bigger fish are carried to a tree limb and beaten against it. A pair may have to catch 100 fish a day to feed their hungry nestlings.

Black stork (left)

A wading bird, the black stork feeds in the shallow waters of rivers, marshes, and ponds of the warmer parts of Europe. This broad-winged bird flies with its long neck outstretched and migrates to Africa for the winter.

Common rabbit
Oryctolagus cuniculus

Muskrat
Ondatra zibethica

Black stork
Ciconia nigra

Souslik
Citillus citillus

European sea sturgeon
Acipenser sturio

Layers of life (above)

A cross-section of a river valley reveals layers of life, each reliant on the other. Water supports nutrients and vegetation in the river and along its banks. This first link in the food chain leads to insects, invertebrates, fish, birds, and mammals. No two river valleys are the same, so speciation occurs. Climate, topography, and humans help determine which species are found where.

European beaver

Once hunted to near extinction for its fur and scent glands, which are thought to have medicinal properties, this largest of European rodents is semi-aquatic. It dams streams with sticks and mud and creates lodges where it can find protection from predators. The dams also help to create ponds for easier access to food. Today the European beaver is found in parts of Eastern and Central Europe and Scandinavia.

European hedgehog
Erinaceus europaeus

Eurasian otter (above)

The Eurasian otter is well-adapted to aquatic life, with its slim body, webbed toes, and rudder-like tail. The otter can close its ears and nostrils while underwater and uses its sensitive whiskers to detect the movement of its prey.

RIVER VALLEYS
THE DELTA OF COTO DOÑANA

The Guadalquivir is the second longest river in Spain, beginning in the Cazorla Mountains and emptying into the Gulf of Cádiz. Its delta is a complex system of marshes, dunes, and coastal lagoons, much of it protected as Doñana National Park. The array of habitats translates into a rich concentration of wildlife. Some 750 plant species live here, along with 20 species of fish, 10 amphibians, 19 reptiles, and 30 mammals, including the rare Iberian lynx, small-spotted genet, and wildcat. More than half Europe's birds occur here, including flocks of up to 70,000 greylag geese and 200,000 teal.

Horseshoe bat (below)
Mediterranean horseshoe bats live in colonies called clouds, roosting in caves and tunnels where the average temperature is 50°F (10°C). They use echolocation to find their prey.

Lataste's viper (left)
Lataste's viper is one of five venomous snakes found in Spain. Stout with a triangular head, it is recognizable by the wavy or zigzag stripe that runs along its back.

Spiny-footed lizard (right)
The spiny-footed lizard owes its name to the comblike spines along its back legs, which allow it to run on sand. This species is found widely in the Mediterranean.

European weasel (right)
It may be small, but the European weasel is known as a ferocious species. Medieval legend recognizes the weasel for killing the mythical basilisk.

Glossy ibis
The glossy ibis breeds in the warmer regions of Europe, where it nests colonially in trees. A strong flier and gregarious feeder, this widespread species migrates to Africa for the winter.

Common spoonbill
The common, or black-billed, spoonbill occurs in the intertidal flats and shallows of fresh and saltwater wetlands. It sweeps its bill from side to side in its quest to trap tiny fish.

Bird beaks

Birds have evolved to occupy certain niches, even in the same ecosystem, such as a delta. The most important function of a bird's bill is feeding, and it is shaped according to what the bird eats. For waterbirds, long, pointed bills suit probing and spearing; flat bills are adapted for straining and scooping.

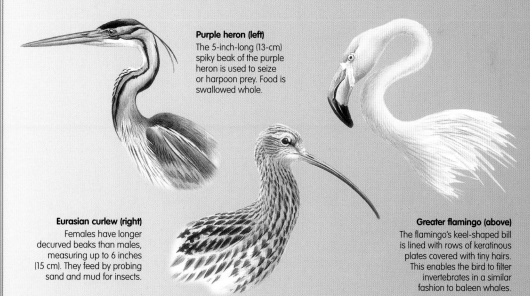

Purple heron (left)
The 5-inch-long (13-cm) spiky beak of the purple heron is used to seize or harpoon prey. Food is swallowed whole.

Eurasian curlew (right)
Females have longer decurved beaks than males, measuring up to 6 inches (15 cm). They feed by probing sand and mud for insects.

Greater flamingo (above)
The flamingo's keel-shaped bill is lined with rows of keratinous plates covered with tiny hairs. This enables the bird to filter invertebrates in a similar fashion to baleen whales.

MOUNTAIN RANGES

Like folds in skin, the European continent is creased with mountain ranges created by the collision of the tectonic plates that form Earth's crust. Collectively, the Alps, Scandes, Pyrenees, Carpathians, Rhodopes, Urals, Caucasia, and Dinaric landforms constitute what is known as the alpine biogeographic region. While the mountainous areas share common features, their varying gradients, climate, and soil types have influenced the distribution and diversity of species. The result is an amazing array of wildlife that includes 129 mammal species, 359 birds, 40 amphibians, and 65 reptiles.

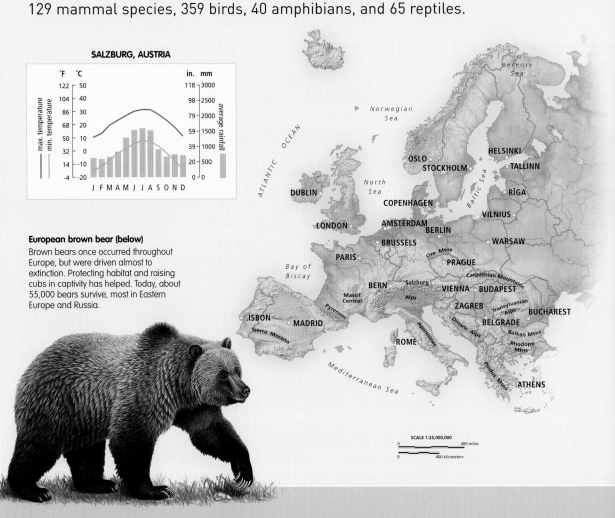

SALZBURG, AUSTRIA

European brown bear (below)
Brown bears once occurred throughout Europe, but were driven almost to extinction. Protecting habitat and raising cubs in captivity has helped. Today, about 55,000 bears survive, most in Eastern Europe and Russia.

SCALE 1:25,000,000

Apollo butterfly (left)

The beautiful Apollo butterfly, with distinctive "eye" marks on its wings, can be found in flowery alpine meadows as high as 6,400 feet (1,950 m). Life in a rugged mountain habitat has led to the development of many subspecies, some restricted to a single alpine valley. Medium-sized and tail-less, the Apollo has three pairs of walking legs.

Wildcat (left)

Once found throughout Europe, the wildcat dates back to the Early Pleistocene. Hunting and habitat loss have reduced its range and numbers. It is generally solitary and is one-third larger, and has a thicker coat, than its direct descendant, the domestic cat.

Dormouse (right)

The dormouse's feet are adapted for grasping trees: the soles have cushioned pads and the toes have curved claws. Its hind feet can be turned backward, which allows it to dangle from a branch.

Relics of the glaciers

Plant and animal species that survived the Ice Age are known as glacial relics. A mountainous region of Poland, now protected as Karkonoski National Park, has a high proportion of glacial relics, including the arctic whorl snail, Sudetic wolf spider, and the bird known as the ring ouzel.

Rivers of ice

Glaciers are rivers of ice, always moving and churning up rocky debris. When they melt or retreat, they leave this debris behind in moraines.

Dotterel (left)

A small wader, a member of the plover family, the migrating dotterel winters in the semiarid deserts of North Africa and the Middle East and breeds in the Alps and northern Europe, nesting in a bare ground scrape. The males are responsible for incubation.

Tengmalm's owl (right)

A small, ancient bird, Tengmalm's owl is found in boreal forests. It builds its nest in a tree cavity drilled by woodpeckers, and successive generations occupy the same site. The male sings to attract a mate.

MOUNTAIN RANGES

THE MOUNTAINEERS

Animals that live in the mountains have developed physical characteristics that help them cope with cold, rugged topography, and reduced oxygen. With the exception of some insects, most animals living at altitude are warm-blooded. These animals adapt to the cold by hibernating in winter, like the marmot; migrating to lower areas; or huddling in burrows. Mountain animals tend to have shorter appendages to reduce heat loss, like the alpine hare, which has smaller ears than its lowland relatives. Animals such as the ibex have larger lungs and more blood cells because of the increased pressure and lack of oxygen.

Marmot den (below)
As sociable animals, marmots (pictured above) live in large burrows with several generations of their family. They excavate the burrow using their forepaws and hind feet, and remove stones with their teeth. Entrances are sited between large rocks to avoid detection and flooding, and living areas are lined with dried grass. Burrows are enlarged to accommodate new generations; the newborn remain in the burrow for their first 40 days.

Tunnel to one of several exits

On guard

Concealed entrance

Nesting chamber

Fresh grass is brought into the den

Chamois and ibex

Split hooves that can spread enable chamois and ibex to climb near-vertical cliffs and smooth, slick rock faces. The hooves have a hard, thin rim surrounding a soft and sponge-like interior, and these cushioned pads can grip slippery surfaces. Well-developed leg muscles and a low center of gravity aid in climbing and jumping. A chamois can leap as high as 6.5 feet (2 m) and as long as 20 feet (6 m).

Ibex (left)
Horn size distinguishes male and female ibex. The defensive horns start growing at sexual maturity and never stop, reaching lengths up to 3 feet (1 m) in the male.

Chamois (above)
In summer, herds of chamois graze in alpine meadows above 6,000 feet (1,800 m). As winter approaches, they descend to shelter in forests near steep cliffs. Chamois were once hunted for their hides.

Alpine hare (below)
The hare's brown coat turns white before winter, providing camouflage from predators and greater warmth. Shorter daylight hours trigger hormones that inhibit the production of brown pigment in the new coat. The hollow white hairs improve insulation and allow more sunlight to be absorbed.

Eurasian lynx (above)
Mainly nocturnal and solitary, the Eurasian lynx is seldom seen or heard. A highly efficient hunter, it preys on rabbits, rodents, and deer. Its footpads are broad and well-furred compared to other felines, as an adaptation for walking in snow.

THE MEDITERRANEAN

The Mediterranean Sea's rocky reefs, seagrass meadows, and upwelling areas support enormous biological diversity. Marine mammals include the fin whale, harbor porpoise, and striped dolphin. Coastal areas are also important habitats for wildlife, with wading and shorebirds dependent upon shallow estuaries, and mammals ranging in size from tiny mice to 200-pound (90-kg) deer found in the oak, pine, and wild olive forests. Wildlife, however, is under extreme pressure from coastal development, overfishing, agricultural and industrial runoff, and wildfire.

⚡ Conservation watch: Mediterranean monk seal

The Mediterranean monk seal is one of the most endangered marine mammals, with fewer than 700 individuals. They were once hunted for their pelts and blubber, which was turned into oil, and commercial fishermen considered them pests. The establishment of protected marine zones now holds the key to their continued survival.

Wildfires

On average, 50,000 wildfires take place in the Mediterranean every year. Up to 95 percent are caused by people. Hot, dry summers and a buildup of fuel compound the problem. Natural wildfires keep forests healthy and ensure plant diversity, but too much burning can impoverish habitat and contribute to climate change.

Italian wall lizard
The Italian wall lizard is typical of the small reptiles at risk from wildfires.

Forest fire
Wildfires have devastating effects on animals, from those with limited mobility, such as snails, snakes, and tortoises, to small and large mammals. Though birds can escape the flames, they lose their food supply.

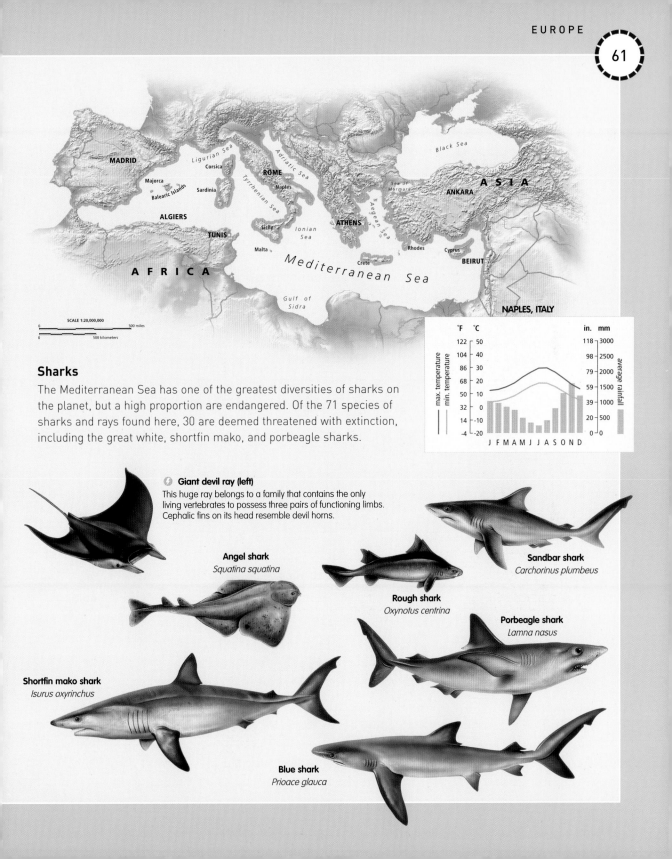

MADRID
Ligurian Sea
Corsica
Majorca
Balearic Islands
Sardinia
ROME
Naples
Tyrrhenian Sea
Adriatic Sea
Black Sea
ANKARA
Sea of Marmara
A S I A
Aegean Sea
ATHENS
ALGIERS
Sicily
Ionian Sea
TUNIS
Malta
Crete
Rhodes
Cyprus
BEIRUT
A F R I C A
Mediterranean Sea
Gulf of Sidra

SCALE 1:20,000,000
0   500 miles
0   500 kilometers

Sharks

The Mediterranean Sea has one of the greatest diversities of sharks on the planet, but a high proportion are endangered. Of the 71 species of sharks and rays found here, 30 are deemed threatened with extinction, including the great white, shortfin mako, and porbeagle sharks.

NAPLES, ITALY

°F °C   in. mm
122 50   118 3000
104 40   98 2500
86 30   79 2000
68 20   59 1500
50 10   39 1000
32 0   20 500
14 -10   0 0
-4 -20
max. temperature
min. temperature
average rainfall
J F M A M J J A S O N D

⚡ **Giant devil ray (left)**
This huge ray belongs to a family that contains the only living vertebrates to possess three pairs of functioning limbs. Cephalic fins on its head resemble devil horns.

Angel shark
Squatina squatina

Sandbar shark
Carchorinus plumbeus

Rough shark
Oxynotus centrina

Porbeagle shark
Lamna nasus

Shortfin mako shark
Isurus oxyrinchus

Blue shark
Prioace glauca

THE MEDITERRANEAN
MEDITERRANEAN ISLANDS

Five thousand islands, ranging from tiny islets to enormous Sicily, pepper the Mediterranean. Variations in size as well as altitude, geology, and isolation produce a wide range of habitats that support a diverse array of species. The limited or non-existent exchange of genetic material between island and mainland species has resulted in an exceptionally high rate of endemism. For example, more than 125 plant species, 10 bird species, and the Cyprus mouflon, a wild sheep, are found on Cyprus and nowhere else.

Bearded vulture (below)
Also known as the Lammergeier, this vulture inhabits high mountains. It feeds almost exclusively on bones, swallowing small ones whole and allowing gastric fluids to digest them. It smashes larger bones on rocks.

Eleonora's falcon
The medium-sized Eleonora's falcon lives in colonies of 100 pairs or more on rocky cliffs in Greece. It winters in Madagascar and is named for the 14th-century Sardinian princess who introduced laws to protect it. In the Middle Ages, falcons were trained and used for hunting.

⚡ Barbary macaque (left)

The endangered Barbary macaque, commonly, but mistakenly called an ape, is the only wild primate found in Europe. It is restricted to Gibraltar, and though there is fossil evidence of the species in other parts of Europe, the 230 surviving macaques actually descended from North African populations that were introduced by the British from the 18th century. The British Army has assumed responsibility for the macaque's care.

Common dolphin (right)

Common dolphins are distinguished from other dolphins by their unique crisscross color pattern: dark on the back, light grey on the flank, with a pale yellow thoracic patch and white abdomen. They live in large schools and jump and splash together.

Conservation watch: mouflon

Hunting and competition from livestock left the population of Cyprus's largest wild land mammal, the mouflon, down to just a few dozen by the beginning of the 20th century. The population has increased, in part, because of the establishment of special watering holes that protect the mouflon from diseases carried by domestic cattle, sheep, and goats.

Sardinian red deer (below)

About 1,500 endemic Sardinian red deer live in mountainous areas of Sardinia. Once close to extinction, the deer is now protected and numbers are growing. Males compete for harems, first by bellowing and trying to chase competitors away, then by battling with their antlers.

EUROPE
FLYWAYS OF EUROPE

The migration of billions of birds every year is one of the most magnificent natural phenomena. Migrants follow overlapping flyways between breeding grounds in the north and wintering grounds in Africa. They cross over two land bridges—one across the Middle East and down the east coast of Africa, and the other over Gibraltar and down the west coast of Africa. These aerial highways include a network of stop-over sites. Flyways tend to follow coastlines and north–south river valleys, narrowing sometimes to just a few hundred yards.

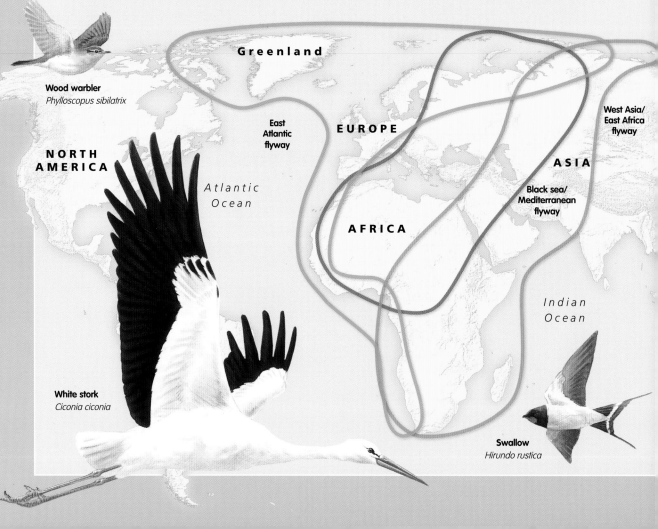

Wood warbler
Phylloscopus sibilatrix

Greenland

East Atlantic flyway

EUROPE

West Asia/East Africa flyway

NORTH AMERICA

Atlantic Ocean

ASIA

Black sea/Mediterranean flyway

AFRICA

Indian Ocean

White stork
Ciconia ciconia

Swallow
Hirundo rustica

Greylag geese

Birds flock for defense, to locate food, and to navigate during migration. The coordinated movements of flocks such as these greylag geese result from the second-to-second decisions of individual birds reacting to their neighbors. Maintaining a V-shaped formation allows birds to gain lift from the bird in front.

SPECIES	WINTERING AREA	MIGRATION DISTANCE
Swallow	South Africa	5,600 miles (9,000 km)
Wood warbler	Central Africa	4,660 miles (7,500 km)
Eurasian teal	East Africa	3,400 miles (5,500 km)
White stork	East Africa	3,400 miles (5,500 km)
Blackcap	East Africa	3,400 miles (5,500 km)
Northern lapwing	North Africa	1,900 miles (3,000 km)

Blackcap
Sylvia atricapilla

Eurasian teal
Anas crecca

Northern lapwing
Vanellus vanellus

Wingspans

A bird's wingspan is measured from the tip of one extended wing to the tip of the other. Feathers provide insulation and help streamline the body and wings, making the bird aerodynamic. Birds adjust their wingspan to control flight.

White stork
60 inches (150 cm)
Riding on thermals of hot air, the white stork has a wingspan twice the length of its body.

Northern lapwing
28 inches (70 cm)
Migration is often wind-assisted for the northern lapwing, whose wings make a lapping sound.

Eurasian teal
20 inches (55 cm)
This dabbling duck flies in large flocks. Fast wing beats make the flocks appear to twist in flight.

Swallow
13 inches (33 cm)
Swallows are fast and acrobatic fliers that prey on insects, which they catch mid-flight.

Wood warbler
9 inches (22 cm)
The entire population of wood warblers flies to tropical Africa to escape harsh European winters.

Flyways (left)

Three major north-to-south flyways pass over Europe. The East Atlantic flyway (green), favored by the teal, bisects the continent and crosses Gibraltar into Africa. The Black Sea/Mediterranean flyway (blue), used by the stork, extends from Russia to West Africa. Many different waterbirds use the West Asia/East Africa flyway (orange), which follows the Ural Mountains through Europe.

EUROPE
BIRDS OF PREY

Birds of prey, also called raptors, are perfectly designed for hunting, with keen eyesight, powerful wings, aerodynamic feathers, and sharp beak and talons. The largest European bird of prey is the Eurasian black vulture, which has a wingspan of up to 10 feet 2 inches (3.1 m). Peregrine falcons are the fastest-moving creatures on Earth, diving at speeds of up to 200 miles per hour (320 km/h).

Eagle wing (left)
Eagle wings are a miracle in lightweight design. Bones are hollow and primary feathers spread like fingers to reduce drag. Most of the power for flying comes from the downward stroke.

Golden eagle (right)
Eagles use several methods for capturing prey, but soaring and swooping are the most common. Snatching the animal by the head with one foot, the eagle drives the talons of its other foot into the prey's lungs as it carries it away.

Red kites (left)

These red kites are circling for prey over a river valley. An extremely agile flier, the red kite has a small body relative to its wing size. If a predator approaches its nest, the mother will signal her young to "play dead."

Lanner falcon (right)

Lanner falcon, also called Feldegg's falcon, resides in southeast Europe and breeds in Africa. It hunts by horizontal pursuit rather than diving from above, and is one of the few raptors that attack its prey head on, often resorting to ambush. Bats are favorite targets.

Peregrine falcon (below)

The peregrine falcon dive-bombs its prey, usually medium-sized birds, such as pigeons, ducks, and shorebirds. As strong as it is speedy, a peregrine can carry off prey half its own body weight.

Osprey (right)

The osprey snatches fish from shallow depths. Before hitting the water, it thrusts its talons forward, pushes out its breast, and holds its wings back, ready to clutch its catch headfirst.

Eurasian black vulture (right)

This huge vulture has a fragmented range stretching from Spain, across southern Europe, to central Asia. It forages for carcasses in mountainous regions and steppe.

EUROPEAN CONIFEROUS FORESTS

The coniferous forest is named for the dominant vegetation: cone-bearing trees, including pine and spruce, that possess needles instead of leaves. Needles contain little sap and do not freeze during the long, cold winters. They are also dark and can better absorb what little sunlight there is. Since they are not deciduous, the trees do not expend energy regenerating during the short growing season. The lack of plant diversity translates into fewer animal species. Resident mammals that have adapted to the conditions include moose, bears, and lynx.

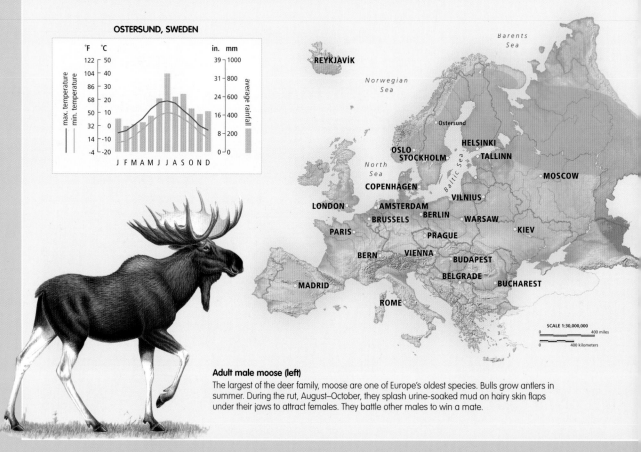

OSTERSUND, SWEDEN

Adult male moose (left)
The largest of the deer family, moose are one of Europe's oldest species. Bulls grow antlers in summer. During the rut, August–October, they splash urine-soaked mud on hairy skin flaps under their jaws to attract females. They battle other males to win a mate.

Red deer (above)
Only male red deer have antlers. Made of bone, the antlers grow about one inch (2.5 cm) a day from spring until they are shed in winter. Red deer graze in the early morning and late evening. They do not migrate.

Pine marten (left)
Semi-retractable claws allow the pine marten to climb trees. A bushy tail helps it balance when scurrying from limb to limb, and fur on the soles of its paws aids insulation and creates built-in snowshoes for winter.

European wolf (above)
Wolves still survive in many European countries despite centuries of hunting and habitat loss. This highly social animal forms packs comprising the extended family of a dominant male.

Black grouse (below)
Black grouse, also known as blackgame, engage in an elaborate courtship ritual. Cocks fan their lyre-shaped tails and make a bubbling, spitting call while competing for hens.

Alpine newt (below)
Though an amphibian, the alpine newt lacks webbed toes and spends much of its time on land, usually in undergrowth. It moves to the cool water of forest pools during the spawning season.

ALONG THE SHORE

Saltmarshes, coastal dunes, rocky cliffs, sandy beaches, and muddy tidal flats are some of the habitats that support an enormous variety of plants and animals. Tidal pools form along the rocky coastline and provide oases for limpets, mussels, crabs, and fish. Bivalve mollusks burrow under the surface on sandy beaches. Deposits of mud and silt in the sheltered waters of estuaries and bays are high in nutrients and provide homes for worms and other invertebrates. These, in turn, satisfy waders and shorebirds, such as the heron, stilt, oystercatcher, and stork.

BREST, FRANCE

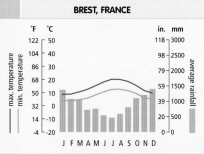

European harbor seal (left)

Common harbor seals can be found from Ireland to the east coast of Sweden and north from Holland to the Arctic. They have two sets of flippers. The pectorals have five webbed digits with claws used for grooming and defense. The hind flippers are kicked for forward propulsion.

Herring gull and chick (left)

A common gull found throughout the North Atlantic, the herring gull can drink either freshwater or sea water. It excretes the salt through special glands located above its eyes. A scavenger, the gull's call is a loud, clear bugle.

Eurasian oystercatcher (right)

The tip of the oystercatcher's bill changes shape. Most of the year it is broad so that the coastal bird can pry open mollusks and hammer through shells. By the time the oystercatchers move inland to breed, the tip has worn down to a point perfectly shaped for digging up worms.

Life in a tidal pool

Inside a tidal pool the environment is always changing with the movement of the sun, wind, and tide. Survival means avoiding being washed away or drying out. The hardiest animals, namely barnacles and whelks, live in the splash zone. Starfish and sea urchins cling to the middle zone, and tiny fish stick to deeper pools. Hermit crabs and sea anemones dwell on the bottom.

Anemone (above)

A sea anemone's body is a column with a single opening, used to ingest food and expel wastes. When touched, surrounding tentacles inject a poison and hold the prey for digestion.

Starfish underside (above)

Starfish are spiny-skinned animals called echinoderms with five or more "arms" that radiate from a disk. Tubelike feet aid starfish locomotion and feeding. The central mouth leads to two stomachs, one of which can be everted so the starfish can digest food outside its body.

Common sea urchin (left)

The common sea urchin's spines offer it protection from predatory fish as it feeds on algae and invertebrates such as worms and barnacles. Strong mouthparts are designed for rasping. Sea urchins belong to the echinoderm group of invertebrates.

MARSHES AND WETLANDS

Wetlands are either continuously submerged or intermittently inundated by seasonal flooding or daily tides. They include marshes, fens, bogs, peatlands, ponds, and coastal estuaries. Among the most biologically diverse habitats on Earth, nearly 900 European wetlands have been declared of international importance. Renowned for their high levels of endemic species, they are a sanctuary for a wide variety of plants, invertebrates, fish, amphibians, reptiles, and mammals, as well as a high concentration of migratory and sedentary waterfowl.

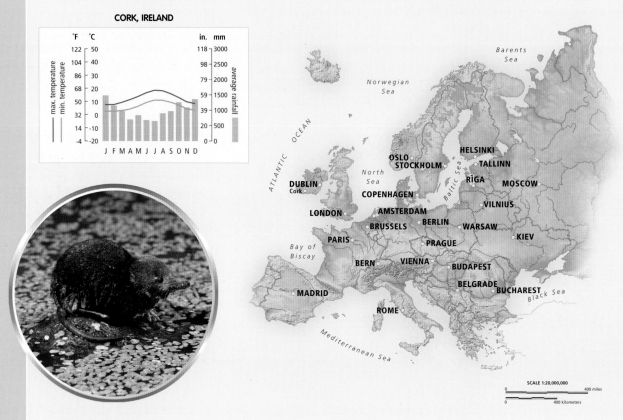

CORK, IRELAND

SCALE 1:20,000,000

Water shrew (above)
The water shrew lives in shallow burrow systems, often with underwater entrances. A fast swimmer, it uses hairs on the underside of its tail as a rudder. Venomous saliva helps immobilize prey, ranging from aquatic larvae and insects to small fish, frogs, slugs, and snails.

Marsh harrier
Circus aeruginosus

Purple heron
Ardea purpurea

Muskrat
Ondatra zibethicus

Azure damselfly
Coenagrion puella

Water shrew
Noemys fodiens

European perch
Perca fluviatilis

Life in a marshland (above)
The entire food chain is represented in a marsh, from plant to prey to predator. The sediment-rich water promotes algal and plant growth, which nourishes invertebrates, insects, and fish. These serve as food for purple heron and semi-aquatic rodents, such as the water shrew and muskrat, which, in turn, provide sustenance for birds of prey, such as the marsh harrier.

Dalmatian pelican (above)
The largest of seven pelican species, the Dalmatian can be distinguished from the more common white pelican by its size, curly nape feathers, and light ash plumage. It catches fish in its huge bill pouch. Habitat loss has made it vulnerable to extinction.

Dragonfly

Dragonflies spend most of their lives as larvae underwater. They metamorphose by crawling onto plants. Exposed to air, their skin splits and the adult dragonflies emerge. Dragonflies have two pairs of wings and can fly at a speed of 100 body-lengths per second.

Green hawker dragonfly (left)
The green hawker is found in wetlands across much of northern and eastern Europe, from Sweden to Ukraine.

Bald eagle

The bald eagle is found throughout North America and as far south as Mexico. It feeds mainly on fish that it plucks from the water, but is also known to steal food from other birds. The bald eagle builds the largest nest of any North American bird, up to 13 feet (4 m) deep and 8 feet (2.5 m) wide.

NORTH AMERICA

Evergreen woods, deserts, temperate rain forests, vast grassy plains, snow-capped mountain peaks, oak forests, swamps, and sandy beaches—all are found in North America. The continent shares some of its wildlife wealth with other continents: brown bears and moose haunt Eurasia, and pumas prey on white-tailed deer in South America. Many of its most beautiful songbirds migrate to and from North America. But many animals are unique, from pronghorns and bison to spotted salamanders and Gila monsters. However, humans have taken their toll: some species, such as passenger pigeons, have disappeared, and some habitats are shadows of their former glory.

The boreal forest
Vast, cold, and remote, the boreal coniferous forest shrouds northern North America from sea to sea below the Arctic and supports a small but splendid wildlife assemblage.

The Great Basin
The forbidding extremes of the Great Basin, a cold desert dominated by sagebrush and species that depend on it, are succumbing to human and plant invaders.

Pacific coniferous forest
Boasting the tallest trees on Earth, the Pacific northwest coniferous forest teems with wildlife, from fish in its coursing rivers to insects living in the treetops.

Deserts of the southwest
In the hot, dry expanses of the deserts of the southwest, diverse plants and animals have evolved ingenious strategies for conserving water and keeping cool.

The Rocky Mountains
The Rocky Mountains' tall peaks and low basins are the home of some of the continent's most spectacular wildlife, including bison, bears, bobcats, and wolves.

Eastern deciduous forest
Rolling mountains and majestic trees that burst into brilliant fall colors define the eastern deciduous forest, where songbirds, salamanders, and flowering shrubs abound.

The Great Plains
The vast expanse of grasses that flowed through the center of North America has nearly vanished, but traces of its glory remain in remnant bison herds and prairie dog towns.

Coastal plains
Swamps, salt marshes, sandy beaches, and pine woods rim the Atlantic and Gulf of Mexico coasts, hosting shorebirds, migrating butterflies, and crabs.

Climate (left)

North America's remarkably varied climates encompass most extremes of weather. In the far north, low temperatures and polar winds keep sea and land frozen for much of the year. To the south, the cold temperate zone experiences heavy winter snowfalls and short summers. Winter snow is also abundant in the northeastern USA, where summers are hot and humid. The greatest aridity occurs in the southwestern USA and northwestern Mexico.

CLIMATE ZONES

Wet tropical	Mediterranean	Cold temperate
Seasonal tropical	Subtropical	Subpolar
Arid	Continental	Highland
Semiarid	Temperate	Polar

Vegetation (right)

A permanent cover of ice swathes most of Greenland. South of the arctic tundra—a barren region of bogs, mosses, and scattered conifers—a huge belt of boreal forest blankets most of Canada and reaches southward along the western ranges. Grasslands flank the Rocky Mountains, stretching across the interior to the broadleaved forests of the east, merging with Mediterranean scrub near the west coast. Deserts extend from the southwestern USA across much of northern Mexico.

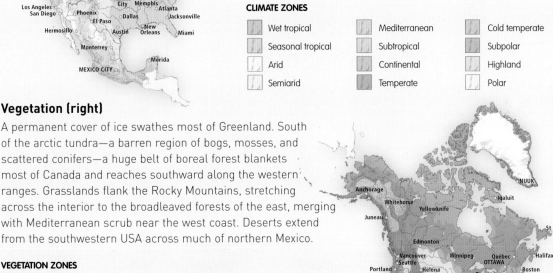

VEGETATION ZONES

Tropical forest	Midlatitude forest
Seasonal tropical forest	Boreal forest
Desert	Tundra
Tropical grassland	Mountain vegetation
Mediterranean forest and scrub	Ice sheet
Midlatitude grassland	

Land cover (right)

Though much diminished, forests still cover a large swath of the continent, chiefly in Canada. Most arable land lies in the north; in the south it is generally restricted to fertile volcanic uplands. Other types of land cover include the large marginal and nonproductive areas in the far north and western mountains, and significant urban sprawl: the USA alone has more than 4 million miles (6.4 million km) of roadways.

PROPORTIONS OF TOTAL LAND AREA

Forest and woodland	
Arable land	
Grazing	
Other land	

31.7% 38.6% 17.2% 12.5%

THE BOREAL FOREST

Covering about one-quarter of North America, the boreal forest is also known as taiga, a Russian word meaning "land of little sticks." Long, cold, snowy winters and infertile soils prevent the coniferous trees that dominate this landscape from growing taller than about 50 feet (15 m). The harsh climate limits wildlife diversity, but about 85 mammal species make their homes here, and in summer 3 billion birds of about 300 species feast on the forest's abundant insects.

Wetlands

Countless lakes, ponds, bogs, and other wetlands dot the boreal forest. More than 13 million migratory ducks breed, feed, and rest in these wetland habitats, as do millions of other waterbirds, including loons, grebes, cranes, and kingfishers. Wetlands and the boreal forest's many rivers are also home to about 130 species of fish and aquatic mammals, such as beavers, whose dams actually create wetlands.

Eared grebe (above)

Eared grebes breed in large, raucous colonies in shallow wetlands in the western boreal forest and other parts of western North America. In summer, they hunt for aquatic insects and spiders on the water's surface and also dive underwater for them.

Whooping crane (below)

Nearly the entire world population of endangered whooping cranes, about 70 breeding pairs, summers in the boreal forest wetlands of Canada's Wood Buffalo National Park and its surrounds. Living 20 to 30 years, whooping cranes raise only one chick a year.

Porcupine (below)

A North American porcupine is studded with about 30,000 barb-tipped quills for protection. If a predator attacks, the porcupine drives its quills into the assailant, injuring and sometimes killing the victim.

Moose (above)

The boreal forest is the primary habitat of the moose, the largest of all deer. In a sense, moose manage the boreal forest. They graze extensively on the forest's aspens and other deciduous trees, preferring them to conifers. As a result, moose grazing makes room for spruces and other conifers to grow. This cow and bull are pictured during the fall mating season.

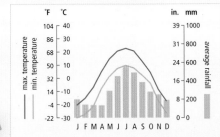

FORT SMITH, CANADA

Adapted to life in the snow

Traveling through the deep snow that blankets the boreal forest for most of the year is hard work that requires a lot of energy. Some mammals, including Canada lynx, snowshoe hares, and caribou, have evolved "snowshoes." Specific adaptations make their feet extra large and this keeps them from sinking far into the snow. The willow ptarmigan, a forest bird, has evolved a different strategy: its feet are densely feathered.

Canada lynx (above)
Medium-sized cats with tufted ears and keen eyesight, Canada lynx specialize in hunting snowshoe hares, which make up about 80 percent of their diet. Predator and prey are so closely linked that fluctuations in hare populations are mirrored in lynx numbers.

Snowshoe hare (left)
Even snowshoes and fur that turns from brown to white to blend into the winter snow do not keep snowshoe hares from the jaws of Canada lynx. The hares dine on willow and aspen, which defend themselves with nasty chemicals when the hares over-browse.

Snowshoe hare paw (left)
Very large hind feet covered in dense fur and stiff hairs, and long toes that spread widely, allow a snowshoe hare to race over deep snow.

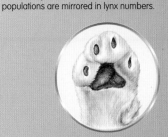

Lynx paw (above)
The Canada lynx's paws are huge for the cat's size. They are furred above and below, serving to improve insulation, much like a pair of mittens.

THE BOREAL FOREST
CARIBOU ON THE MOVE

Caribou, known as reindeer outside of North America, are superbly adapted to life in the cold boreal forest as well as the high Arctic tundra. Two main subspecies occupy parts of the North American boreal forest. The woodland caribou (pictured left) lives here year-round in small groups. Barrenland caribou migrate in huge herds as far as 3,100 miles (5,000 km) a year between summer tundra calving grounds and winter boreal forest habitats. Woodland caribou may migrate too, but over much shorter distances of 9 to 50 miles (15–80 km) within the forest.

Grazing (left)
A caribou's summer fare consists of a variety of grasses, flowering plants, leaves of willows and birches, and even mushrooms. Caribou shed their antlers every alternate year and, unique among deer, females bear them, too.

Conservation watch: caribou

The woodland caribou is classified as endangered. Logging, mining, oil exploration, and roads, are the major reasons for this decline. Barrenland caribou are more secure, but climate change threatens the security of both subspecies. Summer brings swarms of mosquitoes and black, bot, and warble flies that disturb caribou foraging and force them into patches of snow, where there are fewer insects. Higher summer temperatures because of global warming will boost insect numbers, which may compromise caribou health and reproduction.

On the move (below)

Migrating caribou herds are named after their birthing grounds. The Porcupine Herd, named after the Porcupine River, is often considered part of the barrenland caribou subspecies. The herd travels north on fairly fixed routes from their boreal forest wintering habitat, to calve in the northern foothills of the Brooks Range and on the Alaskan coastal plains. In the fall they return along more diffuse routes.

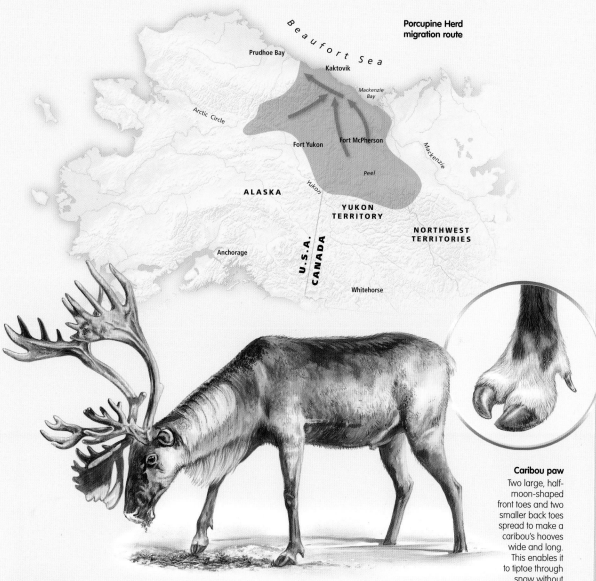

Porcupine Herd migration route

Beaufort Sea

Prudhoe Bay

Kaktovik

Mackenzie Bay

Arctic Circle

Fort Yukon

Fort McPherson

Mackenzie

Peel

ALASKA

Yukon

YUKON TERRITORY

NORTHWEST TERRITORIES

Anchorage

U.S.A.

CANADA

Whitehorse

Caribou paw

Two large, half-moon-shaped front toes and two smaller back toes spread to make a caribou's hooves wide and long. This enables it to tiptoe through snow without getting bogged.

Shoveling for food

Green food is scarce in the boreal forest winter, and the lichen that makes up much of the caribou's winter diet is buried beneath snow. Caribou use their sharp-edged hooves to shovel off the snow. This requires a lot of energy, so caribou try to steal the patches others have cleared.

THE BOREAL FOREST

FOREST MUSTELIDS

Seven of North America's 11 species of mustelids live in various boreal forest habitats. These luxuriously furred carnivores range from tiny least weasels, which weigh just one or two ounces (28–56 g), to husky wolverines that weigh up to 500 times more. Predators with voracious appetites, mustelids eat almost any animal they can catch as well as feeding on carrion.

American marten
Martes americana

Mink
Neovison vison

Least weasel
Mustela vison

Fisher
Martes pennanti

Wolverine
Gulo gulo

Fisher (above)
The fisher is an omnivore, feeding on small animals including snowshoe hares and porcupines, as well as mushrooms and berries. Although it is a good climber, it spends most of its time on the forest floor. Male fishers are up to 4 feet (120 cm) long, while females are a little smaller.

Conservation watch: wolverine

The boreal forest is a stronghold of the solitary wolverine, which ranges widely. It was never abundant but is declining in most of its North American range, and may be extinct elsewhere. Trapping for their fur and poisoning, largely by ranchers, has taken a toll on wolverines, which are easily disturbed and prefer to live and breed in remote wildernesses.

Stoat (right)

The stoat, also known as the short-tailed weasel, is larger and has a longer tail than the closely related least weasel. The stoat molts in spring and fall, changing from its rough, sandy-brown summer fur to its white, dense winter fur. The stoat is often called an ermine when in its winter coat.

Least weasel (below)

Least weasels prefer to live and hunt in grassy meadows intermixed with forest. Their long, slender bodies enable them to follow mice and voles into their burrows and, in winter, through tunnels in the snow. This weasel needs to eat one or two prey a day, equal to about half its body weight.

Northern river otter (left)

Excellent swimmers and divers, semi-aquatic northern river otters ply the rivers and lakes of the boreal forest. They hunt, usually alone and at night, for fish, frogs, turtles, birds, eggs, and sometimes muskrats. A layer of oil underlying their thick fur insulates their bodies in cold water.

PACIFIC CONIFEROUS FOREST

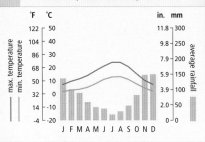

The Pacific northwest coniferous forest is one of the richest forests on Earth. Mild temperatures and abundant rainfall produce dense stands of towering, long-lived evergreen trees, such as Douglas fir, western hemlock, and coast redwood. These old-growth forests, through which many rivers course, are home to a diverse array of wildlife. Some species, such as the northern spotted owl and the Pacific giant salamander, are found nowhere else.

SEATTLE, WASHINGTON, USA

Bald eagle (below)

The majestic bald eagle uses its strong legs and powerful toes, tipped with sharp talons, to snatch salmon and trout, its favorite prey. This large raptor depends on old-growth coniferous or deciduous forest near large bodies of water.

SCALE 1:34,000,000

0   500 miles

0   500 kilometers

Brown bear (left)

Pacific coastal brown bears enjoy a food bonanza in summer, feasting on the abundant salmon swimming upriver to spawn. With food so plentiful, the usually solitary bears gather in numbers at prime fishing spots, often where waterfalls and other obstructions slow the fish down. This bear is leaping on a fish at Katmai National Park, Alaska.

Fish diet (left)

The high-protein, high-fat salmon diet on the Pacific coast produces the largest brown bears in the world. Adult males reach a massive 1,300 pounds (600 kg) or more, and may stand 9 feet (2.8 m) tall.

Pacific banana slug (right)

The second-largest land-living slug does, indeed, reach the size of a banana. The Pacific banana slug inhabits the Pacific Coast's coniferous rain forests, where it eats fungus, dead leaves, and animal droppings on the moist forest floor.

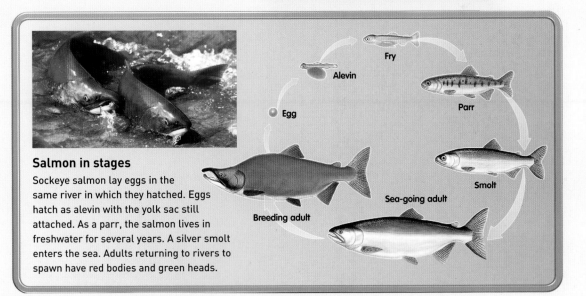

Salmon in stages

Sockeye salmon lay eggs in the same river in which they hatched. Eggs hatch as alevin with the yolk sac still attached. As a parr, the salmon lives in freshwater for several years. A silver smolt enters the sea. Adults returning to rivers to spawn have red bodies and green heads.

Fry

Alevin

Egg

Parr

Smolt

Sea-going adult

Breeding adult

THE ROCKY MOUNTAINS

Habitat diversity in the Rocky Mountains is enormous, ranging from snow-capped peaks to alpine meadows to boreal and deciduous forest and arid steppes, but coniferous forest dominates in the generally cool, dry climate. Wildlife diversity is limited. Relatively few insects, amphibians, and reptiles live here, and many of the fish species in the region's plentiful lakes and rivers have been introduced. However, large mammals include bison, moose, elk, bighorn sheep, mountain goats, mule and white-tailed deer, pronghorn, grizzly and black bears, gray wolves, coyotes, pumas, wolverines, Canada lynx, and bobcats.

JASPER, ALBERTA, CANADA

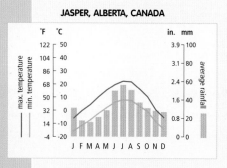

SCALE 1:35,000,000

0	500 miles
0	500 kilometers

American beaver (left)

Energetic American beavers build lodges of tree branches and trunks they fell using their chisel-shaped front teeth. Their lips close behind their front teeth so they can carry branches underwater without fluid entering their lungs. Beavers have dense fur and webbed hind feet.

Common raven (left)

The common raven is one of the Rockies' most conspicuous birds. Sociable and seemingly fearless, it is often seen scavenging gray wolf kills and will even swoop or chase these carnivores to steal a bite for its hungry nestlings.

Western rattlesnake (right)

Although armed with deadly venom, western rattlesnakes are not aggressive and are seldom seen. In hot weather they hunt at night; they spend cold winters hibernating in caves and other animals' burrows.

Rattle structure (left)

Each segment of the rattle is composed of tough skin that is not shed. The loosely interlocking rattles bounce against each other when the snake vibrates its tail.

Mountain goat (left)

Spending most of their time on severely steep, rocky slopes in alpine areas of the northern Rockies, where they are safe from predators, mountain goats nibble small plants that grow among the rocks. Powerful front legs help them to climb and descend the steep slopes, and rough pads on the undersides of their split hooves provide traction. The hooves are capable of pinching around a rock edge or spreading out for braking.

Coyote

Adaptable and opportunistic, coyotes thrive almost everywhere in North America, from the high Rockies to large cities such as Washington DC. They took advantage of the extermination of gray wolves to expand well beyond their original, mostly western, range. However, where wolves reign, as they do once again in Yellowstone National Park, coyote numbers have decreased.

Playful

Combative

Defensive

Friendly

Facial expressions

Among other signals, such as vocalizations and postures, social coyotes use a variety of facial expressions to communicate. They may live alone, in breeding pairs, or packs of several individuals.

THE ROCKY MOUNTAINS
THE GRAY WOLF

Gray wolves once prowled throughout North America. They are still relatively abundant in Alaska and Canada, but extermination programs and habitat loss combined to nearly eliminate these predators from the lower 48 US states by the 1930s. In 1995–1996, 66 wolves were reintroduced to Yellows~~~~ National Park and central Idaho. By 2007, these wolf populations had inc~~~~~~~~~~~ 1,500 animals. Conservation programs and natural re-coloniza~~~~ led to growing wolf numbers in Minnesota, Wisconsin, ~~~~

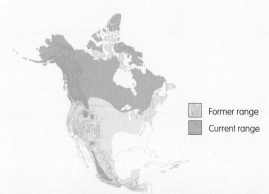

■ Former range
■ Current range

Hunting (above)
Wolves prey mostly on elk, mule deer, and white-tailed deer. They generally hunt in packs of five to 10 or more members, led by a dominant breeding pair, most often accompanied by members of their own recent litters. But a pair or even a single wolf can bring down elk and deer alone, so the benefit of pack hunting may lie in the pair sharing the surplus of their kills with their young.

Wolf cub (left)
A breeding wolf pair produces a litter of five to six cubs in spring or summer after mating about two months earlier. Born helpless, the cubs remain in a den for two months before joining the pack's hunting forays a few weeks later. Cubs do not hunt themselves until aged eight months.

Cascading effects of wolf reintroduction

Elk form about 90 percent of the prey of Yellowstone's wolves. As a result, elk numbers are about half what they were before wolves returned. With fewer elk browsing, streamside vegetation, including willows, aspens, and cottonwoods, is flourishing where once it was disappearing. Wolves have also reduced coyote numbers, which has led to greater survival rates among pronghorn calves, the coyotes' favorite prey. Other species have similarly been advantaged or disadvantaged by the return of the wolves.

Top scavenger
The presence of wolves helps grizzly bears, which are able to usurp wolf kills, particularly when they emerge, starving, from winter hibernation.

Birds abound
The recovery of willows and other streamside vegetation has improved the prospects for songbirds, such as the yellow warbler, that nest in this habitat.

More moose
Willow regrowth has provided new habitat for American beavers, which prefer to eat small willow trees. New beaver dams have created more habitat for water-loving moose.

Rodents on the rise
Semi-aquatic muskrats have found new homes in ponds created by beaver dams, as have river otters.

THE GREAT PLAINS

Once a vast, largely treeless dry sea of perennial grasses, most of the Great Plains now form some of the world's best agricultural land, covered in fields of wheat and corn, and cattle. The climate is dry, but rainfall increases from west to east, dividing the region into western short-grass prairie, eastern tall-grass prairie, and mixed grass in between. Topography ranges from pancake flat to rolling hills. Bison, whose enormous herds once thundered across the plains and supported the region's wolves and grizzly bears, typify this near-vanished ecosystem.

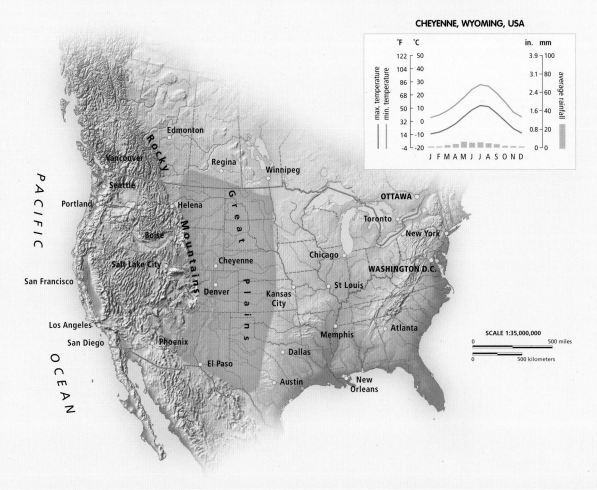

CHEYENNE, WYOMING, USA

SCALE 1:35,000,000

American bison (left)

The largest male bison reach the size of a small car, and can run at speeds of up to 40 miles per hour (64 km/h). A bison's winter coat, with 10 times as many hairs as a cow's, helps keep it from freezing to death when temperatures plummet. The deep black fur, which absorbs the heat of the sun, is shed in summer, but bison still have to pant to lose heat.

Bison's head and neck (left)

A bison's massive head is supported by a short yet wide neck and a large muscular hump between its shoulder blades, connected by a heavy ligament. A bison swings its strong head back and forth to sweep feeding areas clear of snow as deep as two to three feet (60–90 cm).

Greater short-horned lizard (left)

These lizards defend themselves from coyotes and other predators by squirting blood from their eyes. The blood contains formic acid, obtained from the bodies of their primary food—ants.

Western meadowlark
Sturnela neglecta

Bird life (right)

The Great Plains host about 300 species of breeding migratory birds in summer, such as lark buntings, as well as permanent residents, such as greater sage grouse. Here the birds find grasshoppers and other insects, seeds, and herbs to feed their nestlings. However, with so much of the prairie gone, most of these species are in decline.

Grasshopper sparrow
Ammodramus savannarum

Conservation watch: American paddlefish

The long, paddle-shaped snouts that give the American paddlefish its name are densely spotted with electrical sensors. These enable a paddlefish to locate its zooplankton prey in murky water by sensing its electric field. This exquisite sensory system, however, has not protected the paddlefish from overfishing, dams that block access to spawning grounds, and water pollution. The species is considered vulnerable to extinction.

Lark bunting
Calamospiza melanocorys

Greater sage grouse
Centrocercus urophasianus

Snakeweed grasshopper
Hesperotettix viridis

THE GREAT PLAINS
PRAIRIE DOGS

More than 5 billion black-tailed prairie dogs once colonized the Great Plains, living in aggregations large enough to be called towns. The largest recorded single town numbered some 400 million of these burrowing rodents, spread over 25,000 square miles (65,000 km²). Today, the total population of black-tailed prairie dogs may be 10–20 million, occupying only about 1 per cent of its previous Great Plains range thanks to habitat loss and past eradication campaigns. Four other less widespread prairie dog species also inhabit the United States and Mexico.

Model mounds (above)
The mounds around entrances to prairie dog burrows are carefully constructed. Besides offering access, they are elevated so as to allow the animals to scan for predators. The mounds also help prevent flooding during rain storms and improve ventilation in the underground tunnels and chambers.

Dry room

Keystone species

Scientists call prairie dogs keystone species because so many other species are affected by their presence. Many predators, such as coyotes, black-footed ferrets, and golden eagles, eat them. Burrowing owls, rabbits, snakes, insects, and others occupy their burrows, and prairie dog burrowing churns up the soil so it can better support plants. In turn, the plants attract grazers, such as pronghorn and bison, many rodents, and rabbits.

Night visitors
American badgers use their strong claws to dig their own complex burrow systems, but also visit prairie dog towns in search of food. Hunting at night, a badger may dig into a prairie dog burrow to catch one of its sleeping occupants unawares.

Collecting grass (above)
Throughout her 33-day pregnancy, a female prairie dog collects dry grass to line her nesting chamber. Although other parts of the burrow system are shared by all family members, a female aggressively defends her nesting chamber from others that may wish to kill her babies.

Alarmed (right)

With so many prairie dogs active at the same time, a few are always on the lookout for predators. On sighting a threat, a prairie dog instantly sounds the alarm, calling to alert others before diving into the burrow for its own protection.

Emergency exit

Listening room

Food storage

Dry room

Toilet

Sleeping chamber

Nursery chamber

Youngsters (right)

Born in a special nesting chamber in the burrow system, a prairie dog litter ranges in size from one to eight. Newborns are blind, naked, and helpless, but just 40 days later youngsters emerge into the plains' sunshine and begin eating independently.

THE GREAT BASIN

The Great Basin is North America's only cold desert south of the Arctic. At altitudes of 3,900–5,250 feet (1,200–1,600 m) in the rain shadow of western mountains, this is a land of extremes. Years of severe drought may be followed by wet years. Winter temperatures rarely climb above freezing, but summer days may be as hot as 90°F (32°C). Dominated by sagebrush, the Great Basin appears desolate, but 800 plant species eke out a living here and animal life is surprisingly abundant.

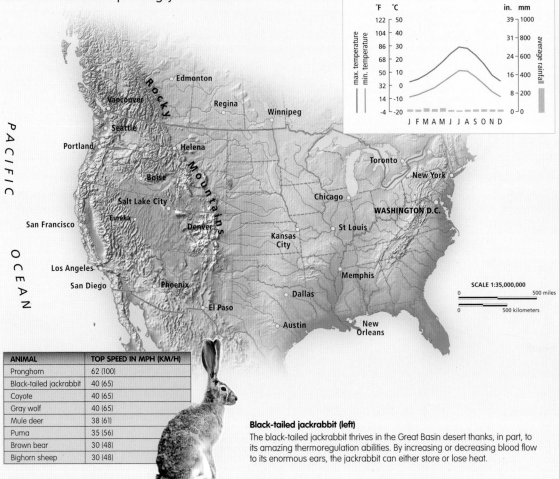

EUREKA, NEVADA, USA

ANIMAL	TOP SPEED IN MPH (KM/H)
Pronghorn	62 (100)
Black-tailed jackrabbit	40 (65)
Coyote	40 (65)
Gray wolf	40 (65)
Mule deer	38 (61)
Puma	35 (56)
Brown bear	30 (48)
Bighorn sheep	30 (48)

Black-tailed jackrabbit (left)

The black-tailed jackrabbit thrives in the Great Basin desert thanks, in part, to its amazing thermoregulation abilities. By increasing or decreasing blood flow to its enormous ears, the jackrabbit can either store or lose heat.

The pronghorn

Speedy hoofed mammals, able to race across the range at up to 62 miles per hour (100 km/h), pronghorns range widely and migrate seasonally in search of nutritious food and to escape deep snow or drought. It remains a puzzle why pronghorns run so fast, clocking up speeds way beyond those required to escape any living predator they might encounter. One intriguing theory is that they evolved alongside speedier hunters, such as the American cheetah, which are now extinct.

Large eyes (right)
Pronghorns have excellent vision and their extra-large, wide-set eye sockets are prominent in their skull. They rely on speed, eyesight, and vigilance for protection. With the exception of the first two weeks of life, when they are easy pickings for coyotes, pronghorns do not hide.

Wild horses (left)
They seem a timeless emblem of the Great Basin but wild horses did not exist here until about 1680. Domestic horses that arrived with the Spanish were soon adopted by Native Americans. Today, the Great Basin hosts the largest number of wild horses, 50,000–75,000, which are descended from released and escaped animals.

Puma (below)
Though not as fast as a pronghorn, a puma can catch one in broken, bushy terrain. It is harder for pronghorns to reach top speeds in these environments and they offer cover for a puma to stealthily approach its quarry.

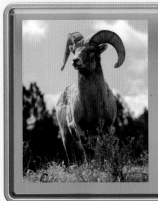

Conservation watch: bighorn sheep

Hunting, habitat loss, and competition with wild horses and domestic livestock, especially sheep that transmit diseases, all conspired to reduce bighorn sheep numbers by 90 percent by the early 1900s. Some populations were completely eliminated. Protection and translocation programs have helped them recover, but several bighorn populations remain endangered.

THE GREAT BASIN
SAGEBRUSH COUNTRY

The country dominated by big sagebrush once blanketed more than 23,000 square miles (60,000 km²) of western North America. This arid, high-elevation habitat is a mosaic of sagebrush species, grasses, shrubs, small green plants, and wildflowers, interspersed with woodlands, streams, and wetlands. Some animals evolved in sagebrush habitats and many, such as the sage grouse and sage vole, can live nowhere else. They get sustenance from sagebrush's soft, evergreen leaves, seek shelter under its branches, or both. Today, about half this habitat is gone, and its 350 associated plants and animals are imperiled.

Mule deer (left)
Named for their large ears, mule deer rely on sagebrush in many parts of their western range to get them through the harsh winter, when other plants are scarce. However, their diet is diverse, including hundreds of plants and shrubs, berries, and acorns.

Mammals 20%
Reptiles 13%
Birds 21%
Invertebrates 46%

SAGEBRUSH COUNTRY ANIMALS

Spiders 36%
Aphids 26%
Beetles 11%
Ants 11%
Gall midges 16%

Conservation watch: greater sage grouse

With greater sage grouse almost entirely dependent on sagebrush for food, it is not surprising that as sagebrush habitat has declined, so too have the grouse. The population of these large, showy birds has fallen by about one-third in the past 40 or so years and they have completely disappeared from five states and one province they once called home.

Courtship display
This male greater sage grouse has inflated his neck sacs during a courtship display. Females nest under a sagebrush canopy, insects attracted to sagebrush are fed to chicks, and the canopy conceals them from predators.

Sagebrush country (right)
Big sagebrush is found only in the dryland of western North America. Growing up to 10 feet (3 m) tall, the plant can live as long as 100 years, but wildfires usually cut short its life.

Sagebrush community (below)
Many animals rely on sagebrush habitats for survival in all or part of their range. Among the mammals and birds, pronghorns, pygmy rabbits, and white-tailed prairie dogs feed on sagebrush, as do Gunnison sage grouse and sage sparrows. In turn, ferruginous hawks hunt the rabbits, jackrabbits, and prairie dogs.

Sagebrush checkerspot
Female butterflies lay their eggs under the leaves of host plants in the sagebrush community. Caterpillars feed in groups on leaves and flowers.

Big sagebrush
The silvery-gray shrub has brilliant yellow flowers in late summer, and year-round bears soft green leaves with fine hairs that may help keep the plant cool and conserve water.

Brewer's sparrow
Brewer's sparrows are abundant in summer in remaining Great Basin sagebrush habitats, but their numbers are declining.

Brown-headed cowbird
Recent additions to the sagebrush community, brown-headed cowbirds arrived only after farms and ranches appeared and created suitable feeding habitat for them.

Desert spiny lizard
The shy desert spiny lizard often shelters in desert woodrat nests and hunts by day for insects.

Desert woodrat
Desert woodrats are common in sagebrush habitats, where they eat leaves and other vegetation.

DESERTS OF THE SOUTHWEST

The Mojave, Sonoran, and Chihuahuan deserts comprise the hot deserts of the southwestern United States and northern Mexico. At fairly high elevations, the Mojave is a transition from the Great Basin and is the smallest of the deserts. Its low elevation makes the Sonoran the hottest and driest of these deserts. The Chihuahuan is the largest desert and fairly temperate.

Despite harsh conditions, many desert-adapted plants and animals populate these arid expanses. Some, such as the saguaro cactus and desert tortoises, live nowhere else.

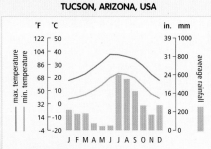

TUCSON, ARIZONA, USA

Hummingbirds (above)
More hummingbird species live in the southwest deserts than anywhere else in the United States and Canada. Southwestern Arizona boasts 15 species, which occur only in the New World.

SCALE 1:30,000,000

0   500 miles

0   500 kilometers

Desert dominants

Major vegetation types distinguish the three southwest deserts. Cacti are rare in the Mojave, where Joshua trees, creosote bush, and bur sage dominate. Most plants are perennial shrubs, many found nowhere else. In the Sonoran, creosote bush (pictured, with a male house finch) and bur sage occur at low elevations, but higher elevations host blue palo verde, ironweed, agave, and many cacti species. Prickly pear, yucca, and acacias characterize the Chihuahuan.

American agave
Found in the Sonoran and Chihuahuan deserts, the American agave blooms just once, then dies. Hummingbirds and insects drink the flower's nectar; birds and small mammals eat its seeds.

Desert tortoises
The only land turtle in its southwestern desert range, the desert tortoise spends most of its time in a burrow. It may go two years without a meal, even though its diet of green plants and wildflowers is its only source of water. Males often fight, using a horn on their shell to flip over their opponent. Fires, disease, urban sprawl, and skyrocketing numbers of ravens that eat hatchlings all threaten desert tortoises. Females do not breed until 15–20 years old.

Conservation watch: gila monster

Gila monsters and closely related beaded lizards are the only venomous lizards, but their toxic bite has not stopped them declining in the face of threats posed by urban sprawl, pets, and cars. They are listed as "Near Threatened."

Ringtail (above)
Although cat-like in appearance, ringtails are closely related to raccoons. Agile climbers, they scamper up and down canyon sides and trees. Their ankles rotate 180 degrees so they can easily descend a tree headfirst.

Burrowing owl (right)
Burrowing owls may be year-long residents or winter migrants from more northerly extremes. These small owls nest and store food in other animals' burrows, such as those of desert tortoises. The owls hunt for insects, scorpions, rodents, frogs and toads, reptiles, and birds.

DESERTS OF THE SOUTHWEST
SAGUARO COMMUNITY

Found only in the Sonoran Desert, the saguaro cactus is a central component of this ecosystem and used by a variety of desert-dwellers. Birds such as gilded flickers dig nest holes in its flesh, and Harris's hawks build stick nests in its arms. Abandoned nest holes are inhabited by other birds, such as finches and sparrows, and hawk nests are often reused by ravens and great horned owls. Bats, birds, and insects, especially bees, sip nectar from the cacti's large flowers, and provide vital pollination services in return. Coyotes, jackrabbits, cactus wrens, and others eat its nutritious, water-rich fruit, then disperse the seeds. The cactus owes its success to amazing adaptations for storing the region's scant water supplies.

Sonoran Desert (below)
With its tall, thick, trunk-bearing arms upturned toward the sky, the saguaro cactus dominates the Sonoran Desert landscape. These stately cacti grow as high as 50 feet (15 m) but attain that height slowly, after more than 125 years of growth. They do not begin to sprout arms until they are 65 to 75 years old and do not flower until about 35 years of age.

Gila woodpecker (above)
A Gila woodpecker pair digs a nest hole in a saguaro but will not make use of it for several months, until the inner pulp has dried into a solid casing around the hole. These birds help the cacti by cutting away flesh infected by disease-causing insect larvae.

Water tank (below)

Saguaro cacti absorb any available water through their shallow roots. This water fills the fleshy pulp inside the exterior woody tissue of their trunk and arms. The vertical pleats of the outer pulp expand like an accordion to store large amounts of water, and can accommodate up to 2,000 pounds (900 kg) without bursting. The interior framework of vertical ribs prevents the turgid plant from collapsing.

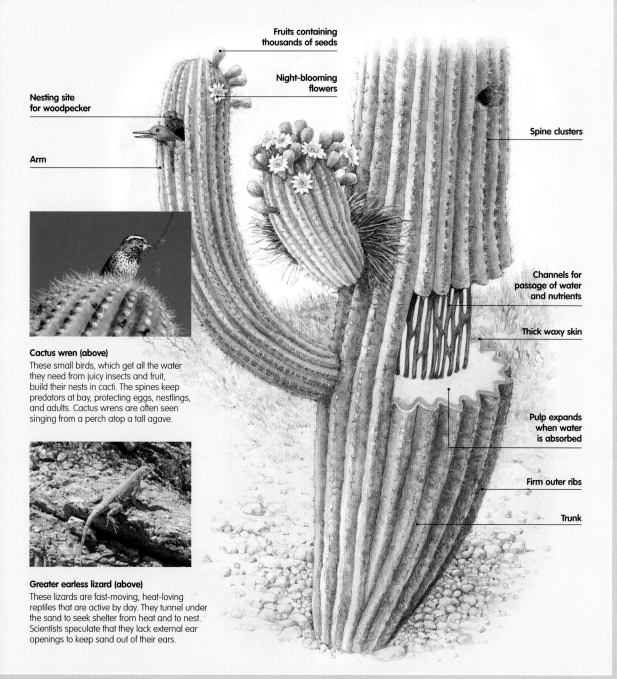

Fruits containing thousands of seeds

Night-blooming flowers

Nesting site for woodpecker

Spine clusters

Arm

Channels for passage of water and nutrients

Thick waxy skin

Pulp expands when water is absorbed

Firm outer ribs

Trunk

Cactus wren (above)

These small birds, which get all the water they need from juicy insects and fruit, build their nests in cacti. The spines keep predators at bay, protecting eggs, nestlings, and adults. Cactus wrens are often seen singing from a perch atop a tall agave.

Greater earless lizard (above)

These lizards are fast-moving, heat-loving reptiles that are active by day. They tunnel under the sand to seek shelter from heat and to nest. Scientists speculate that they lack external ear openings to keep sand out of their ears.

EASTERN DECIDUOUS FOREST AND APPALACHIANS

The great eastern deciduous forest was once unbroken from central Florida to southeastern Canada, and west to the Mississippi River. Much of the forest was logged and farmed between the 1600s and the late 1800s. As the economy changed and many farmers moved west, farms were abandoned. Large fragments of forest have returned, but major urban centers cover much of this region. Dominated by tall trees that drop their leaves in the fall, such as oaks, maples, beech, chestnuts, and hickory, this forest boasts a rich understory of smaller trees, bushes, shrubs, ferns, fungi, and green plants.

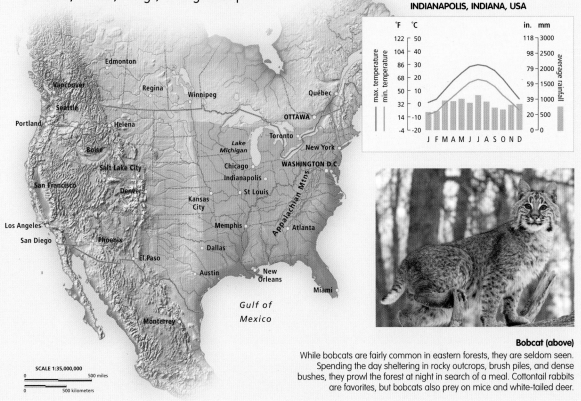

INDIANAPOLIS, INDIANA, USA

SCALE 1:35,000,000

0   500 miles

0   500 kilometers

Bobcat (above)
While bobcats are fairly common in eastern forests, they are seldom seen. Spending the day sheltering in rocky outcrops, brush piles, and dense bushes, they prowl the forest at night in search of a meal. Cottontail rabbits are favorites, but bobcats also prey on mice and white-tailed deer.

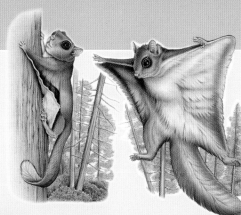

Northern flying squirrel

Widely distributed in northern North America, the northern flying squirrel is found in isolated populations in the southern Appalachians, where it overlaps with the smaller southern flying squirrel. Mushrooms and other fungi are their favorite foods and the squirrels help disperse fungal spores throughout their forested habitats. Active only at night, they forage on the ground and in the treetops, where they are hunted by predators, such as owls and hawks.

Parachuting (above)

Flying squirrels do not fly, but glide 65–295 feet (20–90 m) from tree to tree. The gliding membrane that stretches between their limbs, called a patagium, acts like a parachute. It keeps the squirrel aloft after it launches itself from on high.

American black bear (left)

The only bear in eastern North America is the American black bear, which overlaps with brown bears elsewhere. The black bear occupies diverse habitats, from deciduous forests and rain forests to swamps, tundra, and even suburbia.

Eastern chipmunk (right)

Chattering eastern chipmunks are conspicuous members of the eastern forest community during summer. To endure cold winters, they hibernate in burrows, waking every few days to consume some of the nuts and seeds they cached in the fall.

Striped skunk (right)

Striped skunks emit a foul-smelling spray from their anal glands when threatened, but that does not deter great horned owls from preying on them. Many skunks in eastern North America are also killed by vehicles and disease, such as rabies.

The raccoon

Northern raccoons are North America's ultimate generalist carnivores. With catholic tastes, they find food almost anywhere, from fields and forests to urban backyards, and shelter under porches as well as in tree holes and dens. Bobcats and foxes are among their predators in eastern forests, while the raccoons prey on small mammals, birds, crustaceans, fish, mollusks, and insects, as well as eating fruit, seeds, and carrion.

Handy paws

The skeleton of a raccoon's forepaw bears a striking resemblance to that of a human hand, giving it great manual dexterity. It moves its forepaws through streams and ponds, plucking out crayfish and other aquatic creatures with its "fingers."

Raccoon paw (right)

Human hand (left)

EASTERN DECIDUOUS FOREST AND APPALACHIANS

OAK FORESTS

The eastern United States is dominated by hardwood forests, of which oak forests are the main type. About 30 oak species live here in various associations with maples, beech, hickory, northern conifers, pines, and southern evergreens. Oaks flourish in areas disturbed by both natural and man-made fires, which were frequent in this part of North America until wildfire suppression programs were introduced. Fires removed other tall trees, whose shade prevented oak seedlings from thriving. Today, without fires, oaks have a hard time replacing themselves.

Oak-pine

Oak-chestnut

Oak-hickory

Star-nosed mole (right)
Twenty-two finger-like pink appendages, or stars, ring a star-nosed mole's snout. Each is covered with thousands of receptors that feel earthworms and other prey in the mole's underground habitat. Once a mole senses a worm, it takes only 230 milliseconds for the mole to recognize it and eat the worm.

American robin (left)
American robins nest in small trees under the canopy of oak forests as well as in urban backyards. They forage for earthworms between trees and also eat berries. One of the first birds to breed in the spring, the robin produces up to three clutches of three or four chicks per year.

White-tailed deer (left)

The only hoofed mammal in the eastern deciduous forest today, the white-tailed deer has recovered from habitat loss and overhunting. With forest returning, hunting now carefully managed, and the absence of their one-time wolf predator, the deer are considered "over abundant."

Blue jay (right)

Raucous, boldly colored blue jays are year-round residents of the eastern deciduous forest. To survive winter, they collect and cache thousands of acorns, beechnuts, and pecans in the fall, storing the nuts in the ground. These birds also eat insects, green vegetation, and birds' eggs.

Virginia opossum (left)

The only marsupial in North America north of Mexico, the Virginia opossum is best known for its habit of "playing possum" (acting dead) in response to danger. Although it lives just a year or two, the opossum has high rates of reproduction. A litter averages seven to nine young.

Ecological interaction

Oak trees produce bumper crops of acorns every two to six years, and few in between. About 50 species of acorn-eaters, such as white-tailed deer, white-footed mice, and chipmunks, flourish in the good acorn years, as do their ticks. This raises the risk of humans catching Lyme disease from a tick's bite. On the positive side, chipmunks prey on gypsy moths, an invasive species that defoliates oak trees.

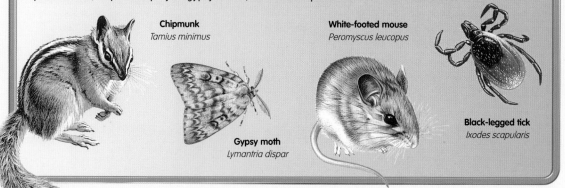

Chipmunk
Tamius minimus

Gypsy moth
Lymantria dispar

White-footed mouse
Peromyscus leucopus

Black-legged tick
Ixodes scapularis

EASTERN DECIDUOUS FOREST AND APPALACHIANS

FOREST SALAMANDERS

At least 55 species of salamander, more than are found anywhere else on Earth, live in the forests of the southern Appalachian Mountains. About 20 are exclusive to the mountains. The lungless salamanders (numbering 34 species), which breathe through their skin, evolved here. The once-towering peaks of the ancient Appalachian range isolated salamanders, which rarely venture far from where they hatch—and here they evolved into new species. Because they live in and along streams and in other moist places on the forest floor, salamanders are threatened by water pollution, habitat degradation, and global warming.

Red salamander (left)
The red salamander eats small insects, worms, and other invertebrates, as well as smaller salamanders. It takes just 11 milliseconds to snatch prey using its long tongue, which is supported by a skeleton and tipped with a sticky pad.

Insect haven

Insects abound in the eastern deciduous forest, from the lofty heights of the canopy to the forest floor. Although mostly small, their combined weight probably exceeds that of the remaining animal life combined. Moths, butterflies, and their caterpillars are important food for many forest birds. Fierce yellowjacket wasps also prey on caterpillars, flies, and bees. Salamanders eat beetles and a host of other insects and their larvae.

Lunar moth
Actius luna

Striped hawk moth
Hyles livornica

Common yellowjacket
Paravespula vulgaris

Stag beetle
Lucanus sp.

Spotted salamander (left)
Found only in deciduous forest, the spotted salamander spends much of its time hiding under logs or within the burrows of other animals. However, on a few warm, wet spring evenings these salamanders emerge in large numbers and migrate to small ponds to breed.

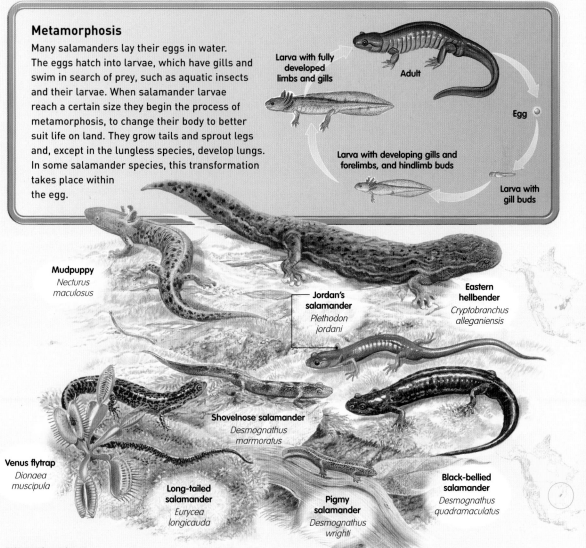

Metamorphosis

Many salamanders lay their eggs in water. The eggs hatch into larvae, which have gills and swim in search of prey, such as aquatic insects and their larvae. When salamander larvae reach a certain size they begin the process of metamorphosis, to change their body to better suit life on land. They grow tails and sprout legs and, except in the lungless species, develop lungs. In some salamander species, this transformation takes place within the egg.

Larva with fully developed limbs and gills

Adult

Egg

Larva with developing gills and forelimbs, and hindlimb buds

Larva with gill buds

Mudpuppy
Necturus maculosus

Jordan's salamander
Plethodon jordani

Eastern hellbender
Cryptobranchus alleganiensis

Shovelnose salamander
Desmognathus marmoratus

Venus flytrap
Dionaea muscipula

Long-tailed salamander
Eurycea longicauda

Pigmy salamander
Desmognathus wrighti

Black-bellied salamander
Desmognathus quadramaculatus

Salamanders (above)
The salamanders of eastern North America range from the diminutive pigmy salamander, which is not as long as a small finger, to the arm's-length eastern hellbender. Whatever their size and secretive habits, salamanders are key players in their ecosystems. They are predators, prey, and nutrient recyclers. Many eat tiny insects, linking these creatures in the food chain to larger vertebrates, such as the birds and mammals that eat salamanders.

THE COASTAL PLAINS

The Atlantic and Gulf of Mexico coastal plains encompass pine woodlands, moist deciduous forest, cypress swamps, salt and brackish marshes, and sandy beaches. However, little of the diverse natural plains habitats remains intact. They are now densely populated and, apart from major urbanization, have been logged and converted to agriculture, and beachside areas have been developed for recreation.

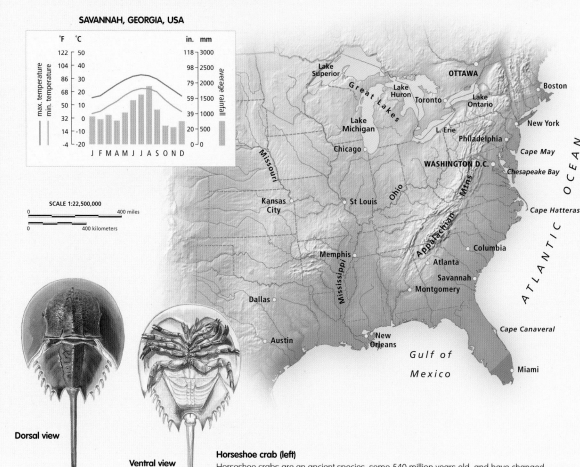

SAVANNAH, GEORGIA, USA

SCALE 1:22,500,000

0   400 miles

0   400 kilometers

Dorsal view

Ventral view

Horseshoe crab (left)

Horseshoe crabs are an ancient species, some 540 million years old, and have changed little. The North American species spawns on Atlantic beaches in spring. The first of six paired appendages on its underside is used to place food into the crab's central mouth.

Black skimmer (above)

The black skimmer's large red and black bill is unusual in that the lower mandible is distinctly longer than the upper. Flying low over the surface of the water, these seabirds skim the water with their lower mandible to catch small fish. They often hunt at night.

Nine-banded armadillo (left)

Its body covered in shell-like plates, the nine-banded armadillo has expanded its range in the southeastern United States. First seen north of the Rio Grande, Texas, in about 1850, it has since ventured as far north as Kansas and Nebraska, and east to Florida.

Canebrakes for cover (below)

Thickets of North American bamboos, called canes, once stood 20 feet (6 m) tall and stretched for miles along the coastal plains. Cut down to make way for farming, these thickets now survive only in scattered stands. They make a great wildlife habitat, providing cover, food, or both, for birds and mammals, and food for the caterpillars of moths and butterflies.

⚡ **Conservation watch: Florida panther**

An isolated subspecies of the puma, the Florida panther lives in the swamps of south Florida. Pumas once ranged throughout eastern North America but hunting and habitat loss eliminated them from all but this retreat. Around 160 of the endangered cats remain in the wild, and they risk collisions with speeding vehicles.

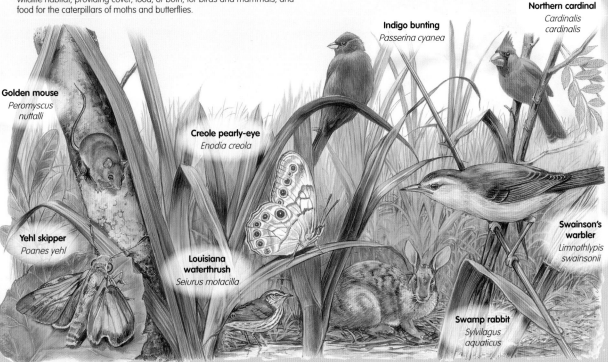

Northern cardinal
Cardinalis cardinalis

Indigo bunting
Passerina cyanea

Golden mouse
Peromyscus nuttalli

Creole pearly-eye
Enodia creola

Swainson's warbler
Limnothlypis swainsonii

Yehl skipper
Poanes yehl

Louisiana waterthrush
Seiurus motacilla

Swamp rabbit
Sylvilagus aquaticus

THE COASTAL PLAINS
BIRD MIGRATION

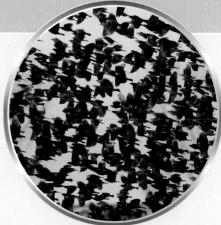

In summer, some 200 bird species breed in North America as far north as the Arctic Circle. They wing their way south as far as Tierra del Fuego, at the southern tip of South America, to avoid the meager fare available to them in winter, then retrace their flight the next spring. It is a spectacular phenomenon involving billions of birds in spring and fall, with huge numbers converging on a few stopover spots, such as Cape May, New Jersey. A million migratory shorebirds break their journey here in spring to feast on horseshoe crab eggs. In the fall, funneled by geography, tens of thousands of migrating seabirds, raptors, and songbirds pour into this small peninsula on a single day.

Red-winged blackbirds (above)
Found throughout North and Central America south of the Arctic, red-winged blackbirds are the continent's most abundant birds. Some populations do not migrate but others, namely those that breed in Canada and the northern United States, migrate to the south. Huge feeding flocks of several million birds may form during winter.

Piping plover (left)
Diminutive piping plovers nest on Atlantic beaches and migrate in winter to similar habitats further south, from North Carolina to Mexico and the Caribbean. These ground-nesting birds are endangered due to habitat loss and human disturbance.

Black-throated blue warbler (right)
Climate change threatens birds such as the black-throated blue warbler because it may influence food availability at breeding, stopover, and wintering sites.

Rose-breasted grosbeak (above)
Rose-breasted grosbeaks that breed in the eastern parts of their range follow the Atlantic flyway through Central America and northwest South America to winter in southern Mexico. Those breeding in the north and west follow the Mississippi flyway.

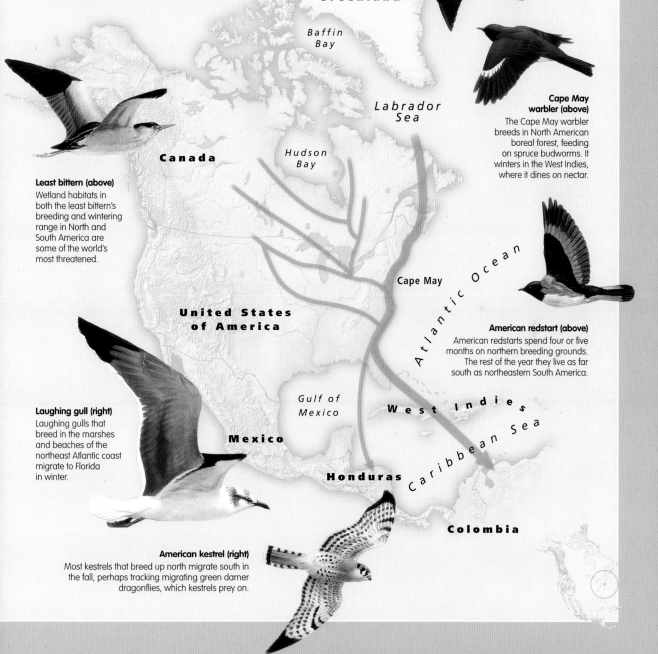

The Atlantic flyway (below)
The heaviest concentration of birds at Cape May occurs during fall, or southbound, migration—from June 23 to January 10—as birds travel down the Atlantic coast. Spring, or northbound, migration runs from January 10 through to June 10. Birds tend to favor the same migratory paths, but do not necessarily take identical routes each year. For example, there are thousands of hawks in Cape May in fall but relatively few in spring because they are dispersed by differences in air currents.

Rusty blackbird (left)
The increasingly rare rusty blackbird winters in the wooded wetlands of the southeastern United States.

Cape May warbler (above)
The Cape May warbler breeds in North American boreal forest, feeding on spruce budworms. It winters in the West Indies, where it dines on nectar.

Least bittern (above)
Wetland habitats in both the least bittern's breeding and wintering range in North and South America are some of the world's most threatened.

American redstart (above)
American redstarts spend four or five months on northern breeding grounds. The rest of the year they live as far south as northeastern South America.

Laughing gull (right)
Laughing gulls that breed in the marshes and beaches of the northeast Atlantic coast migrate to Florida in winter.

American kestrel (right)
Most kestrels that breed up north migrate south in the fall, perhaps tracking migrating green darner dragonflies, which kestrels prey on.

Greenland

Baffin Bay

Labrador Sea

Canada

Hudson Bay

United States of America

Cape May

Atlantic Ocean

Gulf of Mexico

West Indies

Mexico

Caribbean Sea

Honduras

Colombia

THE COASTAL PLAINS
BUTTERFLIES OF CAPE MAY

Cape May is home to 105 butterfly species. Many are permanent residents but others are migrants that stop here in the fall to refuel on goldenrod and other fall-flowering plants. Most spectacular are the monarchs, large black and orange butterflies that blanket small pine trees overnight and flit constantly across the sky during the day. These brave insects undertake a perilous journey across the sea to reach their winter home in Mexico.

Migrating monarchs

Monarch butterflies escape the winter's cold by migrating up to 2,000 miles (3,200 km) from Canada to Mexico and coastal California. Tens of thousands of monarchs descend on Cape May during their annual fall migration.

Mourning cloak (left)

The mourning cloak, known as Camberwell beauty in the UK, lives for 11–12 months, one of the longest life spans of any butterfly. It is common in North America and northern Eurasia. In North America, mourning cloaks are often one of the first butterflies to be seen in spring, as they overwinter in sheltered spots such as tree cavities rather than migrating.

Painted lady (right)

Painted lady butterflies migrate from the deserts of northern Mexico to spend summer throughout North America.

Red-spotted purple (below)

Bird predators avoid the striking red-spotted purple butterfly because it mimics the coloration and pattern of the bad-tasting pipevine swallowtail. Both species are common in the eastern United States.

Tiger swallowtail (above)

Spectacular eastern tiger swallowtails overwinter in their eastern North American range and emerge early in the spring to sip nectar from early flowering plants. These solitary butterflies are high fliers and can be seen soaring among tall trees.

Common buckeye (below)

Successive broods of common buckeyes move north from Mexico through the United States, then late summer broods head south again. Along the Atlantic coast, this beautiful butterfly prefers sandy beaches.

CHAPTER FOUR

CENTRAL & SOUTH AMERICA

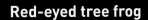

Red-eyed tree frog

This remarkably colored red-eyed tree frog clasps a branch in a Costa Rican rain forest. Most tree frogs have adhesive pads on their fingers and toes that help them stick to leaves and branches. Some even have an opposable first finger, like a thumb, that allows them to grasp twigs and stems.

CENTRAL & SOUTH AMERICA

Highly distinctive species from every class in the animal kingdom are found in Central and South America. Biodiversity is particularly remarkable in Central America, which supports around 7 percent of Earth's species on less than half a percent of its land. The region is dominated by large river systems and wetlands, but also renowned for its imposing mountain chains and volcanoes, deserts, lakes, vast grasslands, and tropical forests. Coastal and marine life is abundant amid the tropical coral reefs, mangroves, and seagrass beds. At its southernmost tip, South America also supports sea ice.

Central America
Located at the junction of two continental masses and the world's largest oceans, this region is rich in biodiversity.

Amazon rain forest
The largest rain forest in the world, which crosses nine international borders, features wildlife and ecosystems barely seen elsewhere.

The Gran Chaco
Climatic extremes and wooded grasslands that become swamps in the rainy season are typical of this region.

The Andes wilderness
Low valleys grazed by camelids and snowy peaks patrolled by the spectacular condor typify the wild beauty of these mountains.

Patagonia
Dramatic mountainous landscape at America's southern extreme adjoins the rugged coast, where Antarctic animals are regular visitors.

The Galápagos Islands
The fascinating species found here are supremely adapted to the harsh life on one of Earth's major tropical archipelagos.

Life in the Caribbean
Shallow warm waters harbor magnificent coral reefs and their resident turtles, fish, and crustaceans in the stunning Caribbean.

Climate (left)

The northwest coast, parts of the northeast and east coasts, and much of the Amazon Basin experience hot, wet weather year-round. Moist onshore winds are the main drivers of the subtropical conditions that extend down the east coast. Cold ocean currents off the west coast dry the air, producing an arid coastal strip. Conditions vary across the Andes: generally it is hot and wet in the north, hot and dry in the center, and cold and wet in the far south. Patagonia, east of the Andes, has low rainfall.

CLIMATE ZONES

Wet tropical	Semiarid	Continental
Seasonal tropical	Mediterranean	Temperate
Arid	Subtropical	Cold temperate

Vegetation (right)

Amazon rain forests extend over much of the great river basin, giving way to cloud forest in the Andes and tropical deciduous woodlands in the north and east. The savanna grasslands that characterize the Gran Chaco and the Brazilian Highlands merge to the southeast with more temperate grasses on the Pampas. Thick stands of temperate rain forest occur on the southern Andes, but the Central Andes and Patagonia are sparsely vegetated. The Atacama Desert is virtually devoid of plant life.

VEGETATION ZONES

Tropical forest	Mediterranean forest and scrub
Seasonal tropical forest	Midlatitude grassland
Desert	Midlatitude forest
Tropical grassland	Boreal forest

Land cover (right)

More than half the continent is studded with forests that account for one-quarter of the world's entire forest cover. Extensive reserves of land suited to cultivation characterize South America, but most of it is prized as pasture. The continent's remaining land cover includes wetlands, sprawling coastal settlements, the barren Andean uplands, and the deserts of the west and south.

PROPORTIONS OF TOTAL LAND AREA

Forest and woodland	53.1%
Arable land	28.7%
Grazing	6.6%
Other land	11.6%

CENTRAL AMERICA

The near-equatorial isthmus of Central America holds a greater concentration of plant and animal life than anywhere else in the world. Central America is characterized by contrasting landscapes, ranging from dry, sea-level forests to those shrouded in mist, and from lofty peaks and coastal marshes to fertile valleys that continue to be shaped by volcanic activity. The abundant natural bounty here includes rivers and lakes, islands, thermal springs, lagoons, estuaries, beaches, and reefs. Distinct climates meet and merge in Central America as a result of topography rather than seasonal change.

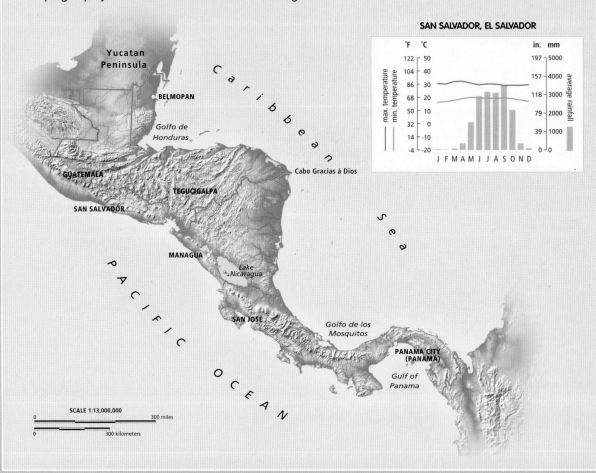

SAN SALVADOR, EL SALVADOR

Yucatan Peninsula

BELMOPAN

Caribbean Sea

Golfo de Honduras

GUATEMALA

Cabo Gracias á Dios

TEGUCIGALPA

SAN SALVADOR

MANAGUA

Lake Nicaragua

PACIFIC OCEAN

SAN JOSÉ

Golfo de los Mosquitos

PANAMA CITY (PANAMÁ)

Gulf of Panama

SCALE 1:13,000,000

0   300 miles

0   300 kilometers

Scarlet macaws (left)

Scarlet macaws are large, colorful parrots that are often seen perched on cliffs, where they consume clay, which helps them digest poisonous chemicals found in the unripe fruit they feed on. Macaws fly in pairs or small groups and can reach speeds of 35 miles per hour (56 km/h).

Boa constrictor (right)

The boa constrictor is a large, solitary snake with powerful muscles that allow it to squeeze its prey until it suffocates. The snake can open its jaws wide and swallows its prey whole, head-first. Strong acids in its stomach help the constrictor digest its meal.

White-faced capuchin (left)

The white-faced capuchin is easy to spot in the wild. Small and inquisitive, it usually travels in groups from tree to tree with the aid of its prehensile tail. These monkeys forage for fruit and insects at all forest levels and communicate using chatters and shrieks.

Mantled howler monkey (right)

The mantled howler monkey is often heard before it is seen. Even in dense rain forest its roars and piglike grunts travel for more than half a mile (0.8 km). A particularly large hyoid bone in the monkey's throat allows it to make such a resonant noise.

Tayra (left)

The tayra is a mustelid related to the otter, but it lives in trees. It hunts small vertebrates, such as rabbits and lizards, and also feeds on carrion and fruits. Similar to a weasel, this skilled climber is able to jump from tree to tree when threatened.

Tent-making bats

Honduran white bats are among the few bat species that construct their own roosts. They bite the veins of large heliconia leaves until they collapse downward, forming a partially enclosed, tent-like space beneath which the bats hang upside down. These "tents" provide protection from jungle rains, sunlight, and predators such as snakes. One male and five or six females usually roost together.

Making a tent (left)

Bats chew away the connection between the midrib and edge of the leaf until it droops.

Protected roost (left)

The little Honduran white bats roost in the tent they have created.

CENTRAL AMERICA
RAIN FORESTS

Central American rain forests are found in the tropical zone between the Tropic of Cancer and Tropic of Capricorn, where the weather is hot and humid year-round. The tree canopy is an evergreen cover of towering trees that reach heights of 60 to 150 feet (20–50 m). These giants are laced with vines and lianas, and their trunks coated with epiphytes, bromeliads, and orchids. The forest's lower layers are densely planted with smaller trees and shrubs, and the deeply shaded forest floor is covered with decaying plant material. Birds, bats, monkeys, reptiles, and ants are found here, and many other insects that share a symbiotic relationship with plants as seed dispersers.

DEFORESTATION

- 1800
- 1960
- Present

Blue morpho butterfly (above)
The blue morpho butterfly owes its coloring to tiny ridges on its wings that reflect light, giving it dazzling visibility. By contrast, the wing undersides are brown. Generally the butterfly rests with its wings closed to make it less visible to enemies.

Margay (left)
An accomplished climber, the margay spends most of its life in the forest canopy. This agile cat has specially adapted claws and rotating ankle joints that enable it to climb down trees headfirst and run upside down beneath branches.

Frogs and toads

The frogs and toads of Central American rain forests include climbers that inhabit the canopy and ground-dwelling species that shelter in caves, burrows, or rock crevices. Most, however, live in ponds and streams. Their bulging eyes enable them to see in any direction, and their sticky tongues are adept at capturing insect prey. Rain forests echo with loud frog and toad calls during the mating season.

Poison dart frog (below)

While some frogs rely on camouflage to remain unobtrusive, the brilliant red skin and blue legs of the poison dart frog serve as a warning to predators. The toxic excretions of this 2.3-inch (6-cm) frog were used by native people on the tips of their arrows.

Harlequin frog
Atelopus varius

Golden toad (above)

The golden toad, an endemic species of Costa Rica, is thought to be extinct in the wild. During the rainy season, hundreds of black females and yellow males used to gather in small ponds to mate. Females produced 200 to 400 eggs and, after hatching, the larvae remained in water for about five weeks as they progressed toward adulthood.

Most tadpoles must stay in water, but the rain forest air is so moist that the poison dart frog can carry its young on its back.

Three-toed sloth (left)

Although sometimes taken for a primate, the brown-throated three-toed sloth is more closely related to the armadillo. Its movements and metabolism are slow: the sloth takes almost a month to digest a single meal and moves at an average speed of 1.2 miles per hour (2 km/h). Sloths are strictly arboreal and descend to the ground only to defecate.

Kinkajou (right)

The kinkajou is also known as the sugar bear because of its habit of eating honey, nectar, and sweet fruits. It licks nectar from flowers with its flexible tongue. Pollen that sticks to its fur is carried from flower to flower, making it an important pollinator.

Resplendent quetzal (above and left)

The quetzal is often found in wild avocado trees, the fruits of which it swallows whole. This bird constructs its nest in the cavity of a dead tree, choosing a soft trunk that is in an advanced state of decomposition. The two feathers that form its tail, which can be 23 inches (59 cm) long, protrude from the nest to protect them from damage.

Keel-billed toucan (left)

Although it appears weighty, the keel-billed toucan's bill is light and hollow, and supported by thin rods of bone. The toucan employs its bill skillfully; using its feather-like tongue to catch insects and flick fruits down its throat.

CENTRAL AMERICA
THE JAGUAR

The jaguar is a top terrestrial predator in Central and South America, and plays an important role in regulating the populations of its prey species. Factors that influence the jaguar's future prospects include its persecution by humans, because it is seen as a threat to people and livestock; hunting for fur and sport; a shortage of prey; loss of habitat, including the conversion of land for cattle ranching; and inadequate protection measures.

Forest habitat (above)
Jaguars depend on forest for their survival; it is their original and preferred habitat for hunting. They climb trees to lie in wait for wild prey below. But because of forest loss as a result of new settlements and clearing for pasture, some jaguars now also kill domestic animals and livestock in areas close to human populations.

Conservation watch: jaguar

Historically, the jaguar's range stretched from the southwestern United States to southern Argentina, but today it is extinct in the United States and numbers have drastically declined in Mexico and Argentina. Recovery programs have included on-the-ground monitoring, predator controls, minimizing livestock conflicts, and creating jaguar reserves.

☐ Present
☐ Former

Swimming
The jaguar is an excellent swimmer and thrives near rivers, lakes, and streams. When hunting fish it stalks, under cover, in its target's blind spot, before leaping into the water to catch its prey. The jaguar is also capable of carrying a large kill while swimming.

Coat

The jaguar can be distinguished by the presence of small dots within the larger rosette markings on its magnificent coat. Each marking has a unique pattern that is like a fingerprint.

Teeth

Four canine teeth, up to 2 inches (5 cm) long, are used for killing, while the sharp, scissor-like carnassial teeth enable the jaguar to crush bones, or to hold meat and cut it at the same time.

Leopard-like ancestors

Jaguars are thought to have evolved from leopard-like ancestors in Eurasia, and to have arrived on the American continent 1.8 million to 10,000 years ago via the Bering land bridge. The modern jaguar is smaller than its cousin the leopard, but both have muscular bodies, roar, climb trees, and enjoy swimming.

Eyes

The pupils of the night-hunting jaguar can contract to mere slits and its night vision is up to seven times better than that of a human. It also has excellent binocular vision for judging distances.

Prey

Jaguars are known to eat more than 85 species of prey, taking advantage of the diversity of animals that are found in rain forests. They prefer to hunt at night, but may capture prey during the day if it is available. Jaguar prey ranges from domestic livestock to tapirs, deer, sloths, peccaries, capybaras, agoutis, crocodiles, snakes, monkeys, and fish. They can consume up to 55 pounds (25 kg) of meat in one sitting, followed by periods of famine.

Capybara

Because capybaras live in groups, a jaguar has a good chance of taking at least one while it feeds underwater, or catching one on land, where capybaras are less agile.

AMAZON RAIN FOREST

The Amazon rain forest is the oldest and largest tropical forest in the world. It extends across the Amazon River basin, a region of 2.6 million square miles (6.7 million km²) drained by the Amazon River. This huge expanse of rain forest contains an amazing collection of wildlife, including tarantulas, caterpillars, scorpions, anacondas, caimans, jaguars, sloths, tamarins, toucans, and vampire bats. Since 1970, more than 232,000 square miles (600,000 km²) of the forest has been destroyed, occupied, or altered by human activity.

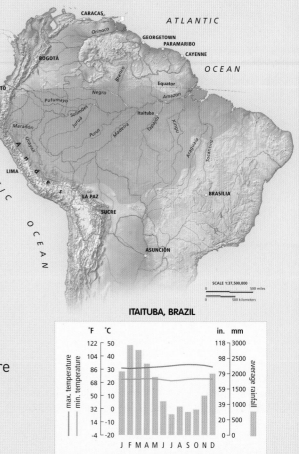

SCALE 1:37,500,000
500 miles
500 kilometers

ITAITUBA, BRAZIL

River creatures

At 3,976 miles (6,400 km) long, the Amazon River is the world's second longest river. Its waters have a high diversity of fish, estimated at more than 3,000 species. During each rainy season extensive forested areas adjacent to the river are flooded and many fish, reptiles, and mammals move into the newly flooded areas to feed, mainly on fallen fruits from the trees. They also reproduce here, returning to the main channels when the floodwaters recede.

Giant river otter (left)
Only a few thousand giant river otters are thought to survive in the wild because of hunting by humans. With a body length of 80 inches (2 m), this is the world's longest river otter.

Black caiman (right)
The black caiman is the largest member of the *Alligatorinae* family. Its prey includes capybaras, fish, turtles, and deer.

Layers of the rain forest (right)

The Amazon rain forest can be divided vertically into four layers, each representing a unique ecosystem. At the emergent level, eagles and parrots inhabit the tallest trees. The broad crowns of these giants form the canopy, which is home to snakes, toucans, tree frogs, monkeys, parakeets, orchids, and bromeliads. In the understory, shrubs and ferns grow larger leaves to capture sunlight, but only a thin layer of decaying organic matter is found on the forest floor.

Pygmy marmoset (right)

Inhabitants of rain forests canopies, pygmy marmosets are the smallest monkeys. Habitat destruction does not seem to have affected these primates, but some populations have declined because of the pet trade.

Hoatzin (above)

The hoatzin, which belongs to a primitive bird family, lives in flocks of 50 or more. These birds perch on low or middle branches that overhang water, and eat green leaves and buds. They have a large food-storage pouch and esophagus for converting plant carbohydrates into sugars they can digest.

Pink river dolphin (above)

The pink river dolphin is the largest and most common of the world's five freshwater dolphins. It uses echolocation to find prey in the muddy rivers of flooded jungles.

Pirarucu (below)

The carnivorous, air-breathing pirarucu, the world's largest freshwater fish, is thought to be 200 million years old. It can grow to up to 120 inches (3 m) in length.

EMERGENTS

Orange-winged amazon
Amazona amazonicas

CANOPY

Black spider monkey
Ateles belzebuth

Maned three-toed sloth
Bradypus torquatus

Orange-winged amazon
Amazona amazonicas

UNDERSTORY

Channel bill toucan
Ramphastos Vitellinus

FOREST FLOOR

Green anaconda
Eunectes murinus

AMAZON RAIN FOREST
LIFE IN THE TREETOPS

Most of the species diversity within tropical rain forests is concentrated in the canopy, just below the top, emergent, layer. It is estimated that biodiversity within the canopy includes 40 percent of all plant and animal species globally. Some of the world's loudest birds and primates, which rely on sound signals to communicate because the dense leaf cover precludes visual territorial displays, are found here. All creatures of the canopy are adapted to take advantage of treetop resources, such as nesting sites, transit routes, hiding places, and a diet of insects, fruits, seeds, flowers, and leaves.

Storing carbon, releasing oxygen (above)
Forest canopies absorb carbon dioxide from the atmosphere and convert it into oxygen. The canopy thereby plays an important part in global climate regulation because it enables the exchange of heat, water vapor, and atmospheric gases.

Julia butterfly (left)
A yellow-orange tropical butterfly with long forewings, the Julia butterfly is a fast-flying, long-lived species. It is active during the day, feeding on the nectar of flowers, such as lantana and shepherd's needle.

Hairy protection (left)
Julia butterfly females lay their eggs on new passionflowers, the leaves of which nourish their larvae. Caterpillars rely on their short antennae to locate food, and defend themselves with fine, irritating bristles that lodge in the skin of their predators.

⚡ Conservation watch: pied tamarin

The pied tamarin, which has one of the smallest ranges of any primate, is dying out in the forests of the Amazon. Its habitat is reduced and fragmented because of urban expansion and agriculture. This small monkey, which weighs just 0.9 pounds (400 g), lives in groups of two to 10.

Red howler monkey (right)

The red howler monkey travels through the forest by clambering along tree branches and lianas, but also descends to the ground, where it walks and runs. It is most active in the morning and evening. Its calls carry more than 1.5 miles (3 km) through the forest.

Emperor tamarin (left)

The emperor tamarin lives in groups and communicates using strident squeaks. The male is an attentive father, assisting at the birth of its offspring and taking responsibility for their grooming and transportation. This tiny monkey is territorial and fiercely defends its area.

Brown-eared woolly opossum (below left)

The woolly opossum's large, protruding eyes face forward, giving it a monkey-like appearance. Its hands and feet are adapted for climbing and gripping, and its flexible prehensile tail provides extra support. It is usually solitary, but opossums gather where fruit is plentiful.

Harpy eagle (below)

The largest and most powerful raptor of the tropical rain forest is the harpy eagle, which preys upon tree-dwelling mammals. Like other birds of prey, it brings green twigs to its nest to protect its young from insects and parasites, and to ensure a cooler home environment.

Orange-winged parrot (above)

The sociable orange-winged parrot moves through the crowns of tall trees searching for ripe fruits and nuts. True to its name, this parrot has a brilliant orange patch on its wings, visible as it flies over the forest at dawn.

THE ANDES

The Andes is the world's longest mountain range, stretching for 5,000 miles (8,000 km) and with mountain peaks reaching higher than 12,000 feet (3,600 m) along half its length. Glaciers, snow-capped volcanoes, desert plateaus, cloud forests, deep gorges incised by rivers, and peaceful valleys characterize the landscape. Conifers and ferns abound and wildlife is richly varied: 50 percent of the plant and animal species found here are unique to the area.

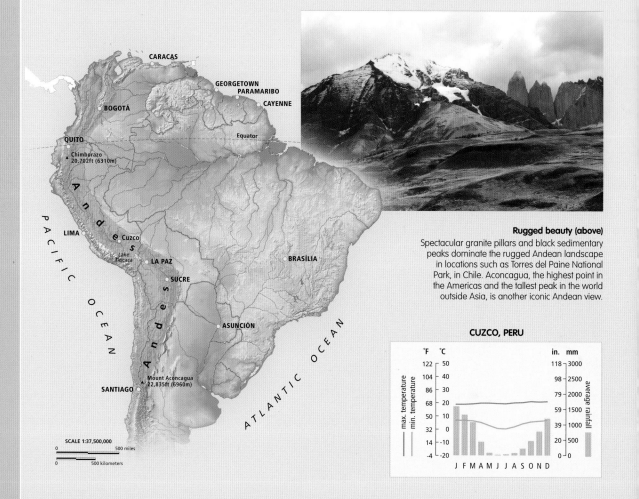

Rugged beauty (above)
Spectacular granite pillars and black sedimentary peaks dominate the rugged Andean landscape in locations such as Torres del Paine National Park, in Chile. Aconcagua, the highest point in the Americas and the tallest peak in the world outside Asia, is another iconic Andean view.

CARACAS

GEORGETOWN
PARAMARIBO
CAYENNE

BOGOTÁ

QUITO
Chimborazo
20,702ft (6310m)
Equator

LIMA
Cuzco
Lake
Titicaca
LA PAZ
SUCRE

BRASÍLIA

ASUNCIÓN

Mount Aconcagua
22,835ft (6960m)
SANTIAGO

PACIFIC OCEAN

ATLANTIC OCEAN

Andes

SCALE 1:37,500,000
0   500 miles
0   500 kilometers

CUZCO, PERU

°F °C   in. mm
122 50   118 3000
104 40   98 2500
86 30   79 2000
68 20   59 1500
50 10   39 1000
32 0   20 500
14 -10   0 0
-4 -20

max. temperature
min. temperature
average rainfall

J F M A M J J A S O N D

Spectacled bear

The spectacled or Andean bear lives mainly in cloud forests. It is the only representative of the family *Ursidae* in South America and the only surviving member of the genus *Tremarctos*, thanks largely to its ability to climb even the tallest trees. It has good eyesight and is named for the markings around its eyes.

Bear's nest

Guandera
Clusia flaviflora

Bromeliad
Neoregellia sp.

Epiphytic ferns

Orchid
Encyclia sp.

Treetop platform (right)
The spectacled bear's diet consists of fruits and bromeliads, which grow on high tree branches that cannot support the animal's weight. To reach the fruit and flowers, the bear bends the branches toward itself. Smaller branches that snap off are used by the bear to build a rough nest that serves as a strong feeding and sleeping platform for several days.

Andean cock-of-the-rock display (left)
The female cock-of-the-rock builds a shallow nest of mud and vegetation on rock walls, hence the bird's name. The polygamous males compete in a mating ritual (pictured here) that includes dances, gymnastics, plumage displays, and vocal challenges.

Giant anteater (below)
As its name suggests, the giant anteater feeds voraciously on ants and termites, consuming up to 30,000 in a day. It claws open termite mounds and uses its tubular snout and long sticky tongue to gather up insects. Though generally docile, it can defend itself against pumas and jaguars.

Conservation watch: Brazilian tapir

The Brazilian tapir, a large animal with a distinctive fleshy snout, prefers water to land. Its peaceful nature and meaty physique make it a favorite hunting target. However, the tapir is now vulnerable because of such illegal hunting, combined with the destruction of its tropical forest habitat. After a gestation of 400 days, females produce just one offspring.

THE ANDES
THE CONDOR

Considered to be the largest flying bird, the Andean condor is threatened by aggressive hunting, loss of habitat, food and air pollution, and water contamination. This bird of prey and its close cousin, the California condor, are part of the New World vultures, a family more closely related to storks than to the vultures of Africa. Standing nearly 3 feet (90 cm) tall, the condor feeds on the carrion of animals such as deer, elk, cows, and llamas.

In flight (left)
Condors flap their wings to lift off the ground, but rarely do so when flying. Instead, they rely on thermal air currents to stay aloft. A condor's wingspan can exceed 10 feet (3 m), which enables it to fly in a way that expends as little energy as possible.

Preying on newborns
Condors prefer open areas to search for carrion, newborns, and dying animals, which are their main food sources. If a meal has been particularly large, they may have to spend hours on the ground or perched on a low branch before they are able to take off again. Condors can travel 200 miles (320 km) a day soaring at great heights while foraging for food. They are able to survive without a meal for at least two weeks.

⚡ Northern pudu
The world's smallest deer, the 12-inch (30-cm) tall pudu is one of the condor's favorite meals. It also feeds on the remains of sheep, llama, vicuña, cattle, seals, and the eggs of seabirds.

Inflatable neck

Condors do not possess vocal cords, so they inflate air sacs in their neck when agitated or excited. This gives them the appearance of being larger than they really are.

Naked head

A naked head and neck enables the condor to feed off carcasses without soiling its feathers. Blood vessels concentrated over the head help to radiate heat and keep the bird cool.

Feet

The condor has strong legs but relatively weak, blunt nails that are more like toenails than talons. The feet are thus better adapted to walking than grasping.

The largest bird of prey (left)

Condors are well-adapted carcass feeders. Since they are not outfitted to stalk, their feet have rounded claws instead of the sharp talons of raptors. Bare skin on a condor's head and neck keeps it safe from bacteria when it sticks its heads into carcasses, and its beak is tailored for tearing fleshy tissue.

THE ANDES
LLAMAS AND RELATIVES

The South American or New World camelids belong to the *Camelidae* family composed of llamas, alpacas, guanacos, and vicuñas, although the term llama is commonly used to refer to all four races. Their habitat includes near-waterless environments located in cool, dry mountain valleys and the Altiplano—the high Andean plateau distinguished by its steep, rocky mountain ledges that extends through Bolivia, Peru, Argentina, and Chile. While the guanaco and vicuña live in the wild, the llama and alpaca were domesticated between 4000 and 3500 BCE and used for transportation, milk, meat, and fiber.

High altitude habitat
Camelids are adapted to life at high altitude: thick wool coats protect them from the cold temperatures, and their extra-large lungs and hearts supply their bodies with sufficient oxygen to cope with the thin air.

Curious camelids

Camelids are herbivores that use their protruding lower incisor teeth and cleft upper lip to snip grass and tear off leaves. They have long legs, necks, and eyelashes, and slender heads. Camelids lack functional hooves and, instead, have feet made up of just two toes covered by a nail. These social herd animals require little water and can rest on their stomachs by bending their hind limbs when seated.

Guanaco

Considered as ancestors of llamas and alpacas, guanacos can survive for long periods without drinking. While grass constitutes the bulk of their diet, they also graze on trees and range from sea level to elevations of 13,000 feet (4,000 m).

Vicuña

Mountain-grazing vicuñas range from elevations of 10,000 to 16,000 feet (3,000–5,000 m). They use one territory for day foraging and a higher, and therefore safer, territory for sleeping. Their fleece once clothed Inca royalty.

Alpaca

The most numerous camelid, the alpaca, is reared in the Andean mountains for its fiber, which is finer than cashmere. Most concentrated in the southern highlands of Puno, the alpaca can be distinguished by its bangs.

Llama

The llama was one of the first animals to be domesticated, some 6000 years ago. As pack animals, they can carry loads of 50 to 75 pounds (25–35 kg) and cover up to 20 miles (30 km) in a day.

Wool

A llama's coat consists of a double layer of fibers. About 20 percent is the protective outer coat of long and coarse guard hairs, while the inner layer comprises short, wavy fibers that are fine and soft.

Small intestine

Third stomach chamber

First stomach chamber

Second stomach chamber behind first

Digestion

Llamas have a three-chambered stomach and chew their cud, a mouthful of swallowed food that is regurgitated from the first stomach. Once swallowed, the cud moves to the next two chambers to be fully digested, thereby extracting as much energy as possible from the food. Llamas spit their mouth contents or a foul-smelling fluid from their first stomach chamber to defend themselves.

GALÁPAGOS ISLANDS

The Galápagos archipelago is located in the Pacific Ocean some 620 miles (1,000 km) off the coast of Ecuador. All the Galápagos reptiles, half the birds, 32 percent of the plants and 25 percent of the fish, as well as many invertebrates, are found nowhere else. The islands' isolation, combined with ocean currents, the merging of cold and warmer waters, warm air temperatures, high rainfall, and a lack of predators have all contributed to the evolution of this unique suite of species. Endemic mockingbirds, seabirds, finches, and marine life inspired Charles Darwin's theory of evolution following his visit in 1835.

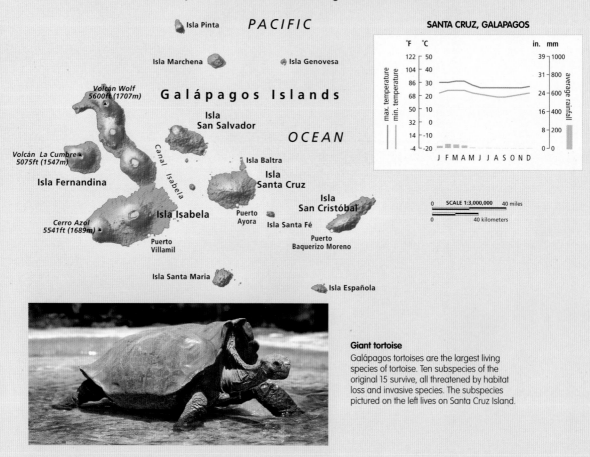

Isla Pinta

PACIFIC

Isla Marchena

Isla Genovesa

Volcán Wolf
5600ft (1707m)

G a l á p a g o s   I s l a n d s

Isla
San Salvador

OCEAN

Volcán La Cumbre
5075ft (1547m)

Isla Fernandina

Canal Isabela

Isla Baltra

Isla
Santa Cruz

Isla
San Cristóbal

Cerro Azol
5541ft (1689m)

Isla Isabela

Puerto
Ayora

Isla Santa Fé

Puerto
Villamil

Puerto
Baquerizo Moreno

Isla Santa Maria

Isla Española

SANTA CRUZ, GALAPAGOS

°F	°C		in. mm
122	50		39 – 1000
104	40		31 – 800
86	30		24 – 600
68	20		
50	10		16 – 400
32	0		8 – 200
14	-10		0 – 0
-4	-20		

max. temperature
min. temperature

average rainfall

J F M A M J J A S O N D

SCALE 1:3,000,000   40 miles

0   40 kilometers

Giant tortoise
Galápagos tortoises are the largest living species of tortoise. Ten subspecies of the original 15 survive, all threatened by habitat loss and invasive species. The subspecies pictured on the left lives on Santa Cruz Island.

Galápagos land iguana (above)
Galápagos land iguanas are vegetarians, subsisting mostly on the fruit and pads of *Opuntia* cactus. They use their front feet to scrape away larger cactus thorns, then gulp down cactus fruit in a few swallows.

Marine iguana (left)
The only seagoing lizard, the marine iguana develops its colors with age. Young iguanas are black, while adults can be shades of green, red, gray, or black, depending on their island home. Males favor sunny, rocky shores during the day, where sea breezes keep them cool.

Blue-footed booby (below)
Male blue-footed boobies pick up their distinctive blue feet and perform an exaggerated step-walk during their courtship dance (pictured below). The world's 40,000 breeding pairs, half of which inhabit the Galápagos Islands, breed opportunistically.

Finches

Thirteen species of finch live on the Galápagos Islands. All evolved from a single pair of birds similar to the blue-black grassquit finch found along the Pacific Coast of South America. Finches have bills of varying size and shape, suited to their diet and lifestyle. According to Darwin's theory of evolution, beaks changed as the birds developed different tastes for fruits, seeds, or insects.

Ancestral ground finch
Probably ate seeds

Sharp-billed finch
Pecks seabirds to drink blood

Warbler finch
Extracts insects from twigs

Woodpecker finch
Raps rotten wood for insects

Large ground finch
Cracks and eats large seeds

Large cactus ground finch
Feeds on cactus flowers and seeds

THE GRAN CHACO

The Gran Chaco comprises savannas and thorn forests so impenetrable that until relatively recently they had barely been explored. As this region is a low, flat, alluvial plain, the climate is hot and dry in summer, but river flooding during the rainy season converts large areas into swamps. The resident wildlife continues to amaze scientists, with animals such as the Chacoan peccary, rediscovered in 1975, and at least 18 species of armadillo. However, the Chaco is threatened by unrestricted forest clearing, overgrazing, and oil and gas exploration.

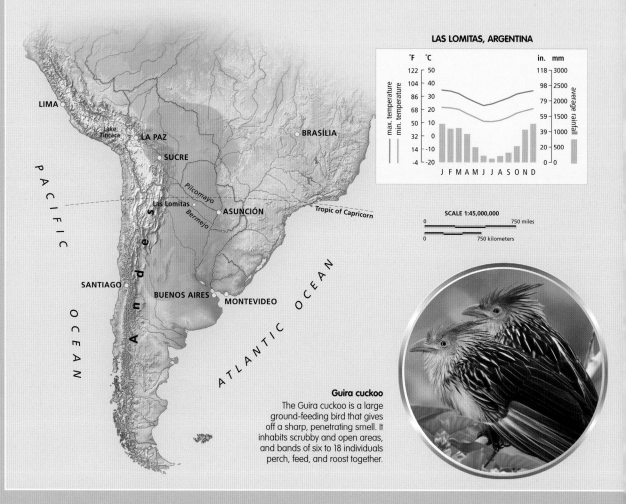

LAS LOMITAS, ARGENTINA

max. temperature
min. temperature
average rainfall

J F M A M J J A S O N D

SCALE 1:45,000,000

0 — 750 miles

0 — 750 kilometers

LIMA

LA PAZ

SUCRE

BRASÍLIA

Pilcomayo

Las Lomitas

Bermejo

ASUNCIÓN

Tropic of Capricorn

SANTIAGO

BUENOS AIRES

MONTEVIDEO

PACIFIC OCEAN

ATLANTIC OCEAN

Lake Titicaca

Andes

Guira cuckoo
The Guira cuckoo is a large ground-feeding bird that gives off a sharp, penetrating smell. It inhabits scrubby and open areas, and bands of six to 18 individuals perch, feed, and roost together.

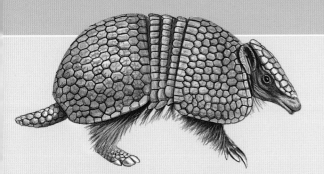

To defend itself from predators the three-banded armadillo rolls into a tight ball using its thick bony plating like armor.

Three-banded armadillo (above)

Largely solitary and nocturnal, but more diurnal during winter, the armadillo's armored skin is composed of hard, bony plates. The three-banded armadillo is the only species of armadillo capable of rolling completely into a ball—others have too many dermal plates.

Blue-fronted parrot (left)

In parrot society, the blue-fronted parrot is regarded as one of the best talkers and singers. It uses a repertoire of whistles, shrieks, and yapping notes. Active, intelligent, and graceful, this bird is commonly kept as a pet.

Maned wolf (right)

The maned wolf looks like a cross between a wolf and a fox. It has evolved long legs for roaming long distances in tall grass. This wolf takes one partner for life, but only interacts with its mate during the breeding season. Just 1,500 maned wolves remain in the wild, and numbers continue to decline because of threats such as habitat loss, agriculture, and hunting.

Chacoan peccary

The Chacoan peccary emits a strong odor from a scent gland on its back when frightened or to mark its territory. It is the largest of the four peccary species that live in South America, and is distinguished by its long bristles and shaggy appearance. The Chacoan peccary was thought to be extinct until 1975, when it was rediscovered.

PATAGONIA

At the southern end of the American continent, stretching from the Atlantic to the Pacific Ocean through the Andes, is Patagonia. It is a region of immense beauty, and includes habitats as varied as treeless plains, forests, snow-capped mountains, large deserts, fertile valleys, wide seashores, impressive lakes, and gigantic glaciers. Some parts of Patagonia preserve untouched vegetation, others are sparsely populated, while the human influences of ranching and mining prevail elsewhere.

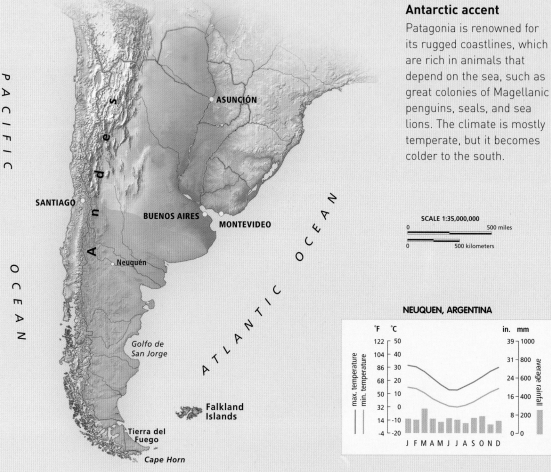

Antarctic accent

Patagonia is renowned for its rugged coastlines, which are rich in animals that depend on the sea, such as great colonies of Magellanic penguins, seals, and sea lions. The climate is mostly temperate, but it becomes colder to the south.

PACIFIC OCEAN

ASUNCIÓN

SANTIAGO

BUENOS AIRES

MONTEVIDEO

Andes

Neuquén

ATLANTIC OCEAN

Golfo de San Jorge

Falkland Islands

Tierra del Fuego

Cape Horn

SCALE 1:35,000,000

0   500 miles

0   500 kilometers

NEUQUEN, ARGENTINA

max. temperature
min. temperature

average rainfall

J F M A M J J A S O N D

Southern elephant seal (left)

The southern elephant seal is so named for its enormous size and the bull's habit of inflating its trunk to impress rivals. The female comes ashore to give birth and does not leave the beach until her pup is weaned, losing weight as her offspring thrives.

Magellanic penguins (right)

Magellanic penguins return to breed at the rookery where they were born. Parents share the task of incubating the eggs for 42 days, then raise the chicks together for the next 29 days.

Geoffroy's cat (left)

A small, solitary wild cat, Geoffroy's cat has razor-sharp claws that help it climb trees. These claws are also used to stab and secure prey, such as small lizards, rodents, insects, frogs, and fish. Humans are the cat's only predators.

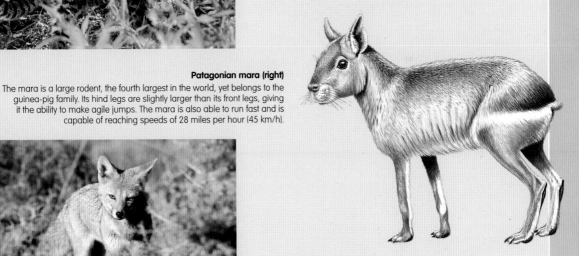

Patagonian mara (right)

The mara is a large rodent, the fourth largest in the world, yet belongs to the guinea-pig family. Its hind legs are slightly larger than its front legs, giving it the ability to make agile jumps. The mara is also able to run fast and is capable of reaching speeds of 28 miles per hour (45 km/h).

Patagonian gray fox (left)

The survival of the Patagonian gray fox has depended on its ability to eat everything from meat and fruit to eggs and carrion. When eating cooperatively, foxes without litters bring food to families with pups. This fox evolved from the wolf family 6 to 7 million years ago.

PATAGONIA

BIRDS OF THE PAMPAS

The Pampas is one of the richest grazing lowland areas in the world, but also one of the most endangered habitats on Earth. Found primarily in Argentina and Uruguay, it covers an area of 300,000 square miles (800,000 km²) from the Andes mountains to the Atlantic Ocean. Migration has enabled birds to adapt to life in these windy grasslands. Marine and coastal birds make a stopover in the region, and more than 300 bird species have been recorded here. Land birds are not as common, but among the most notable is the rhea.

Great pampas finch (right)
The great pampas finch feeds on seeds and grain. It lives near marshes and in association with tall grasses and shrubs, and is usually seen in a bush calling, or on top of a tree or branch singing. It belongs to one of the most diverse terrestrial vertebrate orders, the Passeriformes, which encompass more than half of all bird species.

⚡ Conservation watch: greater rhea
The greater rhea is the largest South American bird. Although flightless, it can run at speeds of 37 miles per hour (60 km/h). The number of greater rheas is declining due to habitat loss caused by the conversion of grasslands to farmland and ranchland, as well as increased hunting.

Chalk-browed mockingbird (above)
The chalk-browed mockingbird is skilled at imitating the melodies of other birds. During the breeding season the male performs a nuptial dance that involves flying from branch to branch and landing slowly with its tail splayed.

Buff-necked ibis (left)

The buff-necked ibis, also known as the white-throated ibis, uses its curved bill to feed on insects, reptiles, frogs, and small mammals. It is easy to spot on the pampas.

Toco toucan (below)

The toco toucan is the largest of nearly 40 species in the toucan family. It feeds on fruit, but when nesting it also consumes a variety of insects as a source of protein. The toucan resides in the jungle canopy and actively flies in noisy flocks of six birds.

THE CARIBBEAN SEA

The warm, tropical waters of the Caribbean Sea are renowned for their coral reefs and red mangroves. A nursery ground for an array of marine animals, the sea is home to saltwater crocodiles, dozens of species of stony corals, sea snails, spiny lobsters, and more than 500 species of fish.

SAN JUAN, PUERTO RICO

ATLANTIC

OCEAN

Tropic of Cancer

HAVANA

Yucatan Peninsula

Greater

Grand Cayman

PORT-AU-PRINCE

SANTO DOMINGO

Leeward Islands

SAN JUAN

Antilles

Lesser Antilles

Windward Islands

Caribbean Sea

SAN JOSÉ

CARACAS

PANAMA CITY

PACIFIC OCEAN

SCALE 1:20,000,000

500 miles

500 kilometers

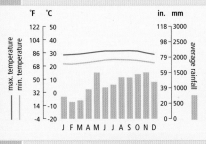

Cuban tody (above)
The Cuban tody is endemic to Cuba and the oldest survivor of five tody species confined to the Greater Antilles. The bird often appears inactive as it feeds on flies from a perch. However, its bright red throat bristles when issuing its "tot-tot-tot" call.

Whale shark (right)
The whale shark is the biggest fish in the world. It feeds on plankton by sucking in huge quantities of plankton-rich water, then expelling the water through its gills.

Red mangroves

Red mangroves are one of the key habitats of the region, providing food and shelter, above and below the water, for creatures such as manatees, kingfishers, crabs, egrets, common black hawks, and boa constrictors. Mangroves, fringing the shores, also protect against land erosion and storm damage, and filter pollutants.

West Indian manatee (right)
Ancient mariners mistook manatees for sirens or mermaids. This gentle mammal can swim vertically or upside down, and dense bones enable it to stay suspended at, or below, the water's surface.

Mesoamerican Reef

The world's second largest reef system, the Mesoamerican Reef covers the northern end of the Yucatán Peninsula in Mexico, the coasts of Belize and Guatemala, and stretches to the Bay Islands in northern Honduras. This region hosts productive ecosystems, such as barrier and fringing reefs, atolls, patch reefs, and seagrass beds. It is at risk from rising water temperatures and increasing tourism.

Stoplight parrotfish (right)
The parrotfish grazes on algae that grows on rocks or coral, pulverizing the algae with its grinding teeth to aid digestion. It later excretes the undigested coral, which then forms much of the sand in the fish's range.

Solenodon (below)
Endemic to Cuba, the solenodon is one of the world's few poisonous mammals. It lives in burrows and is nocturnal. Venomous saliva is secreted by the submaxillary gland that flows through the grooved second lower incisor, which delivers the poisonous bite—only inflicted when the solenodon is provoked by one of its own kind.

Reef octopus (left)
The Caribbean reef octopus is able to squeeze its body through cracks in the reef that are only the size of a keyhole.

CHAPTER FIVE

ASIA

Bengal tiger

The Bengal tiger is found in India, Bangladesh, Nepal, Bhutan, and Burma. Fewer than 2,500 individuals remain in the wild. The tiger can swim rivers more than 3 miles (5 km) wide and is a formidable predator. Its large canines, sharp, retractable claws, and massive forelimbs and shoulders allow it to single-handedly overpower prey much bigger than itself.

ASIA

Asia is the world's largest continent, covering 8.6 percent of Earth's surface area. This vast area has many different kinds of climate, with some of the coldest and some of the hottest, some of the wettest and some of the driest places on Earth. Several biogeographic areas are considered biodiversity hot spots, harboring unique plants and animals. Among the many rivers that traverse the Asian continent, 32 rivers exceed 1,000 miles (1,600 km) in length. The Yangtze River in China is the longest at 3,915 miles (6,300 km).

The steppes of Central Asia
The steppes are Asia's unique grassland ecosystem that harbors grazing herbivores and burrowing rodents. The flat-bottomed lakes here attract numerous waterbirds.

The Siberian wilderness
This is the world's largest remaining wilderness, dominated by taiga forests. The wildlife includes carnivores such as the brown bear and the Siberian tiger.

Hot and cold deserts
These are semiarid areas with extremely harsh climates. Many of the wildlife species here burrow underground for insulation against the extreme heat and aridity.

The Himalayas
This is the world's longest and highest mountain range. About one-third of the mountain animals in the world occur here, and are well adapted for the environment.

The Indian Subcontinent
The junction between the east and the west, this region has a great diversity of natural forest and wetland ecosystems that harbor a rich wildlife.

The mountains of southwest China
This region is known to be the most botanically rich temperate region in the world. Many species of rare and threatened wildlife, including the giant panda, live here.

East Asia
Located at the intersection of three of Earth's tectonic plates, this region contains numerous volcanoes, hot springs, and mountains, and is prone to earthquakes.

The lower Mekong
The lower catchment of the Mekong River and its floodplains are host to a wide variety of natural vegetation types and rich aquatic and terrestrial wildlife.

The Sundaland
An area of high tectonic movement, the Sundaland consists of some 17,000 islands, with vast areas of tropical rain forest. Many species here are in danger of extinction.

Philippine Archipelago
The Philippine Archipelago has an ancient geological history, unique palms, and a tiny primate, the tarsier, that has, for its size, the largest eyes of any known mammal.

Climate (left)

The Malay Archipelago and Malay Peninsula climate is dominated by heat and humidity. Southern Asia and the Indochina Peninsula experience more seasonal rains, often associated with monsoonal winds. The arid interior owes its temperature extremes largely to the Himalayas, which block moisture-bearing winds. A band of almost constant high pressure creates hot, arid conditions in the southwest. Cold polar air prevails in the north.

CLIMATE ZONES

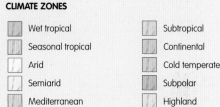

Wet tropical		Subtropical	
Seasonal tropical		Continental	
Arid		Cold temperate	
Semiarid		Subpolar	
Mediterranean		Highland	

Vegetation (right)

The Arctic Ocean is flanked by a strip of tundra. To its south, stretching from the Urals to northern Japan, is a broad belt of coniferous forest that yields to deciduous and mixed forests that extend down the east coast, steppe grasslands, and scrub. Either sparse, arid-adapted plants or none at all typify large areas of the interior and southwest. In Southeast Asia, high rainfall supports some of the most extensive tropical forests in the world.

VEGETATION ZONES

Tropical forest		Midlatitude grassland	
Seasonal tropical forest		Midlatitude forest	
Desert		Boreal forest	
Tropical grassland		Tundra	
Mediterranean forest and scrub		Mountain vegetation	

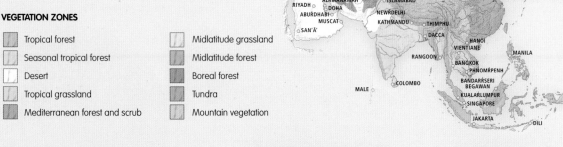

Land cover (right)

Siberia still wears a cloak of conifer forests, the largest in the world. Much of Asia is arable land, but has to support some of the highest population densities on Earth.

PROPORTIONS OF TOTAL LAND AREA

- Forest and woodland
- Arable land
- Grazing
- Other land

18.0%
17.6%
35.8%
28.6%

ASIA

BIG CATS

The Asian big cats are the top mammalian predators in Asia. They include the Asiatic lion, tiger, and seven subspecies of leopard. All the big cats in Asia are threatened with extinction, because of loss of habitats, poaching, and increasing human–wildlife conflict.

BIG CAT	GROUP SIZE	LITTER SIZE	LIFE EXPECTANCY IN THE WILD
Bengal tiger	Solitary	2–4	15–20 years
Sri Lankan leopard	Solitary	2–3	10–15 years
Asiatic lion	2–5	1–4	12–16 years
Snow leopard	Solitary	1–4	15–18 years

Sri Lankan leopard
The Sri Lankan leopard is a subspecies of leopard endemic to Sri Lanka. A solitary hunter, it is the island's top mammalian predator and occurs widely in a variety of habitats, including dry monsoon forests, montane forests, thorn scrub, and lowland tropical rain forests.

Asiatic lion
The Asiatic lion is a subspecies of lion restricted to the Gir Forest National Park of western India. They are highly social animals that live in prides led, usually, by two adult females. The males are less social, and associate with the pride mostly for mating and during the hunting of large prey.

Tigers

The tiger is the largest wild cat in the world. There are six surviving subspecies. The Bengal tiger is found in the Indian subcontinent and Burma, the Siberian tiger in eastern Siberia, the Indochinese tiger in the Mekong region, the Malayan tiger on the Malay Peninsula, the Sumatran tiger (pictured) in Sumatra, Indonesia, and the South China tiger in South China. The last three subspecies are critically endangered. As the tiger is a territorial animal that needs large contiguous areas of habitat that support its prey, it often faces conflicts with humans. Tigers feed mostly on prey such as deer, sambar, and buffalo, but will feed on small mammals, ground-dwelling birds, and reptiles if larger prey is scarce. After a careful stalk, tigers make a short rush toward prey. If a kill is made in the open, a tiger usually drags the carcass into dense cover before beginning to feed.

Bengal tigers fighting (above)

The Bengal tiger is a solitary and extremely territorial animal. Adult tigers guard their territories fiercely. Males in particular will not tolerate any incursions by other males, leading to fights that can end in death or severe wounds.

Former range
Current range

Bengal tiger cub and mother (left)

A tiger litter is made up of two to four cubs, which are raised by the mother. They do not become independent of her for about 18 months.

Conservation watch: snow leopard

The wild population of the snow leopard is estimated to be 3,900–6,400 individuals. It lives in the rugged mountainous regions—up to 17,000 feet (5,180 m)—of Central Asia. Snow leopards are illegally hunted because of the high demand for their thick pelt. They also run into conflict with humans when they attack livestock.

THE CENTRAL ASIAN STEPPES

The steppes are a unique grassland ecosystem that occurs in the lower slopes, foothills, and basins of Central Asia's mountain ranges. These areas may be semidesert, or covered with grasses and shrubs, depending on the season and the latitude. The climate is continental and temperate, with hot, windy summers, periodic droughts, and cold winters. The wildlife is dominated by grazing species, such as antelope, sheep, and wild horses, and small burrowing rodents.

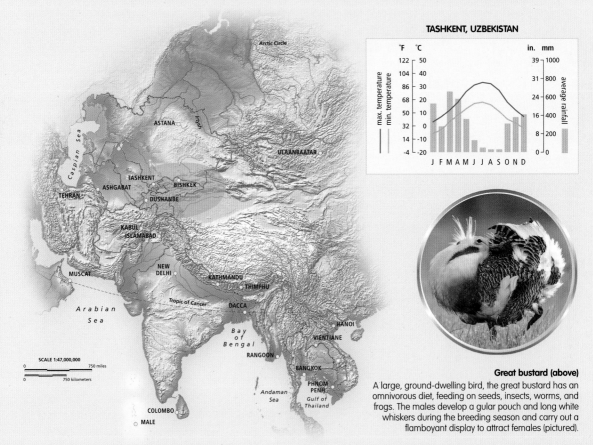

TASHKENT, UZBEKISTAN

SCALE 1:47,000,000

Great bustard (above)

A large, ground-dwelling bird, the great bustard has an omnivorous diet, feeding on seeds, insects, worms, and frogs. The males develop a gular pouch and long white whiskers during the breeding season and carry out a flamboyant display to attract females (pictured).

Ground dwellers

The small ground-dwelling animals of the steppe include a variety of rodents such as ground squirrels, hamsters, voles, jerboas, and marmots, and lagomorphs such as pikas and hares. They contribute to the natural disturbance regime in the steppes because their burrowing habits cause the recycling of nutrients, which sustains the ecosystem.

Daurian pika (right)
Pikas are small relatives of rabbits and hares. During late summer and early fall, Daurian pikas make communal hay piles, which they use to survive through the winter.

Black-bellied hamster (right)
This, the largest species of hamster, lives solitarily in burrows. Stores of cereal grains, seeds, and peas are kept in its winter burrow, which can reach more than 6 feet (2 m) below the surface.

Saiga antelope (right)
The saiga is recognizable by its oversized, flexible nose, which is thought to warm the air as it breathes in winter and to filter out the dust in summer. Saigas occur in large herds that move across the semidesert steppes grazing on several species of plants, including some that are poisonous to other animals. Males compete for females, fighting with their horns and head-butting.

⚡ Conservation watch: Przewalski's horse

Przewalski's horse is the last surviving subspecies of wild horse. Przewalski's horse once roamed freely on the steppe along the Mongolia–China border. The wild population declined in the 20th century because of hunting, harsh climate, and habitat loss. It was dying out in Mongolia in the 1960s and was designated "extinct in the wild." These horses have since been bred in captivity and reintroduced in Mongolia.

THE SIBERIAN WILDERNESS

The Siberian wilderness is the world's largest remaining wilderness and provides a safe home for many species of plants and animals. The climate is continental, with hot summers and extremely cold winters, below -76°F (-60°C). The area is dominated by taiga forests, characterized by widely spaced coniferous trees such as spruce and pines. The wildlife here includes large herbivores such as moose and reindeer (caribou), and carnivores such as the red fox, lynx, and wolves.

VERKHOYANSK, RUSSIAN FEDERATION

Siberian jay (below)

The small-bodied Siberian jay is a widely distributed species in the wild coniferous forests of the north. It is commonly found in unspoilt forests with small natural clearings, marshy hollows, and ancient spruce trees. The birds have various alarm calls to warn others if predators are near.

ARCTIC OCEAN

Kara Sea

Laptev Sea

East Siberian Sea

Yenisey

Lena

Verkhoyansk

Arctic Circle

Sea of Okhotsk

ASTANA

Lake Baikal

ULAANBAATAR

Sea of Japan

TOKYO

BISHKEK

P'Y¬NGYANG
SEOUL

BEIJING

Yellow Sea

East China Sea

SCALE 1:50,000,000

0   750 miles

0   750 kilometers

Kamchatka brown bear (above)

This subspecies of the brown bear (*Ursus arctos*) is the largest bear in Eurasia. It has an omnivorous diet, feeding on fish, fruit, and nuts. Kamchatka bears are at risk from hunting.

Ural owl (above right)

The Ural owl, a medium- to large-sized bird, has a wide distribution in the taiga forests, where it feeds at night on rodents and other medium-sized birds. It is an aggressive owl and will chase birds of prey from its territory. It nests in hollow tree trunks.

Reindeer (below)

Reindeer are large herbivores that live in herds and travel long distances annually. They feed on the leaves of willows and birches, as well as grazing on sedges and grasses. During winter, when snow covers much of their range, their main food source is lichens.

⚡ **Conservation watch: Siberian tiger**

The Siberian tiger is a rare subspecies that is confined to the Amur region in the Russian far east, where it preys primarily on wild boar and red deer. It is considered to be the largest wild cat in the world but is endangered, with only about 480 to 560 individuals occurring in the wild.

HOT AND COLD DESERTS

The hot and cold deserts of Central Asia are semiarid regions with extremely harsh climates. Wide temperature variations are experienced on a daily basis, with fiercely hot temperatures during the day and below freezing temperatures at night. The landscape in these areas consists of sand dunes, barren mountains, and pebble grounds that cover vast plains. The plant cover is sparse and limited to species that tolerate drought. Animals that live in desert regions have developed adaptations that allow them to cope with the lack of water, the extreme temperatures, and the shortage of food.

Cold desert

A cold desert is one that has snow in winter, such as the Gobi Desert in China, with temperatures as low as -40°F (-40°C). The small animals that live here burrow underground to keep warm. These deserts are also home to animals such as gazelles, jerboas, Bactrian camels, and sand grouse.

Bactrian camel (above)
The critically endangered Bactrian camel occurs in northwestern China and Mongolia. It is identifiable by the two humps on its back, where it stores fat that can be converted into water and energy. These camels develop a thick, shaggy coat in winter.

Jerboa

Jerboas are small jumping rodents in the *Dipodidae* family. The several species all have long hind legs, a long tail, and nocturnal feeding habits. The great jerboa (pictured above right) is found in the steppes and northern deserts of Asia. It hibernates from the first frosts till spring.

Jerboa skeleton (right)
A jerboa's hind legs are immensely long in relation to the rest of its body. It is these legs that give the jerboa its agile, jumping gait.

ULAANBAATAR

ASTANA

TASHKENT
Karakum
Desert
BISHKEK
DUSHANBE
KABUL
ISLAMABAD

Taklimakan Desert

Dalanzadgad

G o b i D e s e r t

BEIJING

P'Y-NGYANG
SEOUL
TOKYO

Sea of
Japan

Yellow
Sea

East China
Sea

Thar Desert

NEW
DELHI

KATHMANDU

THIMPHU

Tropic of Cancer

DACCA

HANOI

VIENTIANE

South
China
Sea

SCALE 1:35,000,000

0   500 miles
0   500 kilometers

B a y
o f
B e n g a l

RANGOON

BANGKOK

PHNOM
PENH

DALANZADGAD, MONGOLIA

°F	°C		in.	mm
104	40		39	1000
86	30		31	800
68	20		24	600
50	10		16	400
32	0		8	200
14	-10			
-4	-20			
-22	-30		0	0

max. temperature
min. temperature
average rainfall

J F M A M J J A S O N D

Hot desert

Hot deserts, such as the Thar Desert in India and Pakistan, are warm throughout the fall and spring seasons and extremely hot during the summer, when temperatures can rise to 129°F (54°C). These areas receive little rainfall during winter. The rodents and reptiles that live in hot deserts often burrow during the day, where they are insulated from the heat and aridity.

Gray monitor (below)

The gray monitor is a burrowing lizard, widely distributed in deserts. It is active during the early hours of the day and feeds on vertebrates such as rodents, lizards, snakes, birds, frogs, and toads. It also eats eggs. These monitors become relatively inactive during the winter period.

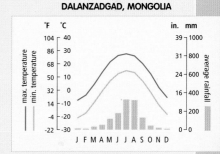

Chinkara (above)

Also known as the Indian gazelle, the chinkara is found in deserts, arid plains, and scrub. Around 80,000 live in India's Thar Desert. They can go without water for long periods, getting all the moisture they need from plants and dew.

THE HIMALAYAS

The Himalayan system is the longest—1,490 miles (2,400 km) west to east—as well as the highest mountain range in the world. The vegetation varies from the unexplored tropical rain forests of the Eastern Himalayas to the sparse vegetation of the cold desert areas of the Transhimalaya. Here the wildlife is characterized by species adapted to cold and mountainous regions and about one-third of the mountain animal species in the world are found in the area. Many species of goat antelope, including the mountain goat, Himalayan tahr, chiru, and takin, make this region their home.

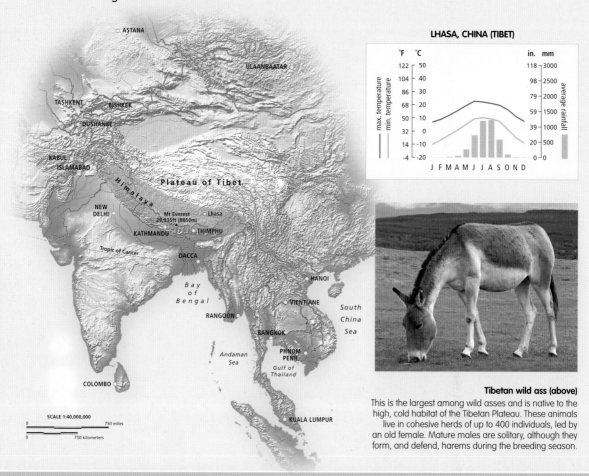

LHASA, CHINA (TIBET)

Tibetan wild ass (above)
This is the largest among wild asses and is native to the high, cold habitat of the Tibetan Plateau. These animals live in cohesive herds of up to 400 individuals, led by an old female. Mature males are solitary, although they form, and defend, harems during the breeding season.

Himalayan tahr (left)

This is a wild goat species that inhabits the rugged wooded hills and mountain slopes in the Himalayas. The tahr spends the summers grazing in high pastures, then descends to lower elevations to form mixed-sex herds in the winter.

🄵 Markhor (below)

The markhor is an Asian mountain goat found in the western Himalayas, at elevations as high as 11,800 feet (3,600 m), in scrub forests of oaks, pines, and junipers. Males are solitary; females and their young live in small herds.

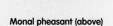

Monal pheasant (above)

This large-sized pheasant is the national bird of Nepal. The males have a long, metallic green crest and brightly colored plumage. They occur in pairs during the breeding season and form large groups that roost communally during the winter.

🄵 Chiru antelope (below)

Chiru antelopes usually congregate in herds of more than 100 individuals and they live in the high mountain grassland and semidesert areas of the Tibetan Plateau. The species has been over-exploited for its skin and is now endangered.

Yak (above)

Wild yaks live in treeless mountains and plateaus feeding on grasses, lichens, and other plants. Vegetation in their habitat is scarce, so they must travel great distances to find sufficient food. They live at altitudes between 10,500 and 17,500 feet (3,200–5,400 m) but are insulated by a thick coat of shaggy hair.

THE INDIAN SUBCONTINENT

The subcontinent has a tropical monsoon climate, with a wet and a dry season. Mainland India harbors a diversity of natural ecosystems, including forests, and an array of wetlands influenced by large rivers such as the Brahmaputra, Ganges, and Indus. The continental island of Sri Lanka is separated from southern India by the Palk Strait. Although the plants and animals in Sri Lanka show affinities with those of peninsular India, many species have evolved in isolation.

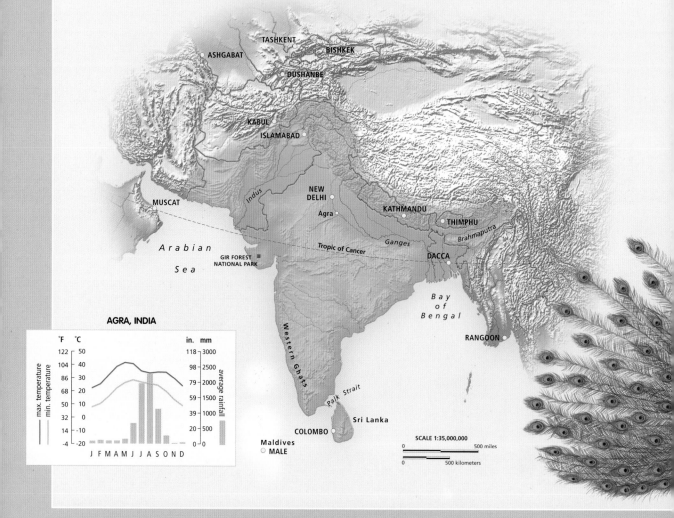

AGRA, INDIA

SCALE 1:35,000,000

0 ... 500 miles

0 ... 500 kilometers

⚡ Conservation watch: Asian elephant

The Asian elephant is the largest terrestrial mammal in Asia. There are two subspecies in the region, occurring in peninsular India and Sri Lanka respectively. A small percentage of the adult males bear tusks. These elephants have a semi-prehensile "finger" at the tip of their trunk, which enables them to gather plant matter for feeding. They live in herds, led by an old female; mature males live a solitary life.

Gaur (right)
A species of wild cattle, the gaur is recognizable by its humped back and large body supported by slim white legs. It is the heaviest and most powerful of all wild cattle and lives in herds of up to 40 individuals, led by an old female. Adult males may be solitary.

Common langur (left)
The common langur is a sub-arboreal species of monkey that spends much of its time on the ground. It lives in medium to large groups of 10 to 64 individuals led by a dominant male. The group is likely to have a home range of 495 to 2,965 acres (200–1,200 ha).

Indian rhinoceros (right)
Indian rhinoceros are generally solitary although their home ranges may overlap and they sometimes gather in small, short-term groups. These large herbivores have one horn, a good sense of smell, but poor eyesight. They can run at speeds of up to 25 miles per hour (40 km/h). Their conservation status is classified vulnerable.

Peacock dance (below)
The male peafowl, the "peacock," bears a group of colorful display feathers on its tail coverts. During the breeding season the peacock expands these feathers and performs a dance in front of peahens to entice them for mating. These feathers are shed annually during the non-breeding season.

King cobra

The largest poisonous snake in the world, the king cobra feeds almost exclusively on other snakes. It hunts its prey during the day, and is able to swallow snakes that are much bigger than its own head. King cobras are capable of killing a human with a single bite.

Mongoose predator (below)
The mongoose is a predator of cobras. When a cobra encounters a mongoose, it flattens its upper body by spreading its ribs, forming a "hood." It hisses and strikes at the predator. The mongoose expands its fur and jumps around the cobra, aiming to give the snake's neck a lethal bite.

THE MOUNTAINS OF SOUTHWEST CHINA

This region includes both temperate and alpine mountains, with a wide variety of vegetation types, including broadleaved and coniferous forests, bamboo groves, scrub communities, savanna, meadow, prairie, freshwater wetlands, and alpine scrub. The wild animals that make their home here include more than 200 mammals and 600 bird species, including many that are rare and globally threatened. The world's best-known flagship species for conservation, the giant panda, is restricted to the shrinking forests of this region.

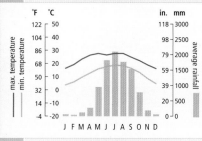

XICHANG, CHINA

SCALE 1:30,000,000

0 — 500 miles

0 — 500 kilometers

Bay of Bengal

Andaman Sea

Gulf of Thailand

South China Sea

KATHMANDU
THIMPHU
DACCA
HANOI
VIENTIANE
RANGOON
BANGKOK
PHNOM PENH
BANDAR SERI BEGAWAN
Gongga Shan
Xichang
Tropic of Cancer

⚡ Golden snub-nosed monkey (left)

Golden snub-nosed monkeys are an arboreal species that inhabit temperate montane forests. These monkeys feed mainly on lichens and other plant matter, supplemented with insects. Found in groups of 20 to 30, they have a large home range of up to 15 square miles (40 km²).

Giant panda

Giant pandas live in dense bamboo and coniferous forests at altitudes of 5,000 to 10,000 feet (1,500–3,000 m). Their diet consists mainly of bamboo leaves, stalks, and roots, which they crush with their powerful jaws and teeth. A single adult panda must eat 20 to 40 pounds (9–18 kg) of food a day to survive, and spends up to 15 hours a day feeding. Although principally terrestrial, pandas can climb trees.

Panda cub (left)

Female pandas give birth to one or two cubs weighing 4 to 8 ounces (100–200 g) each, in a sheltered den. A female in general raises only one cub, if more than one is born.

Former range

Current range

Red goral (left)

The red goral, the smallest of the currently recognized goral species, lives at high elevations of 6,500 to 13,000 feet (2,000–4,000 m). It feeds primarily on lichens, supplemented with tender stems, leaves, and twigs from shrubs. It is agile, moving easily and with speed over rough terrain.

Conservation watch: red panda

Red pandas, which are arboreal and generally solitary, occur in both deciduous and coniferous forests. They rest during the day in the branches of trees and in tree hollows. Their primary food is bamboo, but they also feed on berries, blossoms and leaves of other plants. They are threatened by deforestation and other human activities.

Takin (right)

The takin, a goat-antelope, is found in bamboo forests at altitudes of 6,500 to 14,500 feet (2–4,500 m). It feeds during the day on grasses, buds, and leaves. Takin gather in small herds in winter and herds of up to a hundred individuals in summer.

THE SUNDALAND

The Sundaland covers the western half of the Indo-Malayan archipelago, and consists of some 17,000 equatorial islands. The landscape is dominated by lowland rain forests. Sandy and rocky coastlines support scrubland, muddy shores are lined with mangrove forests, and large peat-swamp forests occur further inland. Montane forests, where plants such as lichens and orchids are plentiful, occur at higher elevations. Higher still, scrubby subalpine forests are dominated by rhododendrons. Sundaland fauna is diverse, with nearly 3,000 species of vertebrates, one-third of them endemic. Many are threatened with extinction.

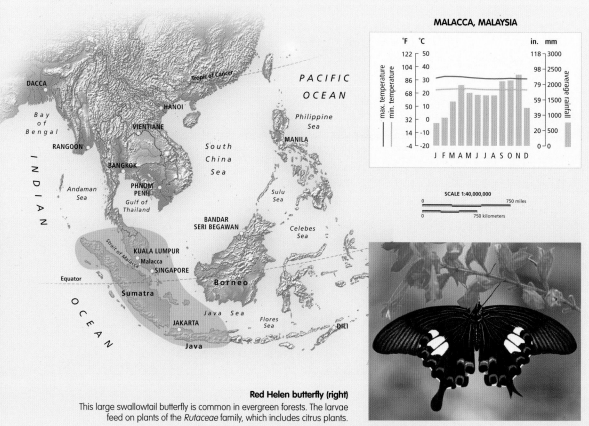

MALACCA, MALAYSIA

SCALE 1:40,000,000

Red Helen butterfly (right)
This large swallowtail butterfly is common in evergreen forests. The larvae feed on plants of the *Rutaceae* family, which includes citrus plants.

Indonesian marine life

The waters around the Indonesian archipelago are relatively shallow and warm, and the rich nutrients support a diversity of marine life. These waters also serve as an important migratory area for more than 30 species of marine mammals.

Nudibranch
These are a group of marine slugs—mollusks without an external shell. They store toxic chemicals in their body for defense.

Marine turtles
Six of the world's seven marine turtle species are found in Indonesia. There are important nesting and foraging grounds on the many islands, and migration routes converge at the crossroads of the Pacific and Indian oceans.

⚡ Sumatran rhinoceros (left)
The Sumatran rhinoceros is the smallest of the living rhino species. A solitary browser, it eats up to 110 pounds (50 kg) of leaves, saplings, twigs, and shoots a day. Individual bulls have territories as large as 20 square miles (50 km^2).

Former range

Current range

Komodo dragon (below)
The world's largest lizard, the Komodo dragon is restricted to Komodo and neighboring islands. Although these lizards usually feed on carrion, they have been known to kill large animals such as goats, deer, and cattle by ambushing them in undergrowth. Previous belief that damaging bites were due to bacterial infection are now better understood as resulting from tissue-destroying venom.

Tail
The dragon's muscular tail is used for balance, capturing prey, and in fights with other males.

Skin
The scales in the dragon's skin have sensory plaques connected to nerves that facilitate its sense of touch.

Claws
Strong claws help the Komodo dragon dig burrows and disembowel prey.

Tongue
The Komodo's sense of smell functions through its tongue, which samples the air then "smells" by touching the roof of its mouth.

SOUTHEAST ASIAN TROPICAL RAIN FORESTS

Lowland tropical rain forests are forests that receive high rainfall, more than 80 inches (2,000 mm) annually, with a mean annual temperature of 75°F (24°C), and an average relative humidity of 85 percent. These forests occur in a belt around the equator, between the Tropic of Cancer and the Tropic of Capricorn, at elevations of less than 3,300 feet (1,000 m). The diverse wildlife in tropical rain forests in Southeast Asia is well adapted to live in the trees, and includes birds, arboreal amphibians, reptiles, and mammals.

Flying frog (left)
A large tree frog with brilliant colors, Wallace's flying frog is well adapted to life in the treetops. Its fingers and toes are webbed and a membrane of skin stretches between the limbs.

Flying lizard (left)
This is an arboreal lizard that can spread out folds of skin attached to its movable ribs to form "wings" that it uses to glide from tree to tree over distances of more than 26 feet (8 m).

Hornbill nest (above)
Hornbills nest in cavities in living trees. The male locates a possible site and invites the female to inspect it. The birds mate and the female then seals herself inside the nest chamber using rotten wood, clay, and regurgitated food supplied by the male. The male delivers food to its mate, and later to the chicks. In most large forest species, the female remains in the nest until the chick is fledged, a total period of incarceration of up to five months.

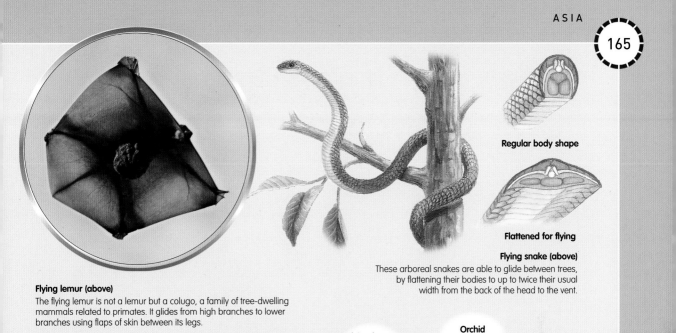

Regular body shape

Flattened for flying

Flying snake (above)
These arboreal snakes are able to glide between trees, by flattening their bodies to up to twice their usual width from the back of the head to the vent.

Flying lemur (above)
The flying lemur is not a lemur but a colugo, a family of tree-dwelling mammals related to primates. It glides from high branches to lower branches using flaps of skin between its legs.

Flying lemur
Galeopterus variegates

Orchid
Vanda sp.

Epiphytic orchid
Phalenopsis sp.

Pygmy tree shrew
Tupaia minor

Red-eyed tree frog
Agalychnis callidryas

Fern
Drymoglossum piloselloides

Rain forest life (right)
An estimated 70 to 90 percent of life in the rain forest exists in the trees above the shaded forest floor. A variety of epiphytes, such as colorful orchids and mosses, occur in the trees. Arboreal animals such as flying squirrels, tree frogs, and flying lizards feed, nest, and rest among the foliage.

Orchid
Coelogyne sp.

Orchid
Dendrobium sp.

Flying lizard
Draco volans

SOUTHEAST ASIAN TROPICAL RAIN FORESTS
FOREST PRIMATES

Primates of the rain forests include apes (orangutans and gibbons), monkeys (including langurs and macaques), and prosimians (lorises and tarsiers). These primates can be found climbing through the canopy or foraging on the forest floor.

⊙ The orangutan

Among the great apes of the world, orangutans are the most arboreal, spending most of their time in trees. They are generally solitary, with large territories. A major portion of their diet consists of fruits, supplemented with young leaves, shoots, seeds, bark, flowers, insects, and small vertebrates. They are remarkably intelligent great apes and are known to use tools for feeding. In the evening they construct a "nest" in a tree, using leaves and branches, and rest there for the night.

Baby orangutan (above)
Females give birth to a single offspring, and care for it for some six to seven years. Newborn infants weigh around 3 pounds (1.5 kg). They begin to take soft food from their mother's lips at about four months. A baby orangutan clings to its mother's abdomen by entwining its fingers in and gripping her fur until it is a year old, then it begins to ride on her back, which it may continue to do for more than two years.

Proboscis monkey (left)

The male of this primate species has a distinct, enlarged, protruding nose, which can be up to 7 inches (17 cm) long. It also has an enlarged belly. It is found in small groups of 10 to 32, living on a diet of seeds, leaves, shoots, and fruit.

White-handed gibbon (below)

The white-handed gibbon is a small, tailless ape with dense, shaggy fur that varies from black to pale gray. It has long, slender arms and the upper side of its hands and feet are white. Its opposable thumb is used for climbing or grooming.

Slow loris (above)

The slow loris, a nocturnal, arboreal primate, is known for its slow, deliberate movements and powerful grasp. It can be difficult to remove the slow loris from a branch. These animals live alone or in small family groups. As opportunistic carnivores, they typically eat insects, birds' eggs, and small vertebrates.

EAST ASIA

This region stretches from humid subtropics in the south to a temperate zone in the north featuring boreal mixed forests. About half the mammal, reptile, and amphibian species in Japan are endemic. The long, north–south stretch of the Korean Peninsula and its complex topography have resulted in wide climatic variations. Wildlife here includes the roe deer, Amur goral, sable, brown bear, tiger, lynx, northern pika, water shrew, and Manchurian ring-necked pheasants. Species such as the black bear, mandarin vole, river deer, fairy pitta, and ring-necked pheasant are found in the lowlands.

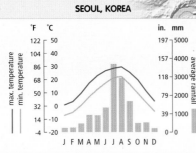

Mandarin duck (above)
The male mandarin duck has a red bill, whiskers on its face, and stunning color patterns on its body feathers. This duck breeds in wooded areas near shallow lakes, marshes, or ponds. It nests in cavities in trees close to water and feeds mainly on plants and seeds.

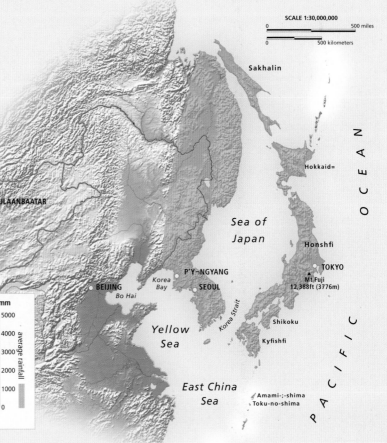

SCALE 1:30,000,000

Sakhalin

Hokkaid=

Sea of Japan

Honshfi

TOKYO
Mt.Fuji
12,388ft (3776m)

P'Y¬NGYANG

Korea Bay

SEOUL

BEIJING

Bo Hai

Korea Strait

Shikoku

Kyfishfi

Yellow Sea

East China Sea

Amami-;-shima
Toku-no-shima

ULAANBAATAR

OCEAN

PACIFIC

SEOUL, KOREA

Asiatic black bear (left)

Asiatic black bears inhabit moist deciduous forests and brushy areas. They migrate into the mountains during summer, returning to valleys for winter. They are excellent tree climbers and strong swimmers.

⚡ Amami rabbit (below)

An endemic rabbit that is restricted to two islands in Japan, Amami-O-shima and Toku-no-shima, the amami rabbit is found mainly in dense old-growth forests. It has primitive morphological traits that resemble those found in fossils from the Miocene Epoch.

Oriental fire-bellied toad (above)

This is a mostly aquatic frog, which spends much of its time in shallow pools. Its bright coloration warns predators of its toxicity. When disturbed, it secretes a milky toxin from its abdominal skin.

Japanese giant salamander (above)

This, the second largest salamander in the world, grows up to 5 feet (1.5 m) in length. It is an aquatic species restricted to mountain streams that have clear, cool water. It has poor eyesight but feeds at night on insects, crabs, frogs, and fish.

Japanese macaques

The Japanese macaque is an omnivorous, semi-terrestrial primate that lives in groups of 10 to 160. It is able to swim distances of 500 yards (0.5 km). In Shiga Heights, in central Japan, macaques remain near hot springs in winter, which helps to maintain their body temperature.

⚡ Conservation watch: red-crowned cranes

These cranes are among the rarest cranes in the world and, weighing from 15 to 20 pounds (7–10 kg), are the heaviest. They breed in Siberia and parts of Mongolia and migrate to East Asia in the fall. Adults reinforce their pair bond in a synchronized courtship dance (pictured). They inhabit wetlands and eat insects, frogs, and grasses.

Staying warm (above)

These macaques have a thick coat of fur, which helps them withstand cold winter temperatures. Mothers protect their young from the cold by huddling closely together.

THE LOWER MEKONG

The Mekong is the longest river in Southeast Asia, with an estimated length of 2,703 miles (4,350 km). The region of the river's lower catchment and floodplains contains a wide variety of vegetation types, including mixed wet evergreen, dry evergreen, deciduous, and montane forests; shrublands; and swamps, mangroves, and seasonally inundated grasslands. The area supports amazing bird diversity, some 1,300 species, and the largest waterbird populations in Southeast Asia. The region also supports the highest diversity of freshwater turtles in the world.

Burmese python (right)
Burmese pythons are among the largest snakes on Earth. They may reach 23 feet (7 m) or more in length and can weigh up to 200 pounds (90 kg). They are nocturnal carnivores, killing by constriction, and survive primarily on small mammals and birds. They are also excellent swimmers.

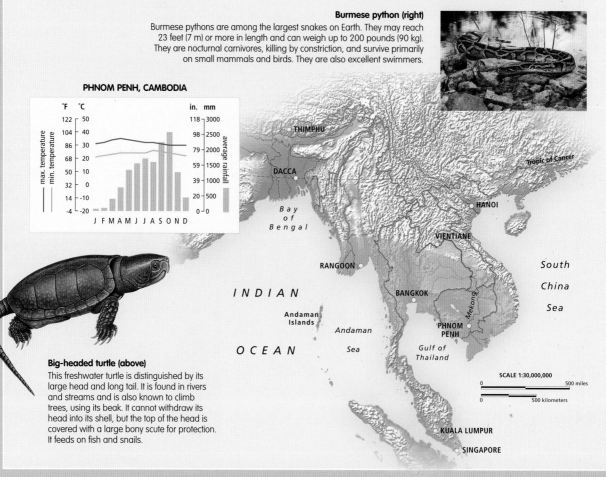

PHNOM PENH, CAMBODIA

Big-headed turtle (above)
This freshwater turtle is distinguished by its large head and long tail. It is found in rivers and streams and is also known to climb trees, using its beak. It cannot withdraw its head into its shell, but the top of the head is covered with a large bony scute for protection. It feeds on fish and snails.

SCALE 1:30,000,000

500 miles

500 kilometers

⚡ Conservation watch: Siamese crocodile

The freshwater Siamese crocodile occurs in swamps, oxbow lakes, and slow-moving sections of streams and rivers. It feeds predominantly on fish, but also amphibians, reptiles, and possibly small mammals. Females construct a mound nest during the annual wet season and lay 20 to 50 eggs. The species is critically endangered in the wild because of habitat destruction, over-exploitation for farming, accidental entanglement in fishing nets, and hunting.

Clouded leopard (above)
This medium-sized wild cat has a tawny coat, bearing cloud-shaped patterns, and a stocky build. It is known to have the longest canine teeth, 2 inches (5 cm), of any living feline. It is tree-dwelling, solitary, and secretive.

Red-shanked douc monkey (right)
This colorful arboreal monkey lives in primary and secondary evergreen forests and moist deciduous forests. It forms groups of 4 to 15 individuals, which socialize by grooming each other, led by dominant males. The monkeys communicate through facial expressions and vocalization. They feed on flowers, leaves, fruits, seeds, and buds.

Life in the river (below)
Riverine wetlands along the lower Mekong consist of a mosaic of habitat types, influenced by the movement of water over the riverbed. Sandbars, mudflats, perennial river channels, rock outcrops, waterfalls, deep pools, and rapids are all found here. The wildlife is richly varied. Crocodiles bask on the muddy banks, turtles and frogs hunt for insects, long-legged waders fish by the shore, and giant carp cruise the waters.

White-throated kingfisher
Halcyon smyrnensis

Black-necked crane
Grus nigricollis

Irrawaddy dolphin
Orcaella brevirostris

Giant ibis
Pseudibis gigantean

Smooth-coated otter
Lutrogale perspicillata

Mekong wagtail
Motacilla samveasnae

Siamese giant carp
Catlocarpio siamensis

Fishing cat
Prionailurus viverrinus

Spiny-breasted giant frog
Paa fasciculispina

Giant Asian pond turtle
Heosemys grandis

THE PHILIPPINE ARCHIPELAGO

The Philippine Archipelago includes more than 7,100 islands. Once covered with thick tropical lowland rain forests, the islands have been cleared extensively and only isolated patches of forest remain. There is still a rich diversity of vascular plants, about one-third of which is endemic, dominated by orchids, palms, begonias, and dipterocarps. Among the many terrestrial vertebrate species in the Philippines, more than 50 percent are endemic. Birds are the largest vertebrate group, with more than 600 species in the region.

⚡ Conservation watch: tamaraw

The tamaraw, or Mindoro dwarf buffalo, is a small hoofed mammal endemic to the island of Mindoro in the Philippines. It is the largest terrestrial mammal in the country, with an average height of 3 feet (1 m). It is a diurnal grazer that feeds on grass and bamboo shoots. Adults live a solitary, reclusive life.

Philippine tarsier

Just the size of a human fist, this small arboreal mammal is a forest-dweller. Its eyes cannot turn in their sockets but a special adaptation in its neck has enabled the tarsier to rotate its head through 180 degrees. Its eyes are considered to be, for its size, the largest of any known mammal. It is primarily an insectivore, but also feeds on lizards and birds.

Sleeping tarsier (above)
The tarsier sleeps during the day, usually in dark hollows close to the ground, in thick bushes and forests. These animals sleep in groups, or as solitary individuals, becoming active at night.

Tarsier hands and feet (left)
The tarsier's second and third toes have sharp claws specially adapted for grooming. Its long digits are tipped with rounded pads that allow it to cling easily to trees.

Philippine eagle (right)
One of the largest and most powerful birds of prey, the Philippine eagle builds a large nest in emergent dipterocarp trees, about 98 feet (30 m) from the ground. The female lays only one egg and the parents care for the hatchling for about 20 months. Each breeding pair requires a home range of 9 to 19 square miles (25–50 km²).

MANILA, PHILIPPINES

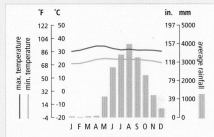

Luzon mangrove snake (left)
This is one of the biggest cat snake species, between 6 and 8 feet (1.8–2.5 m) long, with vividly marked bold yellow bands on a black body. It is a nocturnal feeder and its prey includes small mammals, lizards, frogs, other snakes, and fish.

Philippine crocodile (right)
A relatively small freshwater crocodile endemic to the Philippines, the Philippine crocodile has a broad snout and heavy dorsal armor. It feeds on aquatic invertebrates, fish, and small vertebrates. The female constructs a small nest mound, where 7 to 20 eggs are laid.

Golden-capped fruit bat

One of the largest fruit bats in the world, this species bears a patch of golden-tipped hairs on the top of its head. It roosts in colonies during the day and flies long distances during the night in search of fruits, mainly the fruits of fig trees. It uses its excellent eyesight to locate food, rather than the echolocation used by other bat species.

Wide wingspan
This bat's wingspan is more than 5 feet (1.5 m). It may travel more than 25 miles (40 km) each night in search of food.

CHAPTER SIX

AFRICA

African elephants

African elephants are the largest land animals on Earth. This herd of African elephants moves through the Etosha National Park, Namibia. Three-quarters of an elephant's life is devoted to feeding or moving toward food or water. Female elephants, or cows, live in family groups with their young, but adult bulls roam on their own.

AFRICA

Africa, the world's second largest continent at 11.7 million square miles (30.2 million km²), has unique fauna and flora. Many species are widespread within, and sometimes between, the major habitat types—deserts in the north and south, wet forests in the center, savannas and grasslands between these forests and deserts, and the woodlands and scrub forests of the higher altitude plateaus in the east and southeast. But geological and climatological processes have produced areas of isolation—the Great Rift Valley, the mountains of the Eastern Arc of Tanzania and Kenya, and the great island of Madagascar, where evolution has produced rare and unusual animal and plant forms.

The Sahara and Sahel
The world's largest desert, the Sahara spans nearly the entire top of the continent. Animals are widely dispersed, but they are all adapted to living in the hottest place on Earth.

The Congo Basin
Much of the Congo forest, the world's second largest tropical forest, remains intact and is home to many of humankind's closest ancestors—gorillas, chimpanzees, and bonobos.

The Ethiopian Highlands
The Ethiopian Highlands are high islands cut off from the rest of Africa by their altitude. The Simien and Bale mountains are home to many unique animals species.

East African savanna
Large groups of giraffes still find a home in the savannas of central and eastern Africa. The savannas are also home to the great migrations of antelopes, zebra, and buffalo.

The Albertine Rift
An area of spectacular peaks, deep valleys, and diverse lakes, the Albertine Rift Valley is home to the famed mountain gorilla, and to thousands of unique plant and animal species.

The Miombo woodlands
Little known, but one of the largest ecoregions in Africa, the Miombo woodlands, which provide a habitat for Africa's largest elephant herds, span much of south-central Africa.

The Okavango Delta
The Kavango River floods seasonally into a massive basin in northern Botswana, creating an inland swamp and lake. Hippopotamus and waterbirds abound.

The Kalahari
Africa's "second" desert, the vast Kalahari covers much of Botswana, Namibia, and northern South Africa. The species found here are adapted to life in the extreme heat.

Madagascar
The world's fourth largest island, Madagascar is a laboratory of evolution. The fauna and flora reflect the island's nearly complete isolation for millions of years.

Africa's coral reefs
Fringing the coast and islands of eastern Africa, the coral reefs of the western Indian Ocean are among the most diverse in the world. Climate change presents one threat.

Climate (left)

The equator splices broadly similar climatic zones in Africa. Nearest the equator rainfall is regular and abundant; the duration of the wet season decreases the greater the distance from the equator. High pressure produces arid zones at 30 degrees north, creating the Sahara Desert, and 30 degrees south, where drier conditions are limited to the southwest.

CLIMATE ZONES

	Wet tropical		Mediterranean
	Seasonal tropical		Subtropical
	Arid		Temperate
	Semiarid		Highland

Vegetation (right)

Abundant rain supports extensive tropical rain forests on Africa's west coast and in the Congo Basin. These are bounded by tropical woodlands and savannas, which cover almost half the continent and encircle an expanse of seasonal tropical forest in the south. To the north, the savanna yields to thorn woodlands and sparse grasses. Vegetation is scanty or nonexistent in the Sahara and much of the Namib Desert.

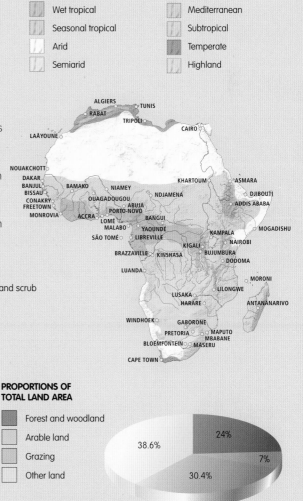

VEGETATION ZONES

	Tropical forest		Mediterranean forest and scrub
	Seasonal tropical forest		Midlatitude grassland
	Desert		Mountain vegetation
	Tropical grassland		

Land cover (right)

Relative to other continents, the proportion of arable land in Africa is low. Two-thirds of the continent is arid or semiarid and suitable only for nomadic grazing. Soil quality varies, from fertile volcanic and alluvial soils to poorer, leached soils in zones of high rainfall. One-fifth of Africa's forests lie within the Democratic Republic of Congo.

PROPORTIONS OF TOTAL LAND AREA

	Forest and woodland
	Arable land
	Grazing
	Other land

24%

7%

30.4%

38.6%

AFRICA
ENDEMIC BIRDS

More than 2,300 bird species, or 23 percent of the current list of 9,917 living birds worldwide, are found across the 58 countries that comprise Africa, Madagascar, and the African island nations. Sixty percent of these are found nowhere else in the world. Like other continents, Africa has many species that are threatened with extinction—about 234 of its birds, slightly less than the international average. But threats are increasing because of a growing population, advancing climate change, increased desertification in the Sahara, and competition for land, water, and wetlands.

Martial eagle (right)
The largest of the African birds of prey, the martial eagle feeds on a variety of mammals and birds, ranging from hyraxes to antelope. Its slow reproduction rate—one egg every two years—makes the eagle vulnerable to population declines in areas where it comes into conflict with humans.

Ground-hornbill (right)
The southern ground-hornbill is a large, terrestrial, turkey-like bird with a booming call. It has bright red skin on its throat, accentuated by a blue patch on the female. Ground-hornbills often breed cooperatively and all family members may assist a female to rear her single chick.

Lesser kestrel (left)
The migratory lesser kestrel spends the winter in the grasslands of sub-Saharan Africa. As a small falcon, it relies on its keen eyesight and gliding abilities to seek out prey, such as small rodents. Rather than build its own nest, the kestrel resumes the nests of other birds.

Secretary birds (right)

The secretary bird is endemic to sub-Saharan Africa. It can fly but often hunts on the ground. It stomps on clumps of grass to flush out grasshoppers and lizards, and, shielded by its large wings, will repeatedly strike a snake. Secretary birds may roost together at night. Nests are enormous structures of interwoven sticks (pictured) that often span 98 inches (2.5 m) across and 20 inches (0.5 m) deep. They may use the same nest for years.

Cape sparrows (left)

Cape sparrows live in many habitats in southern Africa. They typically forage for insects on the ground and can be found in small groups or large flocks. They are monogamous and nest in loose colonies of up to 100 pairs with up to 15 nests in one tree.

Ostrich

Flightless birds such as the ostrich exist in many avian families around the world. As well as being the globe's largest bird, the ostrich is the only bird species with two-toed feet. Its long, strong legs make it one of the fastest animals on land, capable of reaching speeds of up to 45 miles per hour (72 km/h). Once widespread, its range is now restricted to western, eastern, and southwestern Africa.

Ostrich family

Unlike the black and white male, the female ostrich is a brownish-gray, which aids camouflage. Females will lay 12–14 eggs in a clutch, and up to four clutches a year. Males, because of their color, incubate at night. After 40 days, the young hatch, and clutches of several females often join together in large creches.

THE SAHARA AND SAHEL

The Sahara Desert covers 3.3 million square miles (8.6 million km²) and merges with the semiarid savanna of the Sahel to its south. Most of the Sahara's 1,200 plant species are adapted to the heat and low rainfall, being short-lived or possessing thick, rubbery leaves. Diversity of animal species is low, with only 70 mammal species, 90 bird species, and 100 reptile species. Because of these low densities, desert animals are susceptible to hunting, which has decimated ostrich, addax, gazelle, and cheetah populations.

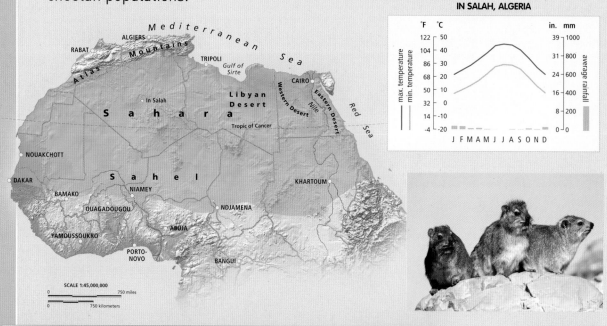

IN SALAH, ALGERIA

Rock hyrax (above)
The rock hyrax is a small ungulate that has a unique call, which sounds like a woman screaming. Despite its size, it is closely related to the elephant and lives in rocky outcrops in colonies averaging 50 individuals. The hyrax's heavily furred feet are equipped with glands that produce sweat, which aids traction in its rocky habitat.

⚡ Conservation watch: scimitar-horned oryx

Formerly found throughout North Africa, the scimitar-horned oryx once congregated in groups of more than 1,000 at water sources. It is now extinct in the wild because of habitat loss and hunting. Captive breeding and reintroductions provide hope that oryx will again roam the desert landscape.

Desert adaptations

Daytime Saharan temperatures often exceed 100°F (38°C) but drop 50°F (28°C) at night. Wildlife must be able to cope with these temperature extremes, excessive dryness, and harsh sunlight. Many animals have evolved behavioral and physiological adaptations, such as sleeping in burrows by day, raising their body temperatures before sweating, and developing kidneys that conserve water.

⚡ Addax (right)
The addax obtains all of its water needs from plants and is adept at tracking and finding patches of desert vegetation after rain. Its broad hooves are adapted to travel over soft sand without sinking.

Fennec fox (above)
The smallest of foxes, the fennec, has large ears that help it to dissipate heat and detect prey. Its sandy coat reflects sunlight, blends into the landscape, and insulates the fox during cold nights, when it is active.

Desert oases (below)
A wadi, or valley in Arabic, is a depression or streambed found in the desert. Wadis remain dry for most of the year but are transformed by heavy rains. Flooding produces lush vegetation that supports a variety of wildlife.

Ostrich
Struthio camelus

Slender-horned gazelles
Gazella leptoceros

Red-fronted gazelles
Gazella rutifrons

Desert jerboa
Jaculus jaculus

THE CONGO BASIN

The Congo Basin forest is second only to the Amazon in size, covering more than 700,000 square miles (1.8 million km²). Unlike much of the Amazon, the Congo is largely undeveloped, but increased road-building, agriculture, mining, and logging destroy up to 2 million acres (810,000 ha) a year. The Congo is not a single ecosystem but a patchwork of ecosystems that includes rivers, swamps, and flooded forests. More than 10,000 species of plants, 1,000 bird species, and 400 species of mammals make their home here.

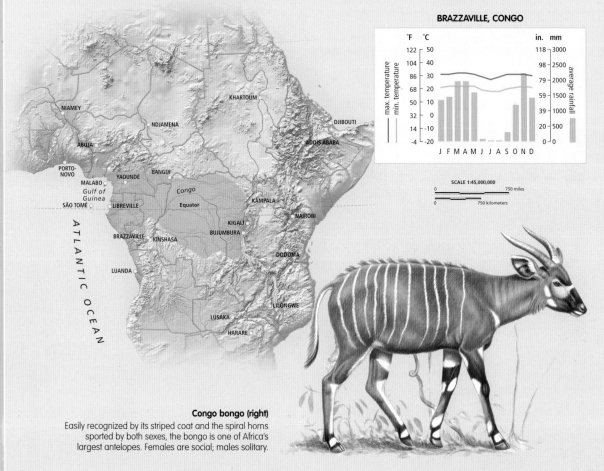

BRAZZAVILLE, CONGO

SCALE 1:45,000,000

0 — 750 miles
0 — 750 kilometers

Congo bongo (right)
Easily recognized by its striped coat and the spiral horns sported by both sexes, the bongo is one of Africa's largest antelopes. Females are social; males solitary.

Complete ecosystem (above)

The Congo Basin's dense vegetation, rivers, and swamps, constitute a self-contained ecosystem. This structure, when combined with the hot and humid conditions, regulates water flow and creates a stable climate that has enabled the forest's biological diversity to evolve and endure.

⚡ Conservation watch: okapi

The okapi resembles a zebra but is in fact the only living relative of the giraffe. Not described by science until 1901, the okapi is found only in the north and east of the Democratic Republic of Congo, formerly Zaire. In the late 1980s, the government established the Okapi Wildlife Reserve to protect the species from hunting and habitat destruction. The initiative has been largely successful, despite near-constant civil war.

Red river hog (left)

Traveling in large groups, or sounders, of up to several dozen animals, red river hogs use their strong snouts to dig for tubers and roots in the forest floor. Adept swimmers, they are often found in swamps. While adults are characterized by a red coat and contrasting black and white stripe down their back, piglets are darker.

Lady Ross's turaco (right)

A social bird that lives in flocks of up to 30 individuals, the Lady Ross's turaco emits a noisy call. Turacos mate while traveling in groups, and the male and female share responsibility for incubating the eggs. The bird's characteristic red crest can rise up to 2 inches (5 cm) when it is excited.

Giant swallowtail (right)

The largest of hundreds of African butterfly species, the giant swallowtail has long, narrow wings. Females tend to remain in the canopy, where they lay their eggs, while males are more frequently encountered near streams on the forest floor, where they engage in territorial disputes.

African gray parrot (left)

With striking red tail feathers, the African gray parrot is endemic to the forests of central and western Africa and renowned for its mimicking ability. Studies suggest that up to 21 percent of these parrots are taken annually for the pet trade.

THE CONGO BASIN
PRIMATES OF THE CONGO

Home to 33 of the 79 African primate species, the forests of the Congo Basin are critical to primate evolution and conservation. All of Africa's great apes, humankind's closest relatives, are found in the Congo—bonobos, gorillas, and chimpanzees. The smaller monkeys—colobus monkeys, drills, and guenons—are keystone species, eating fruits and dispersing their seeds, which helps regenerate the forest.

The habitat is under threat from logging and mining, but the greatest threat to primates is hunting by humans for food.

Black and white colobus (left)
Widely distributed across the Congo, the black and white colobus, like other colobines, has a specialized digestive tract that allows it to feed on a diet composed primarily of leaves.

Mandrill (below)
One of the largest and most striking of the terrestrial monkeys, mandrills are distinguished by the vibrant coloration of the snout and hindquarters of males. While males are higher ranking, the enduring bonds in these highly social animals, which form groups of up to 1,350 individuals, are among females.

Bonobo (below)
Bonobos are the gentlest of the great apes, living in large, cohesive groups. Peaceful relations are reinforced by sexual interactions rather than aggression.

Chimpanzee (below)
Chimpanzees are humans' closest relative and share 98 percent of our DNA. Highly intelligent, they are often observed using tools.

Playful

Frightened

Hungry

Submissive

Aggressive

Attentive

Making faces (above)
Wild chimpanzees communicate with a greater range of facial expressions than any of the other large primates, except for humans.

Drill
With a restricted range in west Africa, the drill is one of the most endangered primates. Drills live in social units of up to 20 individuals, but groups may merge to form troops of up to 200 individuals. Males may be twice the size of females, some weighing 55 pounds (25 kg).

Western gorilla (below left)
The western gorilla has the widest distribution of any gorilla subspecies and is often found in swampy habitats or forest clearings feeding on fruits and herbs. The population estimate stands at 150,000–200,000 gorillas.

Conservation watch: mountain gorilla

Mountain gorillas live in small groups of about nine individuals, led by a large silverback male. Although the largest of the primates, mountain gorillas are rarely aggressive and spend most of the day eating leaves and stems. In the late 1970s, hopes for the conservation of mountain gorillas were few. Populations were in decline and habitat shrinking. Since then, focused conservation action and a vibrant gorilla tourism program have led to stable or increasing populations and declining threats from poaching and habitat loss, despite years of military conflict and instability in many parts of the subspecies' range.

THE ETHIOPIAN HIGHLANDS

The Ethiopian Highlands encompass a vast expanse of high-altitude habitat, mainly contained within modern-day Ethiopia and divided by the Great Rift Valley. The base of the highlands is a plateau that begins at 5,000 feet (1,500 m), but rises to up to 15,000 feet (4,570 m), completely isolating the region's flora and fauna. The region's unique flora and fauna bears its own name—Afromontane. The highlands are home to 193 mammal species, 63 of them endemic; 59 amphibian species, 23 endemic; 80 reptile species; and 680 bird species.

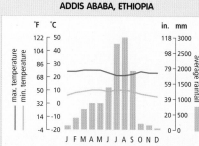

ADDIS ABABA, ETHIOPIA

SCALE 1:25,000,000

0 ——— 500 miles
0 ——— 500 kilometers

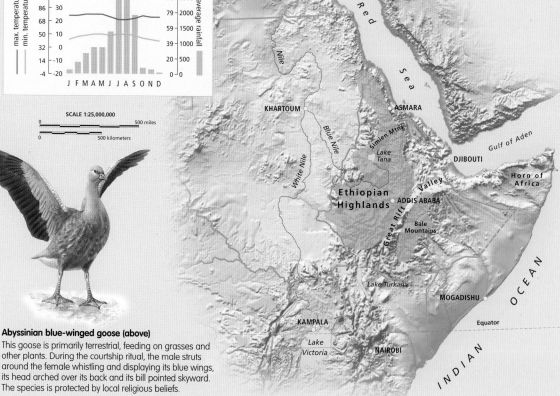

Abyssinian blue-winged goose (above)
This goose is primarily terrestrial, feeding on grasses and other plants. During the courtship ritual, the male struts around the female whistling and displaying its blue wings, its head arched over its back and its bill pointed skyward. The species is protected by local religious beliefs.

⚡ Conservation watch: Ethiopian wolf

The Ethiopian wolf, an ancient lineage, is more closely related to the gray wolf than any African canid. The wolf is found in six isolated populations, with the largest single population of several hundred individuals surviving in the Bale Mountains. Habitat conversion is the primary cause of its decline, but domestic dogs also bring a multitude of threats to small wolf populations: disease, competition for prey, and hybridization.

Gelada baboon (right)

Found only in the high plateaus of Ethiopia, the gelada travels in small harems dominated by a large male. Dozens of these harems often gather to escape predators, with herds of up to 600 individuals sometimes sleeping on cliffs. The chest skin is a dramatic red color, replacing the sexual signaling usually visible on the hindquarters of other baboons.

🐐 Walia ibex (left)

The walia ibex, a mountain goat, is another rare endemic species of the Ethiopian Highlands. It has large horns, most prominent in the males. Once avidly hunted, it survives in the Simien Mountains, within a 500-strong remnant population.

Rouget's rail (right)

Typically found at high elevations, this bird is commonly associated with water, where it searches for aquatic insects, crustaceans, and snails. It is primarily threatened by the loss of its habitat to domestic livestock grazing and the collection, for building construction, of thatch.

🐐 Mountain nyala

The mountain nyala, only the males of which have spiraled horns, was the last African antelope to become known to science, in 1910. Its endangered status can, in part, be attributed to hunting for meat and medicinal use.

EAST AFRICAN SAVANNA

Though considered the cradle of humankind, the savannas of East Africa are best known for their animals—elephants, giraffes, rhinoceros, wildebeest, impala, gazelles, lions, hyenas, and jackals, to name a few. Savanna vegetation ranges from dry forest and scrub to the spectacular grasslands of Tanzania's Serengeti and the Masai Mara of Kenya. With seasonal rainfall varying from 12 to 47 inches (300–1,200 mm) annually, animals often migrate, following the rains and subsequent grass growth.

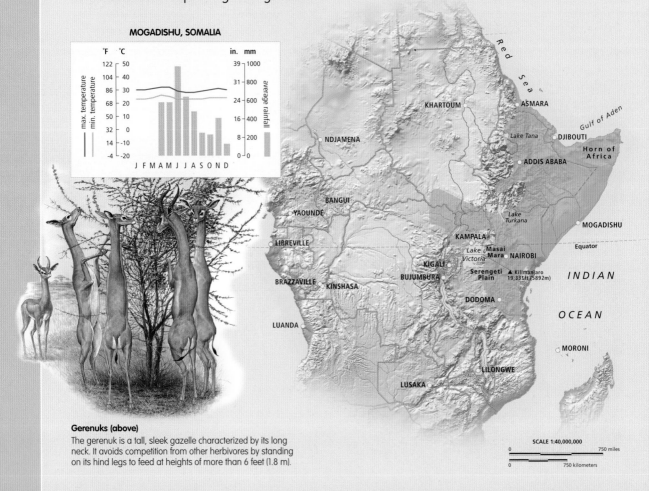

MOGADISHU, SOMALIA

Gerenuks (above)
The gerenuk is a tall, sleek gazelle characterized by its long neck. It avoids competition from other herbivores by standing on its hind legs to feed at heights of more than 6 feet (1.8 m).

SCALE 1:40,000,000

0   750 miles

0   750 kilometers

Safari ants (left)
Safari or army ants may live in colonies of 20 million individuals. When food is scarce, columns containing up to 50 million ants from several colonies may form to find resources. In this photograph, a column of workers is guarded by soldier ants.

Termites (above)
Termites, which are incredibly abundant, play a key role in savanna structure and function. They increase soil porosity, allowing water to infiltrate the soil. They also bring nutrients to the surface in mounds up to 9 feet (3 m) high. These nutrients influence larger-scale patterns of vegetation, and hence animal distribution.

Giraffes (above)
At 18 feet (5.5 m) tall, the giraffe is the tallest land mammal. Genetic evidence suggests that there may be as many as six species of giraffe, with variations in pattern. Males swing their long necks in combat and when competing for partners.

African elephant (left)
Males are primarily solitary so elephant societies are dominated by female groups, led by an old matriarch. Elephants rely on their good memory to recall widely dispersed water holes. They also communicate across distances using rumbling infrasound, which can carry for 3 miles (4.8 km).

Weaver birds

Weaver birds are small, gregarious, finchlike birds that eat seeds. Each pair weaves an intricate, basket-shaped nest that is suspended from a tree branch. The nests—constructed by males from grass, leaf shreds, and twigs—usually hang separately, but may be massed apartment-style, with 100 to 300 pairs occupying separate chambers.

EAST AFRICAN SAVANNA
GRASSLAND GRAZERS

Grasslands are dominated by hoofed animals, or ungulates. Some of these animals browse or eat woody vegetation, but the greatest densities are among those species that live off seasonally abundant and nutritious grasses—the grazers. Zebra eat the taller, rougher grasses, allowing wildebeest to follow in their wake and clip off the shorter, more nourishing grasses. This grazing pattern spurs new growth, on which small gazelles are among the first to dine. This succession of grazers enhances grassland productivity.

African buffalo (right)
The African buffalo is one of Africa's most abundant large herbivores. It usually lives in herds of up to a few hundred but buffalo sometimes congregate in their thousands. Although their sight and hearing is poor, a well-developed sense of smell allows them to detect predators on the open plains.

Conservation watch: white rhino

The two subspecies of white rhino have different histories. Nearly extinct in the early 1900s, the southern white rhino has staged a remarkable recovery, with more than 17,000 now living in southern Africa. However, the northern white is now virtually extinct, with only five surviving, in captivity. The declines are because of demand for rhino horn.

Migration miles

Each year, 2 million animals follow a migration path around the vast plains of the Serengeti. More than 1 million wildebeest, half a million zebras, and tens of thousands of African buffalo and Thomson's gazelles make the annual move, covering more than 1,000 miles (1,600 km). Not all paths traverse national parks; migrating animals still spend up to 10 percent of their journey in unprotected areas.

MIGRATION MAP
➡ Migration routes

Lining up (above)
A winding column of blue wildebeest crosses the Serengeti–Masai Mara Nature Reserve, tracing a route used annually as they migrate across the grasslands.

Birth on the run (above)
Approximately 400,000 wildebeest are born in the rainy season preceding migration, but births also occur along the way, placing calves at great risk. However, youngsters can stand and run within an hour of birth.

Zebra (right)
The plains zebra (pictured), found across eastern and southern Africa, is one of three zebra species. Grevy's zebra, found only in northern Kenya and southern Ethiopia, has fine stripes and a white belly. The mountain zebra of South Africa and Namibia has wide stripes over its hindquarters. Studies suggest that a zebra's stripes may play a role in thermoregulation—the maintenance of a stable body temperature.

Thomson's gazelle (left)
The Thomson's gazelle is known for its graceful leaps, which often reach more than 8 feet (2.5 m) in height. When stalked by predators, it will bounce or "stot" to signal that it is escaping. During migration, males establish territories that they rigorously defend in the hope of herding passing females.

EAST AFRICAN SAVANNA
BIG CARNIVORES

Lions, hyenas, cheetahs, leopards, and wild dogs are among the widest-ranging species found in Africa, but their pattern of vast movement puts them in conflict with an ever-growing human population. As available habitat is reduced, these animals compete with one another for food and a hierarchy operates, governed by those species that can steal a kill from the others. The lion remains the king of beasts; hyenas trump wild dogs and cheetah; almost all species can steal from leopards, which drag their prey into trees to avoid such theft; and cheetahs employ their speed to outpace the competition.

AFRICAN CARNIVORE	TOP SPEED IN MILES PER HOUR (KM/H)	GROUP SIZE	LITTER SIZE
Cheetah	70 (112)	1–4	3–5
Lion	50 (80)	5–15	3–5
African wild dog	45 (72)	3–25	5–17
Hyena	40 (60)	2–90	1–2
Leopard	40 (60)	1	2–3

Spotted hyena (above)
Spotted hyenas are among the most effective hunters on the African plains. They kill most of their own food and hunt in packs, chasing down weak or young animals. They efficiently crush bones using their massive teeth and strong jaw muscles, ingesting and digesting body parts that many other predators leave behind. An alpha or dominant female leads each complex hyena clan, which may number up to 80.

⚡ Conservation watch: African wild dog

Once found across Africa in every habitat except rain forest, the African wild dog has been exterminated from 32 African countries and around 7,000 remain. Disease contracted from domestic dogs, habitat fragmentation, roads, and snaring have all contributed to the decline. Recent conservation efforts appear to be helping the species recover. Wild dogs hunt in packs of up to 20 adults and communally rear a single litter of puppies born to the dominant female.

Leopard (below)

The leopard is an opportunistic, solitary hunter that prefers mid-sized antelope. It silently stalks its prey. Like the cheetah and wild dog, the leopard hunts in areas and at times not favored by lions and hyenas.

Cheetah (above)

The cheetah is best known for its speed and has been clocked at up to 70 miles per hour (112 km/h). It can achieve such speed because of its streamlined body and enlarged heart and lungs. Cheetahs range over large areas and are threatened by habitat loss.

CHEETAH POPULATION

Kenya
Somalia
Tanzania
Angola Zambia
Zimbabwe
Namibia
Botswana
South Africa

| | Cheetah population circa 1900 |

Cheetah population circa 2000

	Low population density
	Medium population density
	High population density
•	Protected area

The lion

Once found across Africa, southern Europe, and western Asia, lions are now restricted to the savannas and grasslands of eastern and southern Africa. The largest of the African carnivores, they live in prides consisting of five to 10 related females and a coalition of two to three males. Loss of habitat forces them into conflict with humans and livestock, and populations have recently plummeted.

Mane (above)

Only male lions have manes. The mane size and color indicates male quality, but not without a cost. The dark manes preferred by females raise a male's body temperature, demanding more energy use, and make the male more conspicuous.

Cubs (left)

A lioness gives birth to a litter of up to four cubs, which are introduced to the pride at six weeks. Females may synchronize the timing of births and often nurse each others' offspring.

Hunting (above)

Females are the hunters of the pride, chasing down prey as a unit. They kill by strangulation or delivering a bite to the neck or head. Males may feed first, despite contributing little to the kill.

THE ALBERTINE RIFT

Thirty-five million years ago, the African continent almost divided in two. This event created a 6,000-mile (9,600-km) fissure, known as the Great Rift Valley. The northern section of the rift, named for England's Prince Albert, stretches from Lake Albert to the southern tip of Lake Tanganyika. The region is home to a vast array of vertebrates: 39 percent of Africa's mammal species, 50 percent of its birds, 19 percent of its amphibians, 14 percent of its reptiles, and a high number of freshwater fish. Many are found nowhere else, and a high proportion are critically endangered due to habitat loss.

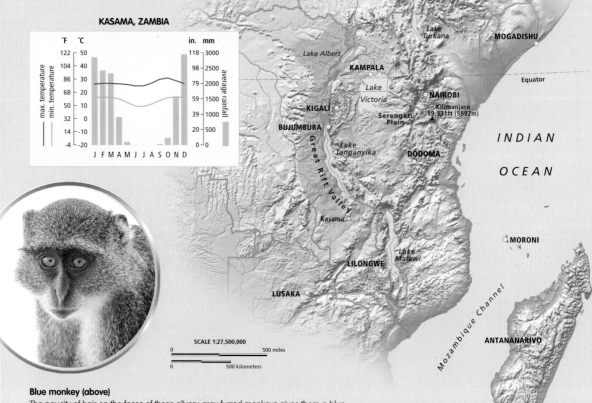

KASAMA, ZAMBIA

SCALE 1:27,500,000

0   500 miles

0   500 kilometers

Blue monkey (above)
The paucity of hair on the faces of these silvery-gray furred monkeys gives them a blue appearance. They often feed and travel in groups with other primates, such as red-tailed monkeys, red colobus, and mangabeys. Such multiple species groups enhance efforts to discover new food sources and afford greater protection from predators.

⚡ Conservation watch: golden monkey

The golden monkey is so closely related to the blue monkey that they were mistakenly classed as a single species. With a soot-black coat, highlighted by a gold-orange mantle across its back and head, this endangered species is found only in the volcanic Virunga Mountains of Central Africa.

Flamingos (below)

Alkaline soda lakes have developed across this region as a result of the deposition of fine volcanic ash. The lakes are home to both the lesser and greater flamingos. Flamingos are filter feeders—they use their bills, which are lined with fine hairs, to strain water and capture small shrimplike animals. The prey contains a red pigment that gives flamingos their pink color.

Bushbaby (left)

The bushbaby is more closely related to the Madagascan lemurs than the monkeys of continental Africa. It uses its large, round eyes and ears to hunt insects and other prey at night. During the day it sleeps in tree-hollow nests.

Chameleons

This family of lizards is best known for the ability to change color. While commonly considered a camouflage strategy, the color variation actually results from physiological changes and may be a means of communication. The upper and lower lids on a chameleon's eyes are fused, leaving it only a pinhole to see through. It grips prey—usually large insects—using suction cups on its tongue.

Strange-nosed chameleon

A popular pet, famed for the bump on its nose, this over-collected chameleon is now threatened and lives only in the Rwenzori Mountains.

Rwenzori double-collared sunbirds
Cinnyris stuhlmanni

Regal sunbird
Cinnyris regia

Giant lobelia
Lobelia rhynchopetalum

Purple-breasted sunbird
Nectarinia purpureiventris

Giant lobelia (right)

At altitudes above 10,000 feet (3,050 m), the giant lobelia provides nectar for many species of sunbirds. The giant lobelia produces one inflorescence (cluster of flowers on a single stem), which grows for several decades, up to 10 feet (3 m) tall. It flowers once before dying.

THE MIOMBO WOODLANDS

The Miombo woodlands covers more than 1.1 million square miles (3 million km²) and takes its name from the Bantu word for the dominant tree genus, *Brachystegia*. The animals of the Miombo woodlands must deal with a long dry season each year. During the single rainy season, when water is plentiful, wildlife densities are low, and animals spread out across the landscape. When water dries up, animals congregate at high densities around the few permanent waterholes.

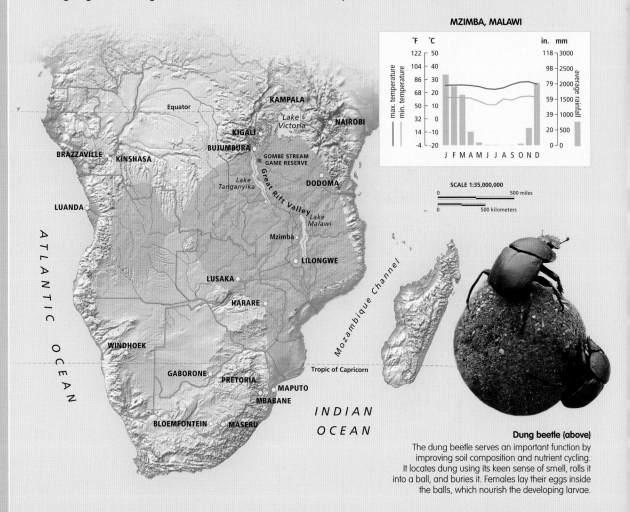

MZIMBA, MALAWI

SCALE 1:35,000,000

Dung beetle (above)
The dung beetle serves an important function by improving soil composition and nutrient cycling. It locates dung using its keen sense of smell, rolls it into a ball, and buries it. Females lay their eggs inside the balls, which nourish the developing larvae.

Horned creatures

The ungulates of the Miombo woodlands are adorned with some of the most spectacular horns of any of the African hoofed animals. Horns, which unlike antlers are not shed, serve a dual function—to protect the animals from predators and as weapons in combat between males for access to females. Males usually have larger, more elaborated horns than females.

Greater kudu (right)
The corkscrew horns of the greater kudu indicate rank among males. Males interlock their horns when fighting, in an attempt to push each other off-balance.

Sable antelope (left)
Male sable antelope drop to their knees when in battle and fight with their horns, which can reach up to 40 inches (1 m) in length. They have been known to successfully defend themselves against lions.

Northern carmine bee-eater (right)
The striking carmine bee-eater catches bees on the wing and hits them against hard surfaces to remove their stings.

Ground pangolin (above)
Pangolins are covered with large plate-like scales. When threatened, they curl up into a ball and the scales form a protective armor. Pangolins do not have teeth; instead, they rely on their specialized tongues to feed on ants.

Puff adder (right)
Short and wide, the puff adder produces an extremely toxic venom and is one of the deadliest snakes in Africa. It lies in wait to ambush prey, such as small mammals and birds. When disturbed, the adder inflates its head and makes a loud hiss.

Nile crocodile (below)
An aggressive and feared predator, the Nile crocodile consumes a variety of mammals, ranging from the sitatunga to the wildebeest. Unlike most reptiles, it buries its eggs. Both parents diligently guard them, and the mother continues to care for the hatchlings. Nile crocodiles have been known to live for up to 100 years.

⚡ Conservation watch: black rhinoceros

The black rhinoceros is critically endangered—only around 4,000 remain in the wild. These rhinoceros have been heavily hunted, particularly for their horns, which are used in traditional medicine. Long, prehensile lips assist the black rhinoceros as it browses for leaves and twigs.

THE OKAVANGO DELTA

The Okavango Delta is one of the largest water systems in the world that does not flow to an ocean. Rains in Angola, beginning in October, swell the Okavango River and flood the delta, covering 6,200 square miles (16,000 km²). By April, dry conditions have returned, and the delta shrinks to nearly half that area. The delta supports a wealth of wildlife—300 species of plants, 450 bird species, and 20 ungulate species.

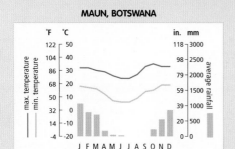

MAUN, BOTSWANA

Red lechwe (above)

The red lechwe, a medium-sized antelope, is an important food source for lions in the delta but is skilled at evading capture. Its hind quarters are longer than its forelimbs, giving it superior leaping abilities. When threatened, members of a lechwe herd disperse in different directions, effectively confusing potential predators.

Sitatunga (below)

Sitatunga are well adapted to swamp life. Strong swimmers with water-resistant coats, they can submerge all but their nostrils and use their splayed hooves to negotiate boggy marshes. However, sitatunga are hunted for their meat.

SCALE 1:30,000,000

0 ————— 500 miles

0 ————— 500 kilometers

The hippopotamus

Hippopotamuses generally live in small groups, or pods, usually containing one male, several females, and their young. They spend much of the day in water, venturing on to land at dusk to feed on grasses. Hippopotamus are hunted for their meat and ivory teeth. When threatened, they express their aggression by opening their mouths wide.

Skin protection
The skin of the hippopotamus is sensitive to the harsh African sun. It secretes a red-tinted fluid that protects it against ultraviolet rays and may also have antibiotic properties.

Community group (above)
Hippopotamus pods are led by a bull, which strongly defends its territory and harem from other males. Congregations of up to 100 individuals have been observed.

Swamp society (below)
The hippopotamus, widespread across Africa, commonly grazes on dry land at night. But in delta swamps it plays a critical role in maintaining pathways through thick vegetation—water lilies, papyrus, and water cabbage. These hippopotamus channels often connect lakes in the permanent swamps where waterbirds, such as the hammerkop and wattled crane, and the Cape clawless otter make their living.

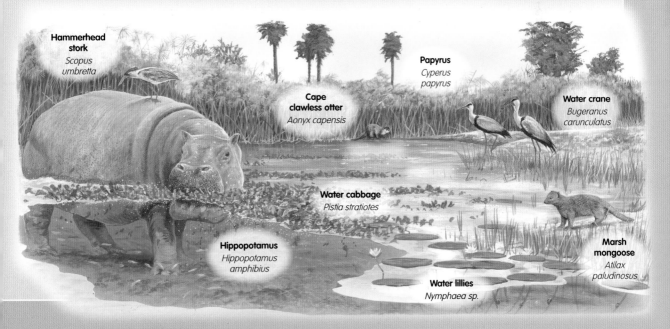

Hammerhead stork
Scopus umbretta

Cape clawless otter
Aonyx capensis

Papyrus
Cyperus papyrus

Water crane
Bugeranus carunculatus

Water cabbage
Pistia stratiotes

Hippopotamus
Hippopotamus amphibius

Water lillies
Nymphaea sp.

Marsh mongoose
Atilax paludinosus

THE KALAHARI

The Kalahari describes a vast plateau in southern Africa. It includes both a desert of about 200,000 square miles (518,000 km²) and a basin twice that size. At an altitude of approximately 3,000 feet (915 m), the Kalahari is not a true desert but a semi-desert, where stationary sand dunes are covered by grasslands, and acacia woodlands and scrub. The flush of grass that follows annual rain supports species once common across Africa, such as the giraffe, elephant, rhinoceros, and lion.

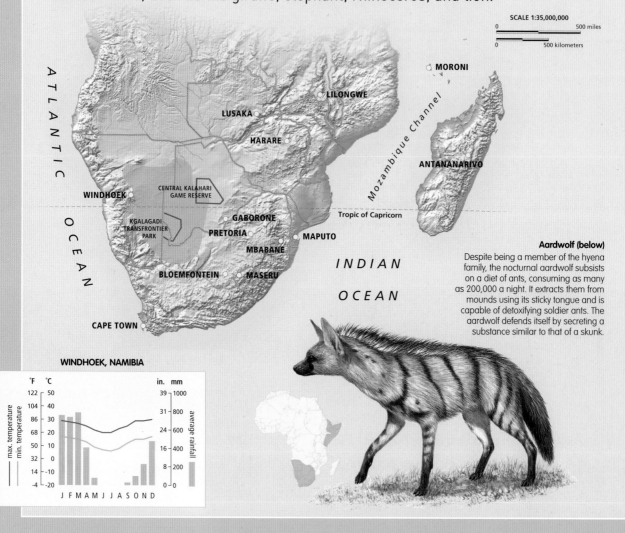

SCALE 1:35,000,000

0   500 miles

0   500 kilometers

ATLANTIC OCEAN

□ MORONI

○ LILONGWE

LUSAKA ○

HARARE ○

ANTANANARIVO

Mozambique Channel

WINDHOEK ○

CENTRAL KALAHARI
GAME RESERVE

KGALAGADI
TRANSFRONTIER
PARK

GABORONE ○

PRETORIA ○

MBABANE ○

MASERU ○

BLOEMFONTEIN ○

Tropic of Capricorn

MAPUTO ○

CAPE TOWN ○

INDIAN

OCEAN

Aardwolf (below)

Despite being a member of the hyena family, the nocturnal aardwolf subsists on a diet of ants, consuming as many as 200,000 a night. It extracts them from mounds using its sticky tongue and is capable of detoxifying soldier ants. The aardwolf defends itself by secreting a substance similar to that of a skunk.

WINDHOEK, NAMIBIA

°F °C   in. mm

122 50   39 1000
104 40   31 800
86 30   24 600
68 20
50 10   16 400
32 0
14 -10   8 200
-4 -20   0 0

max. temperature
min. temperature

average rainfall

J F M A M J J A S O N D

Gemsbok (left)

The gemsbok, or oryx, relies mainly on water contained within grass for moisture. Horns can reach 30 inches (76 cm), with the female growing taller and thinner horns than the male.

Aardvark (above)

Powerful legs, special claws, a long snout, and sticky tongue enable the aardvark to dig through termite mounds and ant nests, its thick skin warding off bites.

Meerkats (left)

Meerkats live in clans of up to 50 individuals, dominated by a single breeding pair. Family members excavate burrows, help raise pups, and watch out for predators. Meerkats mostly eat insects, excavated using their non-retractable claws. While foraging, at least one clan member serves as sentry, scanning for predators. Meerkats often stand in the morning sun to warm their belly skin.

Desert adaptations

Wildlife in the Kalahari has adapted to the harsh environment primarily by living at low densities, being active at night, and traveling vast distances. Water, not food, is the key limiting resource. During the wet season, animals fan out across the Kalahari; they survive the drier periods by retreating to the seasonal riverbeds. Elephants—which excavate water holes in the rivers—are critical to the survival of many other species.

Lion economies (above)

The lions of the desert have lighter fur as an adaptation to the extreme daytime temperatures. They travel in smaller groups, over larger ranges, and hunt smaller mammals than lions elsewhere.

Elephant memory (above)

The desert-dwelling elephants of Namibia are smaller than other elephants and can endure many days without water. Like others of their kind, they have a fine memory and may travel more than 45 miles (70 km) to reach water holes and feeding grounds they recall previously visiting.

Cape foxes (above)

The Cape fox is nocturnal and avoids the heat of day by resting in burrows underground. It enjoys a varied diet of small mammals, insects, and reptiles, and may cache, or hide, its food.

MADAGASCAR

More than 100 million years ago, Madagascar broke off from the African continent. Its isolation and variety of habitats have contributed to the unusual diversity of endemic species. The western and southern regions are dominated by dry forests and thorny deserts. Along the eastern side of the island, habitats are wetter and some of the most diverse tropical forests are found here. Madagascar is home to 5 percent of the world's species, and 80 percent of them are endemic. Best known are the lemurs, a group of approximately 70 primate species.

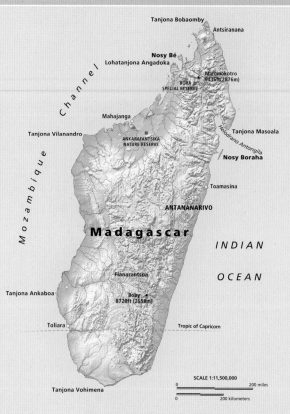

ANTANANARIVO, MADAGASCAR

Fossa (above)
The fossa is the dominant and largest predator on Madagascar. More than 50 percent of its diet is made up of lemurs. Closely related to the mongoose, it is agile both on the ground and in trees.

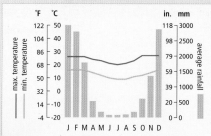

Aye-aye
The aye-aye is the largest nocturnal primate, with big eyes and large, sensitive ears. Pointed claws allow aye-ayes to hang from branches. The elongated middle finger is used to tap tree branches to find and extract insect grubs inside. Aye-ayes live a primarily solitary life.

Lemur diversity

The sifakas, wooly lemurs, and the indri, all in the *Indriidae* family, are the largest lemurs: indris may weigh up to 22 pounds (10 kg). The world's smallest primate, the gray mouse lemur, weighs 1 to 2 ounces (40–60 g). Mid-sized lemurs, such as the red-bellied lemur, weigh about 3 pounds (1.4 kg). The ruffed lemurs are the only primates to produce young in litters.

Red-bellied lemur
Eulemur rubriventer

Ring-tailed lemur (left)
The ring-tailed lemur is the most terrestrial of the lemurs. Like most lemurs, females are dominant. Aggressive interactions often include "stink fights," which involve flicking tails coated with a scent from glands in the wrist.

Gray mouse lemur
Microcebus murinus

Red-ruffed lemur
Varecia variegata rubra

Indri
Indri indri

Conservation watch: Coquerel's sifaka

The striking Coquerel's sifaka, a lemur, has never been numerous. It is found only in the dry deciduous forests of northwestern Madagascar at altitudes of less than 300 feet (90 m). The loss of these forests to agriculture, and habitat degradation, are the main threats to the species.

Reptiles and amphibians

With more than 400 species of reptiles and 300 species of frogs, Madagascar hosts a wide diversity of reptiles and amphibians. Half of the world's chameleon species exist only in Madagascar. Some evolutionary affinities are unexpected: pythons do not occur here but an endemic boa constrictor has its closest relatives in South America.

Tomato frog (right)
Despite its bright red color, the tomato frog sits quietly as it waits to ambush its insect prey. Its coloration acts as a warning to predators; if attacked it puffs up its body and gives off a toxic sticky substance.

Panther chameleon (right)
Found throughout Madagascar's tropical forest, the male panther chameleon is nearly twice the size of the female, and more vibrantly colored.

Spider tortoise (above)
Named for the weblike pattern of yellow lines on its shell, the spider tortoise has adapted to life in dry habitats by burrowing underground during the driest times of the year.

CORAL REEFS

While corals fringe the African continent, true reefs are mostly found off the east coast, from the Red Sea south to Mozambique and across to Madagascar. Coral reefs are biologically diverse, highly productive, and critical to local fisheries and subsistence fishermen. Sea surface temperature increases, industrial run-off and pollutants, untreated sewage, and increasing sediment flows in rivers all threaten these coastal ecosystems.

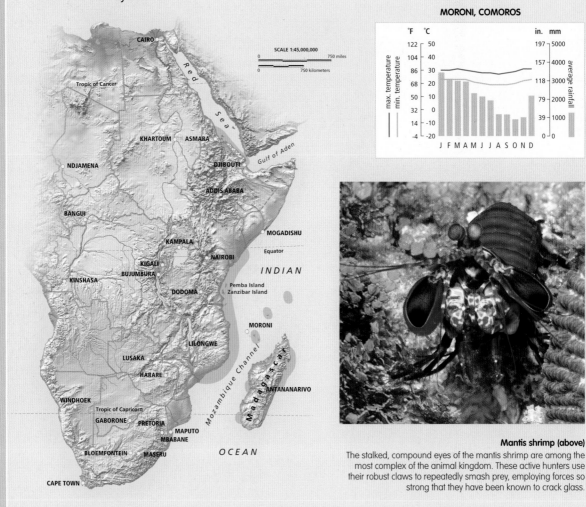

SCALE 1:45,000,000

750 miles

750 kilometers

CAIRO
Tropic of Cancer
Red Sea
KHARTOUM   ASMARA
NDJAMENA   DJIBOUTI
Gulf of Aden
ADDIS ABABA
BANGUI
MOGADISHU
KAMPALA
NAIROBI
Equator
KIGALI
BUJUMBURA   INDIAN
KINSHASA
DODOMA   Pemba Island
Zanzibar Island
MORONI
LILONGWE
LUSAKA
HARARE
Mozambique Channel
Madagascar
ANTANANARIVO
WINDHOEK
Tropic of Capricorn
GABORONE   PRETORIA
MAPUTO
MBABANE
BLOEMFONTEIN   MASERU   OCEAN
CAPE TOWN

MORONI, COMOROS

°F	°C		in.	mm
122	50		197	5000
104	40		157	4000
86	30		118	3000
68	20			
50	10		79	2000
32	0		39	1000
14	-10			
-4	-20	J F M A M J J A S O N D	0	0

max. temperature
min. temperature

average rainfall

Mantis shrimp (above)
The stalked, compound eyes of the mantis shrimp are among the most complex of the animal kingdom. These active hunters use their robust claws to repeatedly smash prey, employing forces so strong that they have been known to crack glass.

Ornamental shells

Mollusk shells are multilayered. The mother-of-pearl layer is made up primarily of calcium carbonate and gives the shell its luster and distinctive pattern. Shells are a protective fortress for the soft-bodied mollusks living within, their color and patterns providing camouflage from a multitude of predators. Algae may live along the lips of clam shells, where they trap sunlight and deliver the clam an energy-rich supply of food.

Maxima clam (left)

Clams are bivalves, having two shells to protect their soft bodies. The maxima clam lives in shallow waters near the top of the reef, where it attaches itself to the coral rubble or limestone surface and filters water to trap plankton.

Cowrie (above and right)

Cowries live under rocks and feed on algae at night. Their smooth, porcelain-like shells are wrapped in a mantle that is often brilliantly colored.

Humphead wrasse (left)

One of the largest fish inhabiting the coral reef, the humphead wrasse is distinguished by a large bulge on its head. Highly sedentary, it is active by day and rests in reef caves at night. A long lifespan—about 32 years—and slow breeding rate make the humphead wrasse vulnerable to overfishing.

Starfish (left and below left)

Starfish lack a centralized brain, but have two stomachs to digest their prey, and at least five arms, which they can regenerate if severed. A covering of spines prevents organisms from colonizing the skin of starfish, all of which can reproduce sexually and asexually.

Sweetlips (below)

As its name suggests, the black-spotted sweetlip that lives in the Indian Ocean can be recognized by its lips and spots. Juveniles have six lines down their back, which later develop into spots. Sweetlips feed at night on invertebrates and can grow up to 18 inches (45 cm) in length.

Hawksbill turtle (above)

An inhabitant of tropical and subtropical waters around the globe, the hawksbill turtle often migrates hundreds, if not thousands, of miles between breeding and feeding grounds. Human development at nesting sites, overhunting, and entanglement in fishermen's nets all take their toll on the population.

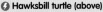

CHAPTER SEVEN

AUSTRALASIA & OCEANIA

Frilled lizard

Frilled lizards are found in New Guinea and the tropical north and east coast of Australia. The capelike frill that lies over the lizard's shoulders flares up when it is frightened or angry, making it appear twice its actual size. The lizard opens its mouth wide, hisses loudly, and pushes up on its front legs to ward off predators.

AUSTRALASIA & OCEANIA

The biogeographic region of Australasia extends from the easternmost islands of the Indonesian archipelago to New Guinea and Australia. The region known as Oceania incorporates all the island groups in the southern Pacific Ocean, including New Zealand. Most of the land in these two regions consists of remnants of what was once the ancient continent Gondwana. The remaining island groups are mainly volcanic in origin or formed as coral atolls perched atop submerged volcanic remnants. The flora and fauna of Australasia and Oceania is rich in old endemic species that had ancestors in the forests of Gondwana, such as the large flightless ratite birds, monotremes, and marsupial mammals.

The Great Barrier Reef
Australia's Great Barrier Reef is the largest fringing coral reef in the world and its abundant coral and fish species make it an important global biodiversity hot spot.

Temperate forests and heathlands
Like the eucalyptus trees on which it feeds, Australia's iconic animal, the koala, is one of the most readily identified inhabitants of the temperate southern forests.

Wildlife of Cape York
Cape York is both the bridge and the barrier between Australia and New Guinea, and its flora and fauna contain a fascinating mix of species from both major landmasses.

New Zealand
The kiwi is synonymous with New Zealand. It is one of the few survivors of an ancient line of flightless birds that once inhabited the great southern continent of Gondwana.

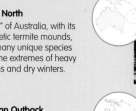

The Tropical North
The "Top End" of Australia, with its iconic magnetic termite mounds, is home to many unique species adapted to the extremes of heavy summer rains and dry winters.

Islands of the southwest Pacific
Lord Howe Island is home to a host of seabirds that nest on its predator-free shores. Other islands are a sanctuary for endemic species including flightless birds.

The Australian Outback
The deserts of central Australia are home to arid-adapted species such as the bearded dragon, but oases in the form of artesian springs and ephemeral lakes occur here, too.

New Guinea highlands
The rain forests of the New Guinea highlands are home to many unique species of mammals and birds, including the tree kangaroos and birds-of-paradise.

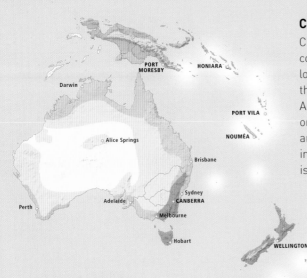

Climate (left)

Close proximity to the equator produces warm, humid conditions across much of Oceania. Hurricanes, known locally as cyclones, occur above 5 degrees south during the summer and extend to the northern latitudes of Australia. The middle latitudes are cooler, and moist onshore winds ensure regular rainfall in New Zealand and on Australia's east coast. However, the Australian interior is arid; less than 12 inches (300 mm) of rainfall is recorded each year across about half the continent.

CLIMATE ZONES

Wet tropical	Mediterranean
Seasonal tropical	Subtropical
Arid	Temperate
Semiarid	Highland

Vegetation (right)

The islands of Oceania have a unique suite of plants—rain forests in the interior, palms and mangroves nearer the coast. The trend is reversed in northern Australia, where lush coastal rain forest pockets yield to grasslands inland. Evergreen sclerophyll forest, dominated by eucalypt and acacia species, typify the southeast. In the arid interior, hummock grasses and mulga trees are widespread. Northern New Zealand's native forests include stands of large kauri trees; elsewhere there are temperate rain forests.

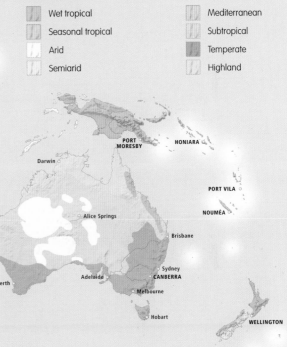

VEGETATION ZONES

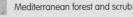

Tropical forest	Mediterranean forest and scrub
Seasonal tropical forest	Midlatitude grassland
Desert	Midlatitude forest
Tropical grassland	Mountain vegetation

Land cover (right)

Most of the Australian continent, as well as New Zealand, is suited to grazing, but in Australia livestock must roam widely to find sufficient food. Overall, one-quarter of Oceania is covered with forests. Arable land is scarce on many Pacific Islands, except where good rainfall and volcanic soils ensure agricultural productivity.

PROPORTIONS OF TOTAL LAND AREA

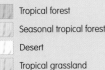

Forest and woodland
Arable land
Grazing
Other land

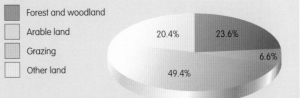

20.4%
23.6%
6.6%
49.4%

AUSTRALIA
MONOTREMES

Australia has unique remnants of the fauna that existed on the southern supercontinent, Gondwana, 200 million years ago. Monotremes, or egg-laying mammals, are the only survivors of the early mammals that arose while dinosaurs dominated Earth. Fossil monotremes are found in South America and Australia, but the surviving species occur only in Australia and New Guinea: the platypus and the four echidna species. Monotremes have advanced mammalian characteristics, such as hair, mammary glands, although not teats, and a large cerebral cortex, but they retain some primitive reptilian features.

Platypus (below)
Platypus swim with their webbed front feet, using their hind feet to steer. When diving, they close their eyes and ears and search for food using electroreceptors within their beak, which detect the movement of prey.

Platypus young (right)
The mother platypus incubates her eggs for two weeks in a nest near the end of a long burrow. Her young lap milk from the mother's mammary glands until they are old enough to forage.

Claws and tongue (left)
Echidnas use their powerful claws to excavate the nests and feeding tunnels of ants and termites. They then insert their long, sticky tongues into the galleries to lap up the insects.

Short-beaked echidna (left)
The short-beaked echidna is a spiky, rotund creature widely distributed throughout Australia and lowland New Guinea. When threatened, it can dig vertically into the soil, leaving only a few spines visible. All monotremes have a daily period of torpor (a deep sleep when the body temperature is lowered) and, in southern latitudes, the short-beaked echidna may hibernate in winter.

Other curious creatures

In addition to monotremes, Australia is home to many other unique animals. Among the most recognizable are the ratites: the emu and cassowary, large flightless birds related to the ostrich of Africa and rheas of South America. Rarely seen inhabitants of inland waters, the lobe-finned lungfish and soft-shelled turtle also have relatives in Africa and South America.

Australian lungfish (below)
These air-breathing fish are restricted to two rivers in Queensland. Their lungs allow them to breathe air when caught in shallow pools but, unlike their African and American cousins, they cannot survive in mud alone.

Pig-nosed turtle (above)
Found only in Australia's far north, pig-nosed turtles are notable for their soft shells, which lack bony dermal plates. They live and breed in freshwater, flood-prone rivers, where the rising waters stimulate their eggs to hatch.

Emu (right)
Widespread over most of Australia, emus eat the leaves and flowers of a variety of native plants, as well as insects. The male incubates the eggs and cares for the young for at least six months. At maturity, emus can reach 8 feet (2.5 m) in height.

AUSTRALIA
MARSUPIALS

Marsupials evolved on the continent of Gondwana around the time it was breaking up, and formed a major part of the early mammal fauna of South America and Australia. Marsupials have a more primitive brain and skeletal features, particularly the skull, than placental mammals. They deliver live young, but the young are born at an embryonic stage of development and attach themselves to a teat, generally enclosed in a pouch on the mother's belly, where they are fed until they are fully furred and able to move around.

Honey possum (above)
Mouselike honey possums feast on pollen and nectar, reaching their brush-tipped tongues into the flowers of banksias and other heathland plants.

Koala (left)
The koala looks sleepy because it lives on a diet of highly toxic eucalypt leaves. It has the ability to detoxify the poisons but the effort required leaves little energy to spare. Koalas do not make nests but simply sleep in the fork of a tree.

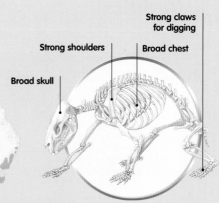

Strong claws for digging
Strong shoulders
Broad chest
Broad skull

Common wombat (left and above)
The stout frame and limbs of the common wombat make it a formidable landscape architect, capable of excavating extensive burrow systems with nesting chambers and multiple entrances. A grazer, the wombat forages for food at night. Its large colon enables it to live, like a horse, on dry grasses.

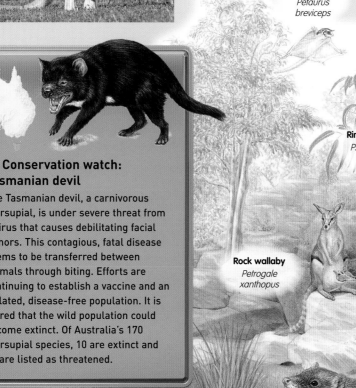

Red kangaroo (left)

Widespread across Australia's inland, the red kangaroo browses on grasses and shrubs. It rests under trees by day, feeding mostly at dawn and dusk. If hungry, tired, or threatened, a joey seeks shelter in its mother's pouch.

Sugar glider
Petaurus breviceps

Greater glider
Petauroides volans

Ringtail possum
Pseudocheirus peregrinus

Rock wallaby
Petrogale xanthopus

⚡ Conservation watch: Tasmanian devil

The Tasmanian devil, a carnivorous marsupial, is under severe threat from a virus that causes debilitating facial tumors. This contagious, fatal disease seems to be transferred between animals through biting. Efforts are continuing to establish a vaccine and an isolated, disease-free population. It is feared that the wild population could become extinct. Of Australia's 170 marsupial species, 10 are extinct and 34 are listed as threatened.

Southern brown bandicoot
Isoodon obesulus

Spotted-tailed quoll
Dasyurus maculatus

Diverse habitats (right)

Marsupials live in a variety of habitats. Trees provide shelter and food for possums, gliders, and the koala; rocky slopes are home to rock wallabies and wallaroos; and grassy nests hide the brown bandicoot. The elusive marsupial mole plows through soft sand without making a permanent burrow.

Marsupial mole
Notoryctes typhlops

AUSTRALIA
PARROTS AND COCKATOOS

Parrots are characteristic of the three southern continents and southern Asia, with only a few species invading the northern tropics. Parrots belong to three superfamilies: "true parrots," cockatoos, and New Zealand parrots. Cockatoos are found across Australia and northward as far as the Philippines. They have showy crests and curved bills, but less colorful plumage than most parrot species.

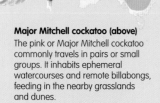

Major Mitchell cockatoo (above)
The pink or Major Mitchell cockatoo commonly travels in pairs or small groups. It inhabits ephemeral watercourses and remote billabongs, feeding in the nearby grasslands and dunes.

King parrot (left)
The king parrot, distinguished by its brilliant red breast and head, is a large, forest-dwelling parrot. It feeds on the seeds of acacias and other understory shrubs and trees.

Black cockatoo (right)
The handsome red-tailed black cockatoo feeds mostly on eucalyptus seeds.

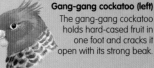

Bill types

A parrot's upper bill is always downcurved but varies in length from species to species. Some are long, ideal for digging into soft wood for insects or for cutting into ripe fruit. Others are short and strong, for breaking open tough seed cases.

Corella (left)
A cockatoo, the corella has a long, narrow bill ideal for extracting seeds from hard-coned plants and digging up bulbs.

Double-eyed fig parrot (left)
This parrot eats the seeds of soft-textured figs, slicing the fruit open neatly with the edge of its sharp bill.

Gang-gang cockatoo (left)
The gang-gang cockatoo holds hard-cased fruit in one foot and cracks it open with its strong beak.

Palm cockatoo (left)
A huge bill and powerful jaw muscles allow the palm cockatoo to break open seed cases and unripe fruit.

Rainbow lorikeet (left)
Instead of using its bill, this lorikeet uses its enlarged, hairy tongue to collect nectar and pollen.

Conservation watch: parrots

Many parrots species are under severe threat from the pet trade, habitat loss, and predation by introduced species. Some are economically important pests. However, a few species have proven their adaptability, despite land clearing and urban development. For example, crimson rosellas are now resident year-round in lowland Sydney, where once they were only winter visitors.

Rainbow lorikeet (right)
The rainbow lorikeet is found in the suburbs of most Australian cities.

Turquoise parrot (left)
A male turquoise parrot displays its beautiful wing and tail feathers as it prepares to land. The parrot occurs mostly in eastern Australia, where it nests in tree hollows.

Eastern rosella (right)
Platycercus eximius

Budgerigar (left)
Sociable budgerigars create colorful spectacles in outback Australia. Flocks containing thousands of birds suddenly erupt from a waterhole and wheel around.

A variety of nests

The nests made by parrots vary according to their range and the availability of safe sites. Hollows in tree trunks or branches are widely used, but nests may also be on the ground, in grass, under rocks, or even in fence posts.

Ground nest (below)
The ground parrot lives in heathland and nests on the ground, concealed by foliage.

Termite nest (left)
The golden-shouldered parrot makes its nest inside a termite mound at the end of a tunnel.

Tree nest (right)
The Australian king parrot makes its nest in a deep hollow in a tree trunk.

Rock nest (left)
Rock parrots, which live close to the coast, make their nest in a depression protected by an overhanging rock.

Communal nest (left)
Budgerigars nest in tree hollows but, unusually, they often nest communally, with several nests in one tree.

GREAT BARRIER REEF

Running parallel to the far northeast coast of Australia, the Great Barrier Reef covers some 134,286 square miles (347,800 km²). Despite its name, the reef is not one long barrier, but a series of 760 separate fringing reefs and more than 2,000 other reefs and cays inside the barrier. The shallow tropical water, with surface temperatures in the range of 75–86°F (24–30°C), is an ideal environment for a wide variety of marine animals.

Loggerhead turtle (left)
The loggerhead turtle is one of several species of marine turtles that coexist in shallow tropical waters. Although sharing the same range, they may have different diets. The loggerhead mainly eats mollusks and its powerful jaws are capable of crushing even large shells.

Dugong (below)
The dugong once inhabited extensive shallow waters around the Indian Ocean but now occurs only as small, remnant populations. On the Barrier Reef, seagrass beds provide food and shelter from predators.

Parrotfish
Sacruss sp.

Marine life (below)
The reef itself is composed of the skeletons of more than 300 species of hard corals. It is home to more than 1,500 species of fish, 4,000 mollusk species, and over 400 species of sponge. Within its protected waters, seagrass beds provide food for dugongs and green turtles, and shelter for countless other creatures.

Staghorn coral
Acropora sp.

Giant clam
Tridacna gigas

Table coral
Acropora sp.

Clown anemonefish
Amphiprion percula

Orangespine unicornfish
Naso lituratus

Crown-of-thorns starfish
Acanthaster planci

TOWNSVILLE, QLD, AUSTRALIA

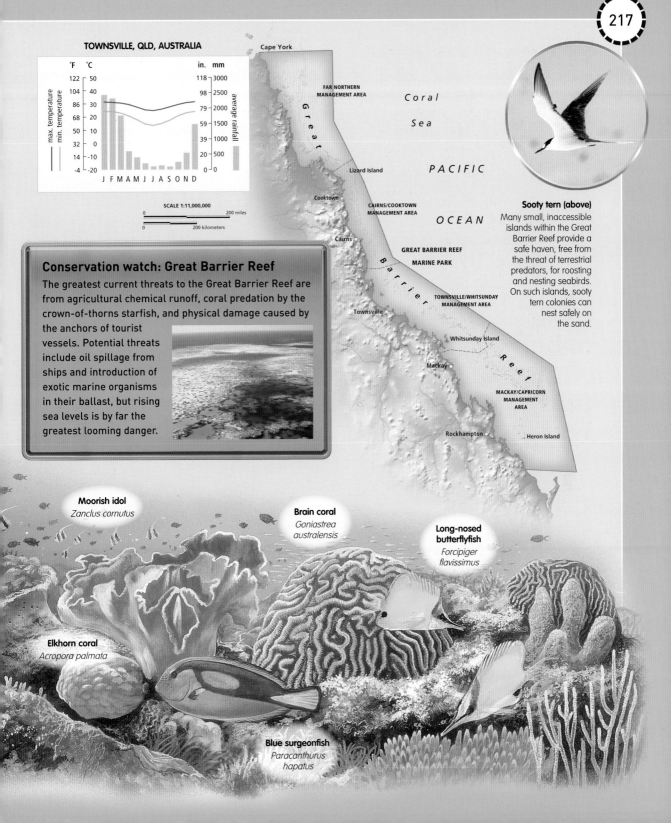

°F   °C   in.   mm
122   50   118   3000
104   40   98   2500
 86   30   79   2000
 68   20   59   1500
 50   10   39   1000
 32   0   20   500
 14 -10
 -4 -20   0   0
     J F M A M J J A S O N D

max. temperature
min. temperature
average rainfall

SCALE 1:11,000,000

0 ————————————— 200 miles
0 ————————————— 200 kilometers

Cape York

FAR NORTHERN
MANAGEMENT AREA

Coral
Sea

PACIFIC

Lizard Island

Cooktown

CAIRNS/COOKTOWN
MANAGEMENT AREA

OCEAN

Cairns

GREAT BARRIER REEF
MARINE PARK

Great

Barrier

TOWNSVILLE/WHITSUNDAY
MANAGEMENT AREA

Townsville

Whitsunday Island

Reef

Mackay

MACKAY/CAPRICORN
MANAGEMENT
AREA

Rockhampton

Heron Island

Conservation watch: Great Barrier Reef

The greatest current threats to the Great Barrier Reef are from agricultural chemical runoff, coral predation by the crown-of-thorns starfish, and physical damage caused by the anchors of tourist vessels. Potential threats include oil spillage from ships and introduction of exotic marine organisms in their ballast, but rising sea levels is by far the greatest looming danger.

Sooty tern (above)

Many small, inaccessible islands within the Great Barrier Reef provide a safe haven, free from the threat of terrestrial predators, for roosting and nesting seabirds. On such islands, sooty tern colonies can nest safely on the sand.

Moorish idol
Zanclus cornutus

Brain coral
Goniastrea australensis

Long-nosed butterflyfish
Forcipiger flavissimus

Elkhorn coral
Acropora palmata

Blue surgeonfish
Paracanthurus hapatus

CAPE YORK

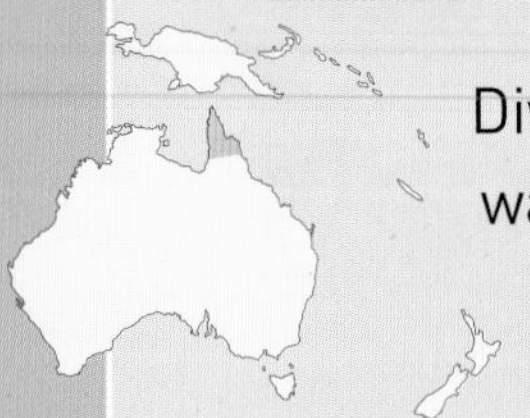

Dividing the Cape York Peninsula from New Guinea, the Torres Strait was not always water, and the flora, fauna, and peoples of this region bear witness to the close relationship between the two regions. Animals with distributions that span the strait include the short-beaked echidna, striped possum, spotted cuscus, palm cockatoo, and birdwing butterfly. Many other groups have closely related, yet distinct species on either side of the strait, such as the tree kangaroos, pademelons, and dasyurids.

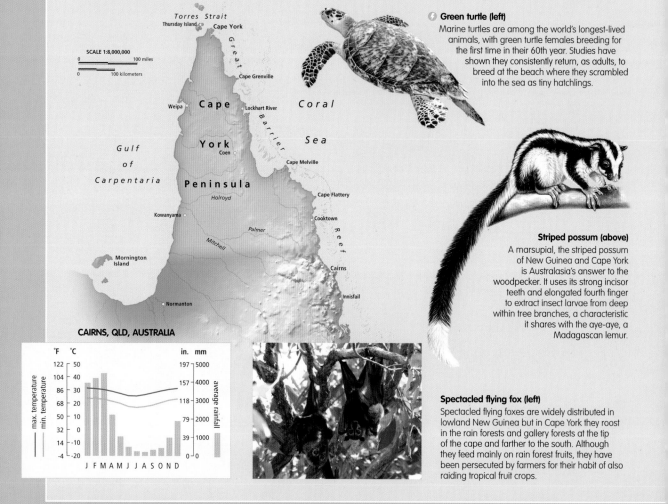

Green turtle (left)
Marine turtles are among the world's longest-lived animals, with green turtle females breeding for the first time in their 60th year. Studies have shown they consistently return, as adults, to breed at the beach where they scrambled into the sea as tiny hatchlings.

Striped possum (above)
A marsupial, the striped possum of New Guinea and Cape York is Australasia's answer to the woodpecker. It uses its strong incisor teeth and elongated fourth finger to extract insect larvae from deep within tree branches, a characteristic it shares with the aye-aye, a Madagascan lemur.

Spectacled flying fox (left)
Spectacled flying foxes are widely distributed in lowland New Guinea but in Cape York they roost in the rain forests and gallery forests at the tip of the cape and farther to the south. Although they feed mainly on rain forest fruits, they have been persecuted by farmers for their habit of also raiding tropical fruit crops.

Map labels: Torres Strait, Thursday Island, Cape York, Great, Cape Grenville, Weipa, Cape, Lockhart River, Coral, Barrier, York, Coen, Sea, Cape Melville, Gulf, of, Carpentaria, Peninsula, Cape Flattery, Holroyd, Kowanyama, Reef, Palmer, Cooktown, Mitchell, Mornington Island, Cairns, Normanton, Innisfail

SCALE 1:8,000,000
0   100 miles
0   100 kilometers

CAIRNS, QLD, AUSTRALIA

°F °C   in. mm
122 50   197 5000
104 40   157 4000
86   30   118 3000
68   20
50   10   79   2000
32   0   39   1000
14   -10   0   0
-4   -20

max. temperature
min. temperature

average rainfall

J F M A M J J A S O N D

Mangrove forest (below)

Mangrove habitats occur in all coastal areas with shallow, calm waters. Around Cape York this includes estuaries and the entire undisturbed coastline inside the Great Barrier Reef. Mangroves have an unusual growth habit, sporting long, arching stilt roots or aerial roots known as pneumatophores. In this habitat, fiddler crabs swarm over the mud at low tide, gobies climb the mangrove roots to escape larger fish, and the archerfish lurks in the shallows, waiting to shoot down passing insects with a jet of water.

Green tree python

The green tree python, unlike most other pythons in the genus *Morelia*, is primarily arboreal in its habits. It is similar to the emerald tree boa of South America, sharing the juvenile boa's yellow coloration, its dietary preference for birds, and the distinctive way in which it rests in a coiled loop on a branch. Although widespread in New Guinea, the green tree python occurs in Australia only in rain forests on mountain ranges in the Cape York Peninsula.

Python jaw (right)

The two halves of the python's lower jaw are attached by an elastic ligament, and the upper jaws are not firmly attached to the cranium. This allows for a ratchet movement that draws large prey into the gullet.

Striated heron
Ardeola striata

Gobies
Gobiidae

Archerfish
Toxotes chatareus

Archerfish (above)

Unerring aim with a forceful jet of water shot from its mouth allows the archerfish to knock insects from overhanging foliage.

Stilt roots

Nursery fish

Fiddler crabs
Uca spp.

CAPE YORK
TROPICAL RAIN FOREST

This region contains some of Australia's largest tracts of tropical rain forest. These ecosystems contain more than 3,000 species of plants from more than 200 families, making this area one of the richest in botanical diversity in the world. The forests are home to several primitive forms of flowering plants and to many unique endemic species of animals, such as the musky rat-kangaroo.

ENDEMIC SPECIES		
CLASS	NO. OF SPECIES	EXAMPLE
Mammals	8	Herbert River ringtail possum
Birds	13	Tooth-billed catbird
Reptiles	18	Chameleon gecko
Amphibians	20	Torrent frog
Fish	78	Cairns rainbowfish
Invertebrates	Thousands	Cairns birdwing butterfly

Lilly pilly
Acmena smithii

Musky rat-kangaroo (below)
The musky rat-kangaroo is the smallest and most primitive member of the kangaroo group of families. It, alone, has retained the opposable first toe common to most other marsupial groups but absent in kangaroos. It forages during the day for fruits and fungi.

Double-eyed fig parrot (left)
The small but colorful double-eyed fig parrot is not often seen. It spends much of its time in the rain forest canopy, where it enjoys a diet of native fig seeds. Its range also extends to New Guinea.

Brush turkey
Alectura lathami

Orange-thighed tree frog
Litoria xanthomera

Rhinoceros beetle
Xylotrupes ulysses

Cassowary (left)

The cassowary's natural habitat is rain forest although it sometimes ranges into gardens and orchards in search of fruit. Like the emu and ostrich, the male incubates the eggs and rears the chicks, which remain in its care for about nine months.

Fruit dispersal (left)

Cassowaries play an important role in forest life by helping disperse the seeds of forest trees, including the quandong. They swallow the fruits whole and their digestive tract activates the seed, which is returned to the earth conveniently encased in fertilizer.

Tropical rain forest floor (below)

The floor of a tropical rain forest is a rich field for fruit- and insect-eaters, and an ideal habitat for a wide range of invertebrates, including centipedes, snails, and beetles. Frogs and lizards find both food and shelter in the leaf litter or in decaying branches. The canopy of dense vegetation overhead prevents much light from reaching the forest floor. Emerging seedlings grow slowly but fungi thrive.

Chameleon gecko
Carpodactylus laevis

Scrub python
Morelia amethistina

**Giant
forest cricket**
Papuaistis sp.

Centipede
Scolopendridae

THE TROPICAL NORTH

Annual rainfall here is high, but it falls during a short monsoonal wet season between November and April. The rest of the year the weather is dominated by hot, dry winds. This results in a different suite of ecosystems from elsewhere in Australia, dominated by grassy woodlands and savannas. Palm forests and vine thickets grow in moister gullies but large areas of rain forest are absent. The area is home to the second largest national park in the world, Kakadu, which contains many of the tropical north's unique plants and animals.

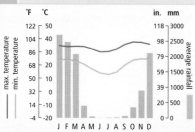

KATHERINE, NT, AUSTRALIA

Saltwater crocodile (right)
Rightly feared as ferocious predators, saltwater crocodiles are found in northern Australian seas, estuaries, large rivers, and during the wet season, coastal flood plains. The female crocodile builds a mound nest of rotting vegetation, which she guards while her eggs incubate.

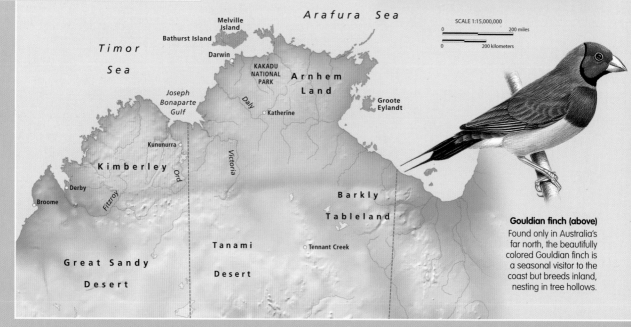

SCALE 1:15,000,000

Arafura Sea

Melville Island

Bathurst Island

Timor
Sea

Darwin

KAKADU NATIONAL PARK

Arnhem Land

Joseph Bonaparte Gulf

Daly

Groote Eylandt

Katherine

Kununurra

Kimberley

Victoria

Ord

Derby

Broome

Fitzroy

Barkly

Tableland

Tanami

Tennant Creek

Great Sandy

Desert

Desert

Gouldian finch (above)
Found only in Australia's far north, the beautifully colored Gouldian finch is a seasonal visitor to the coast but breeds inland, nesting in tree hollows.

Taipan

The taipan is one of Australia's largest and most venomous snakes. It is a "strike and wait" predator, biting its unsuspecting victim once or twice before retreating and waiting for it to die. It is particularly dangerous to humans because of its habit of lurking in long grass, where it waits to strike prey, such as a passing bandicoot, rat, small marsupial, or bird.

Fangs (below)
The taipan's hollow fangs are fixed in the front of the upper jaw. A duct supplying venom leads from a gland in the back of the head.

Venom gland

⚡ Northern quoll

Cane toads, introduced to Australia in 1935, are one of the tropical north's greatest threats. Poison from the toad's parotoid glands is highly toxic to most native animals. Although some species seem to have found ways to avoid or even consume toads, the northern quoll has proven particularly vulnerable. The toad's relentless movement across Arnhem Land and Kakadu has coincided with the deaths of large numbers of quolls. A major effort is being made to save the northern quoll by establishing populations on toad-free islands north of Darwin.

Cane toad (right)
Cane toads have been in the western Gulf of Carpentaria for many years but have recently expanded their range to the west, reaching Darwin in 2005.

Termite fortresses

Most termite species build insignificant nests, either underground or inside a tree or log, but tall termite mounds dot the grasslands and woodlands of Australia's far north. Their shape, often narrow at the top, and their careful alignment in relation to the sun's rays, helps to keep them as cool as possible. Magnetic termites are responsible for many of these mounds, but the tallest, up to 25 feet (7.6 m) high, belong to spinifex termites.

Soldier
Soldiers are armed either with huge jaws or, in the case of the spinifex termite, a snout capable of squirting a sticky, toxic fluid.

King
The king's main role is to fertilize the queen but when the colony is first founded the king also cares for the young.

Strong outer wall

Special chamber for queen

Queen
Queen termites lose their wings once they find a male. Together they establish a temporary shelter, where the first brood is born. The queen may live for 50 years and lay up to 2,000 eggs per day.

Many small cavities and channels in inner section of mound

Goannas often make their nest in the cool environment of a termite mound

THE OUTBACK

The term "Outback" generally refers to the semiarid and arid lands of Australia's interior. Most of the Outback is flat or rolling land sparsely covered with grasslands or low woodlands, featuring stunted trees such as the mulga and mallee. In the deserts of the center, lizards, birds, and small mammals feed on plentiful ants and other insects. Water is a major limiting factor in the desert. Places such as Lake Eyre, rocky gorges, and the myriad mound springs scattered around the rim of the Great Artesian Basin, a vast aquifer, defy notions of a barren continent.

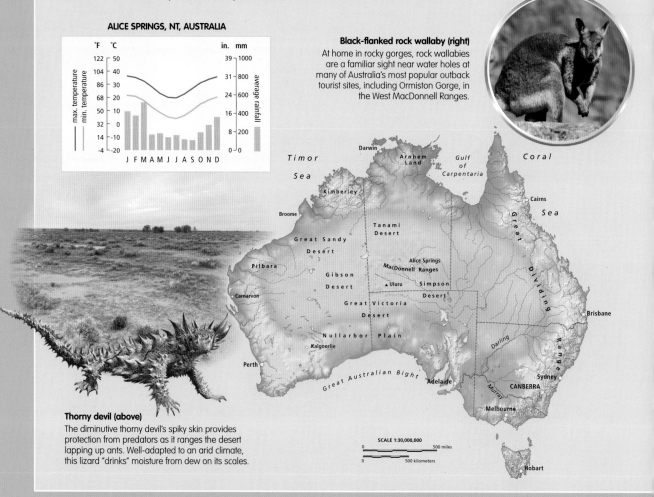

ALICE SPRINGS, NT, AUSTRALIA

Black-flanked rock wallaby (right)
At home in rocky gorges, rock wallabies are a familiar sight near water holes at many of Australia's most popular outback tourist sites, including Ormiston Gorge, in the West MacDonnell Ranges.

Thorny devil (above)
The diminutive thorny devil's spiky skin provides protection from predators as it ranges the desert lapping up ants. Well-adapted to an arid climate, this lizard "drinks" moisture from dew on its scales.

SCALE 1:30,000,000

0   500 miles

0   500 kilometers

Dingo (above)
Members of the dog family, *Canidae*, dingoes occur widely in Australia from coastal to alpine regions, but they remain the quintessential symbol of the outback. They prey upon other mammals and birds, sometimes hunting in packs.

Conservation watch: kowari
The kowari is vulnerable in its range and populations have decreased dramatically over the past century. Its decline, and that of the greater bilby whose burrows it inhabits, appears to be linked to the loss of insect prey associated with the expansion of cattle grazing. A wide-ranging hunter, the kowari requires relatively large protected reserves for its future survival.

Bilby (above)
Once widespread in the Outback, bilbies are now found in only a few refuges. These shy, nocturnal members of the bandicoot family, with ears and gait reminiscent of a rabbit, forage for fungi and insects. They spend the day in burrows to escape the inland heat.

Spinifex grasslands (right)
Spinifex is a perennial, tussock-forming grass that grows into characteristic rings as the plant expands and the older central stems die. Along with its associated shrubs and trees, spinifex provides food and shelter for a wide variety of animals. White-winged fairy-wrens and grasswrens flit about the spinifex, gleaning insects off the spiky leaves.

Sand goanna
Varanus gouldii

Spinifex tussock
Triodia sp.

Mulgara
Dasycercus cristicauda

Bearded dragon
Pogona minor

White-winged fairy wren
Malurus leucopterus

Sand-swimming skink
Lerista sp.

THE OUTBACK
WATER IN THE DESERT

In Australia, the arid-zone rivers begin and end their journeys in the desert, where rainfall is a rare event. When it does rain, as a result of a massive frontal event or a cyclone, the consequences are felt over vast areas and for many months. Rains falling on the inland plains of Australia's northeast, for example, make their way west into the Cooper and Diamantina systems. Rain farther west swells the Finke River. All end up in the Lake Eyre Basin. These infrequent inundations provide the impetus for a massive breeding event, when all forms of life gather in vast numbers and multiply in the swelling lakes and billabongs.

Waiting for the rain (below)

Long periods of drought in inland Australia make life impossible for frogs, which need to keep their skin moist. The water-holding frog has adapted to this harsh climate by burrowing into a chamber underground, shedding layers of skin to form a protective cocoon, and awaiting rain in a state of torpor. It then emerges to feed and mate.

The Lake Eyre drainage basin

Area of the basin that is prone to flooding

Digging in

The frog digs itself a small burrow and prepares to wait for rains to return.

Inactive underground

Enclosed in its cocoon, the frog enters a state of torpor, which may last many months.

Rain arrives

When rainfall softens the soil, the frog digs its way out to the surface.

Waterbirds on wetlands

The desert wetlands attract birds from all over Australia to the temporarily abundant feeding and breeding grounds. Ibis, egrets, spoonbills, and cormorants breed in trees fringing the rivers and billabongs. Pelicans, gulls, and terns nest on islands in the temporary lakes, and black swans, along with several duck species, nest in the reed beds fringing the wetlands.

Pink-eared duck (left)

The pink-eared duck is one of a group of nomadic species that takes advantage of the ephemeral waterways in the interior to breed when conditions are favorable. It retreats to coastal estuaries and lagoons when drought inevitably returns to the inland.

Australian pelican (right)

Australian pelicans breed in several small breeding colonies around the continent's coastal fringe, but the major breeding site for vast numbers of pelicans is Lake Eyre. On the all-too-rare occasions when floodwaters reach the lake, it attracts many hundreds of birds.

Australian white ibis (right)

Swamps are the favored feeding sites of the Australian white ibis, which dines on insects, crustaceans, fish, and frogs. While most birds breed in the Murray–Darling wetlands, some take advantage of ephemeral wetlands further inland on an opportunistic basis.

Royal spoonbill (right)

The nomadic royal spoonbill, one of two species occurring in Australia, nests in small colonies scattered throughout northern and eastern Australia.

Life in a billabong (below)

Inland rivers may overflow their banks and flood surrounding plains after heavy rain, then shrink during drier times to form billabongs—isolated water holes. The stagnant water in the billabong is an ideal habitat for smooth freshwater crayfish, or yabby, frogs, the long-necked tortoise, and myriad small fish and insects. Birds, including long-legged waders, are attracted to these rewarding feeding grounds.

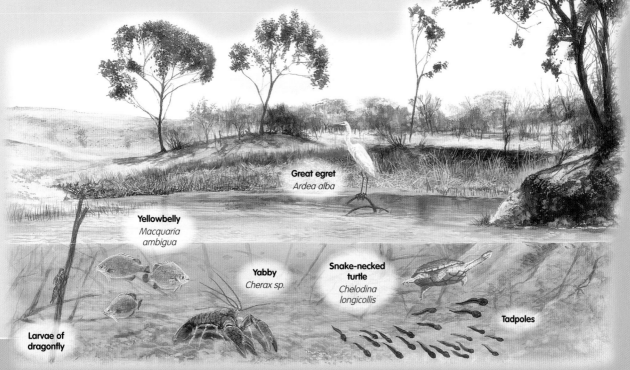

Great egret
Ardea alba

Yellowbelly
Macquaria ambigua

Yabby
Cherax sp.

Snake-necked turtle
Chelodina longicollis

Tadpoles

Larvae of dragonfly

TEMPERATE FORESTS AND HEATHLANDS

Australia's southern forests and heathlands are dominated by two large plant families—the *Myrtaceae*, containing the iconic eucalypts commonly known as gum trees, melaleucas, and bottlebrushes; and the *Proteaceae*, whose banksias and grevilleas regenerate quickly after the fires that periodically raze the landscape. All have massive flowering events that attract nectar-feeding mammals, such as possums and fruit bats, birds such as honeyeaters and lorikeets, and insects, all of which pollinate the plants as they gorge themselves on the abundant nectar.

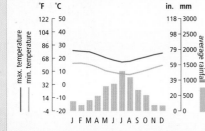

ESPERANCE, WA, AUSTRALIA

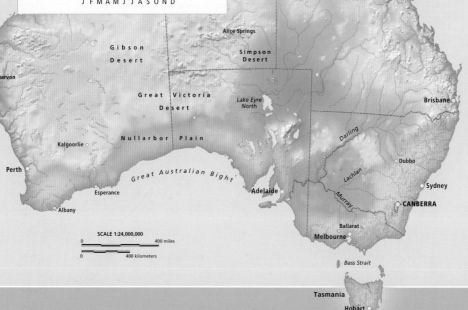

Numbat (above)
The numbat, a marsupial with a bushy tail and a pointed face, is exclusively a termite-eater. Its long tongue is a key player in its search for food as it explores feeding galleries of termites under the soil or in logs.

Kookaburra (below)

The kookaburra is one of Australia's most familiar birds. A dry-land kingfisher, it preys on lizards, snakes, worms, and cicadas and is a highly efficient hunter. Its raucous laughing call, often heard pre-dawn, is a familiar sound in the Australian bush.

⚡ Conservation watch: mountain pygmy possum

The mountain pygmy possum is a true living fossil. It was first described from Pleistocene cave deposits, before living animals were discovered in 1966. Restricted to high alpine heathlands, it is highly endangered because of the threats of fire and global warming.

Red-necked wallaby (below)

The red-necked wallaby, generally solitary, is one of the most common members of the kangaroo family and the only one to live in high alpine areas. Its thick winter fur was highly prized by Aboriginal people for making warm winter capes.

Superb lyrebird (left)

The superb lyrebird, named for the shape of its tail, is one of the oldest members of the songbird group that evolved in Australia before spreading to the rest of the world. The male lyrebird is an amazing mimic, capable of imitating almost any sound it hears.

Satin bowerbird (right)

When the male satin bowerbird inherits or acquires a territory, it changes into its deep blue-black plumage and builds a bower, which it lines with any blue objects it can find. The bird then hovers around the bower, burbling and calling to attract a mate.

NEW ZEALAND

New Zealand's fauna is a mixture of early Gondwanan elements, such as the kiwis, and species that have made the journey across the Tasman Sea or Pacific Ocean unaided. New Zealand has 10 species of native mammals, three bats and seven pinnipeds, but it has 35 species of introduced mammals. Of these, the kiore and dog were introduced by the Maori, and the rest, including a hedgehog, the rabbit, three rodents, and 16 ungulates, were brought by Europeans. Over the past 200 years, these interlopers have had a devastating effect on native fauna and flora.

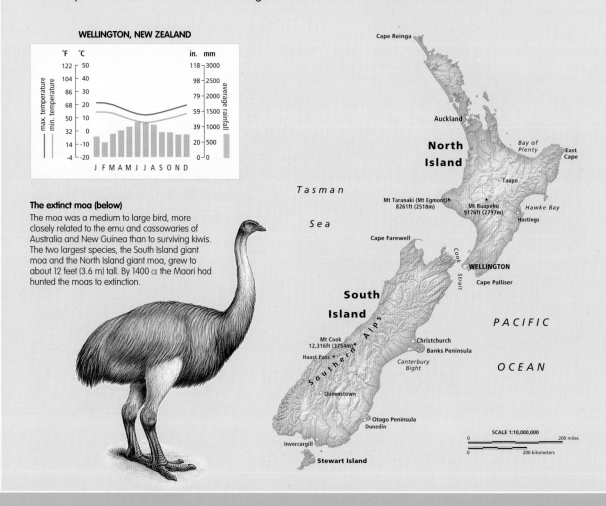

WELLINGTON, NEW ZEALAND

The extinct moa (below)

The moa was a medium to large bird, more closely related to the emu and cassowaries of Australia and New Guinea than to surviving kiwis. The two largest species, the South Island giant moa and the North Island giant moa, grew to about 12 feet (3.6 m) tall. By 1400 CE the Maori had hunted the moas to extinction.

Cape Reinga

Auckland

North Island

Bay of Plenty

East Cape

Taupo

Mt Taranaki (Mt Egmont)▲
8261ft (2518m)

Mt Ruapehu
9176ft (2797m)

Hawke Bay

Hastings

Tasman

Sea

Cape Farewell

Cook Strait

WELLINGTON

Cape Palliser

South Island

Southern Alps

Mt Cook
12,316ft (3754m)▲

Haast Pass

Christchurch

Banks Peninsula

Canterbury Bight

PACIFIC

OCEAN

Queenstown

Otago Peninsula
Dunedin

SCALE 1:10,000,000

0   200 miles

0   200 kilometers

Invercargill

Stewart Island

Tuatara (right)

Two species of tuatara survive on islands off New Zealand's coast. Despite their lizard-like appearance, they are not lizards but belong to an ancient reptile order that predates the dinosaurs. They are now known only in New Zealand, where half the population of the common species (*Sphenodon punctatus*) lives on Stephens Island in Cook Strait.

Weta (above)

About 70 species of weta, forest- and cave-dwelling crickets, are found in New Zealand in all habitats from coastal scrubs to alpine areas.

Hochstetter's frog (left)

Of New Zealand's four frog species, the Hochstetter's frog, found in several locations on the North Island, is the most common. It lays its eggs in damp ground and hatchlings emerge without undergoing a free-living larval stage.

Kea (left)

The kea is the alpine and subalpine parrot familiar to most visitors to New Zealand's Haast Pass, where it vandalizes the windscreen wipers of parked cars. It is also notorious for attacking sheep. Its numbers are declining.

⚡ Conservation watch: kakapo

The kakapo, considered the world's heaviest parrot, was once widespread throughout New Zealand. The clearing of forests and predation have forced it onto a handful of islands. Flightless and nocturnal, it lives on fruits and other plant parts, and breeds only every three to five years.

Great spotted kiwi (right)

The great spotted kiwi is the largest of the four kiwi species but, like the other three, its numbers are declining and it requires conservation. It is threatened by predation from domestic dogs and cats, as well as stoats.

SOUTHWEST PACIFIC ISLANDS

The islands of the tropical southwest Pacific Ocean have two separate origins. New Caledonia is a remnant of the ancient supercontinent Gondwana, and the rest, from the Solomon Islands to Vanuatu, are volcanic uplifted blocks along the Pacific Ring of Fire. New Caledonia is home to many ancient plants that demonstrate its affinity with Australia. The larger islands have a high percentage of endemic land birds, including the kagu of New Caledonia. The smaller, more isolated islands frequently host large breeding colonies of pelagic seabirds.

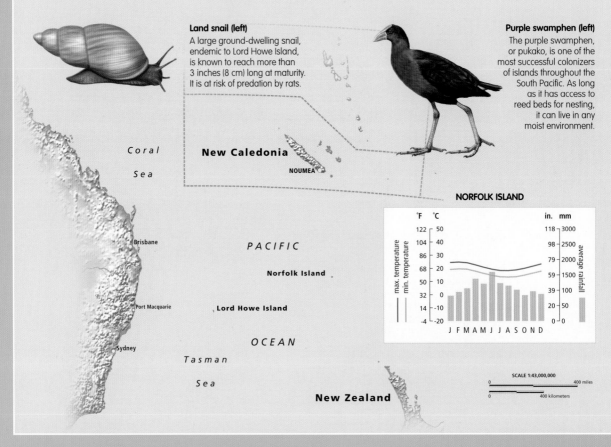

Land snail (left)
A large ground-dwelling snail, endemic to Lord Howe Island, is known to reach more than 3 inches (8 cm) long at maturity. It is at risk of predation by rats.

Purple swamphen (left)
The purple swamphen, or pukako, is one of the most successful colonizers of islands throughout the South Pacific. As long as it has access to reed beds for nesting, it can live in any moist environment.

Coral Sea

New Caledonia

NOUMEA

Brisbane

PACIFIC

Norfolk Island

Port Macquarie

Lord Howe Island

OCEAN

Sydney

Tasman Sea

New Zealand

NORFOLK ISLAND

°F °C   in. mm

max. temperature / min. temperature

average rainfall

J F M A M J J A S O N D

SCALE 1:43,000,000

0 — 400 miles
0 — 400 kilometers

Sooty tern (left)
The large breeding colony of sooty terns on Lord Howe Island's Mount Eliza is one of the island's major natural attractions. Bird breeding colonies are normally found on inaccessible islands, but here the birds gather in large numbers and are readily observed.

⚡ Lord Howe phasmid (right)
The Lord Howe Island phasmid, or stick insect, population on the main island was wiped out by introduced rats, but survivors were discovered in 2001 on an outlying island. A captive colony was established and some of their progeny was reintroduced to a small area on the island, following a rat eradication program.

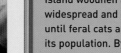

⚡ Conservation watch: Lord Howe Island woodhen

Species of rail tend to evolve into flightless forms after they invade remote islands, of which the Lord Howe Island woodhen is one example. It was widespread and common on the island until feral cats and pigs decimated its population. By 1973 only a few individuals survived on Mount Gower and Mount Lidgbird. A safe breeding colony was established and, by the mid-1980s, 85 captive-bred individuals were reintroduced into the wild. The current population is around 250 birds.

⚡ Kagu (left)
The kagu, a relative of the rails and cranes, is endemic to New Caledonia. Although its wings are a normal size for its bodyweight and shape, it is flightless, so it is found only on the forest floor. It is highly susceptible to predation, particularly by dogs and cats.

Providence petrel

The Providence petrel is a pelagic species with an unusually narrow distribution, occurring mainly in the warmer waters of the southwest Pacific Ocean. During the non-breeding season some individuals migrate to the North Pacific, but during the breeding season dense colonies gather on Lord Howe Island. The birds nest in burrows, the parents taking turns to incubate the egg.

Hatching (left)
The Providence petrel parents share the duty of incubating their egg in a small underground nesting chamber at the end of a burrow.

Nestling (right)
The nestling, which is often alone while the parents fly far out to sea to seek food, is in danger of predation by rats or other birds.

NEW GUINEA HIGHLANDS

In the highlands of New Guinea, the vegetation ranges from palm forests and rain forest in the wettest areas to tree-fern savannas and grasslands on the drier slopes. The largely undisturbed rain forests support flowering, fruit-bearing trees, which attract fruit bats, numerous birds, and some of the world's largest birdwing butterflies. The extensive grasslands characteristic of many highland valleys are known as kunai grasslands. Among the native mammal and bird species there is considerable variability in different regions.

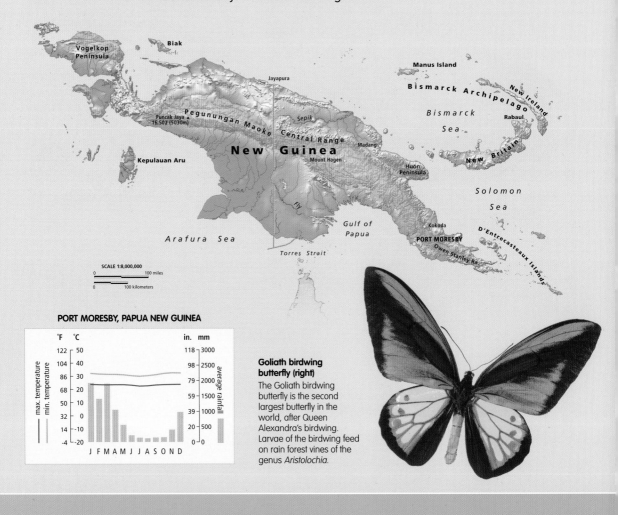

SCALE 1:8,000,000

0 — 100 miles

0 — 100 kilometers

PORT MORESBY, PAPUA NEW GUINEA

°F °C in. mm

122 — 50 ⎪ 118 — 3000
104 — 40 ⎪ 98 — 2500
86 — 30 ⎪ 79 — 2000
68 — 20 ⎪ 59 — 1500
50 — 10 ⎪ 39 — 1000
32 — 0 ⎪ 20 — 500
14 — -10 ⎪ 0 — 0
-4 — -20 ⎪

max. temperature
min. temperature

average rainfall

J F M A M J J A S O N D

Goliath birdwing butterfly (right)
The Goliath birdwing butterfly is the second largest butterfly in the world, after Queen Alexandra's birdwing. Larvae of the birdwing feed on rain forest vines of the genus *Aristolochia*.

Ground cuscus (left)

The cuscuses are a group of nocturnal leaf- and fruit-eating marsupials. The ground cuscus differs from the other cuscuses as it spends its day in burrows rather than in the trees. It is found in forests and scrub on New Guinea and the Aru Islands.

Goodfellow's tree kangaroo (right)

Living in the rain forests of the central highlands, Goodfellow's tree kangaroo has suffered habitat loss because of forest-clearing for agriculture. However, it remains the most widespread species within the ornate tree kangaroo group.

Birds-of-paradise

Birds-of-paradise are synonymous with the island of New Guinea, and the bright plumes the male birds employ in their spectacular acrobatic displays have been adopted by the local peoples in their headdresses. The birds' range extends to Indonesia and subtropical Australia, but the center of diversity is in the New Guinea highlands.

Raggiana bird-of-paradise (above)

The Raggiana bird-of-paradise is the most common species in this family. Males gather in groups known as leks to perform their spectacular dance routines, which are accompanied by high-pitched calls.

King of Saxony (below)

The male King of Saxony is unique, with its two long head plumes, but the female is easily mistaken for a drab honeyeater. Solitary males display from a dead limb high in the canopy.

Blue bird-of-paradise (below)

The male blue bird-of-paradise is solitary, unlike its close relative the Raggiana bird-of-paradise. It is also secretive, displaying in the treetops high on a hillside.

Superb bird-of-paradise (right)

The male superb bird-of-paradise is unmistakable, with electric-blue false wings on its chest and lustrous black erectile back feathers.

Huon astrapia (left)

Huon astrapias are, like other astrapias, quiet birds of the middle to upper canopy. They fly in a characteristic flap-and-glide pattern, with their enormous tails trailing behind.

CHAPTER EIGHT

THE
POLES

Emperor penguins

Emperor penguins live in Antarctica and are one of the few animals to stay during winter. When penguin chicks are about six weeks old, they collect in a group, or crèche, and are looked after by a single adult. This allows other adult penguins to leave the colony and catch food. Emperor penguins feed their own chicks for about nine months.

THE POLES

The north geographic pole is located on sea ice in the middle of a cold, deep ocean. The Antarctic centers on a high continent: the south geographic pole is on an icecap 9,301 feet (2,835 m) above sea level. Latitude for latitude, the high continent makes the Antarctic region much colder than the Arctic. The Arctic is constantly recruiting plants and animals overland from the south. Antarctica receives only the few plants and animals that can swim, fly, or be blown there. It also has fewer habitable areas to offer, hence its relative poverty of species.

The Arctic

In the sunless winter, strong anticyclones form over the central core of pack ice, North America, Greenland, and Siberia, bringing mean temperatures of around -22°F (-30°C) to the central basin, -58°F (-50°C) over land. Through the rest of the year, eastward-moving cyclones bring rain, snow, and winds. Mean monthly temperatures rise above freezing point from May to September.

Arctic sea ice
The Arctic region is home to many land animals, although even the heavily furred polar bear must spend winter in a snow den.

South Georgia
South Sandwich Islands
Scotia Sea
South Orkney Islands
Falkland Islands
Tierra del Fuego
Drake Passage
South Shetland Islands
Bransfield Strait
Antarctic Circle
Larsen Ice Shelf
Antarctic Peninsula
Alexander Island
Bellinghausen Sea
Peter I Island
Amundsen Sea

SOUTHERN OCEAN

Cosmonauts Sea
Fimbul Ice Shelf
Riiser-Larsen Sea
Lazerov Ice Shelf
Lützow-Holm Bay
Cape Ann
Riiser-Larsen Ice Shelf
Brunt Ice Shelf
Queen Maud Land
Enderby Land
Cape Boothby
MacDonald Islands
Heard Island
Weddell Sea
Filchner Ice Shelf
Berkner Island
Ronne Ice Shelf
Cooperation Sea
Prince Charles Mtns
Cape Darnley
Amery Ice Shelf
Prydz Bay
West Ice Shelf
Cape Penck

ANTARCTICA

△ South Pole
▲Vinson Massif 16,066ft (4897m)
South Geomagnetic Pole △
East Antarctica
Shackleton Ice Shelf
West Antarctica
Horlick Mtns
Transantarctic
Davis Sea
Marie Byrd Land
Ross Ice Shelf
Wilkes Land
Vincennes Bay
Cape Poinsett
Getz Ice Shelf
Mt Erebus 12,447ft (3794m)▲
Victoria Land
Adélie Land
Cape Goodenough
Porpoise Bay
Mawson Sea
Cape Morse
Ross Sea
McMurdo Sound
George V Land
South Magnetic Pole △
Mt Minto 13,665ft (4165m)▲
Cape Adare
Fisher Bay
Cape North
Balleny Islands
Somov Sea
Dumont d'Urville Sea

Antarctic Circle

SOUTHERN OCEAN

Macquarie Island

SCALE 1:35,000,000
0   500 miles
0   500 kilometers

Antarctic desert
Antarctica is truly a frozen desert. In winter most animal species migrate, even if only to subantarctic islands. The humpback whale, however, migrates to the tropics.

The Antarctic

A persistent winter anticyclone over the continent makes the highest points of the plateau some of Earth's coldest places. The Russian station Vostok recorded a world-record low temperature of -126.9°F (-88.3°C) in August 1960. Summer monthly mean temperatures rise to around -22°F (-30°C). Coastal stations and the Antarctic Peninsula are much warmer.

ARCTIC TUNDRA

Tundra is the rolling, treeless plains lying north of the boreal forests. Snow-covered in winter, it thaws in spring to reveal stony, wind-swept uplands and greener lowlands dotted with lakes, bogs, and marshes. Though underlain by permafrost, summer tundra supports mosses, grasses, rushes, and knee-high shrubs, brightened by flowering plants. In the harsher north, the tundra thins gradually to near-sterile Arctic desert. Hundreds of kinds of living creatures make their homes on tundra, either year-round or as summer migrants.

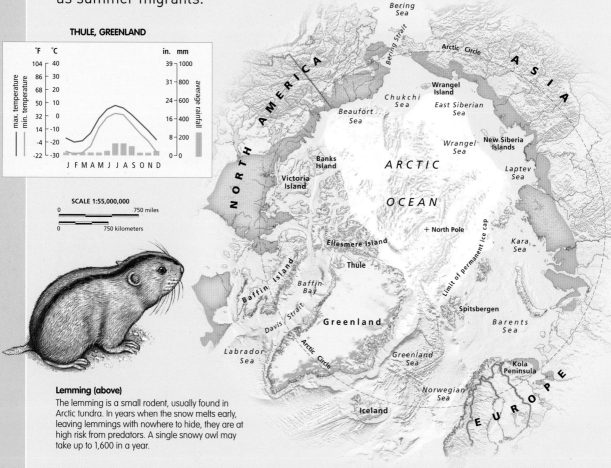

THULE, GREENLAND

SCALE 1:55,000,000

0 — 750 miles

0 — 750 kilometers

Lemming (above)

The lemming is a small rodent, usually found in Arctic tundra. In years when the snow melts early, leaving lemmings with nowhere to hide, they are at high risk from predators. A single snowy owl may take up to 1,600 in a year.

Life on the tundra

In winter much of the tundra lies blanketed in snow. Small animals, such as the ground squirrel (pictured left), mice, and lemmings can continue living under cover—the ground is still warm and the blanket of snow protects them from the worst of the weather outside. Bigger animals cannot do this. Some, such as the caribou, migrate south to the shelter of forests. Others, such as musk oxen, fatten and grow massive coats to see them through winter.

Snowy owl (right)

Snowy owls live year-round on the tundra, generally favoring areas where snow is thin. They perch on rocks or low bushes from which they can watch for prey, then swoop silently and almost invisibly on hares, lemmings, mice, ducks, and other small mammals and birds.

Musk oxen (above)

Musk oxen live in small wandering herds, feeding throughout the year on sedges, dwarf willows, and grasses. In fall they fatten and grow a dense, woolly coat. In winter they live only where the snow lies thin, so they can continue to find food.

Arctic fox (left)

Gray or white in winter, brown or brown-and-white in summer, Arctic foxes live in well-drained hillside burrows, hunting constantly for ground squirrels, lemmings, and nesting birds. In winter many go out onto the sea ice, hunting for seal pups and scavenging after polar bears.

Hibernation

To stay active, warm-blooded animals such as mammals and birds must feed to maintain their body temperature around 99°F (37°C). Big animals like this brown bear (often called a grizzly) carry thick fat and dense fur insulation, but cannot find enough food in winter to keep their temperature up. They find a sheltered den and hibernate: chill down and sleep the winter away.

Insects

Insects disappear in winter, but emerge when the snow melts and the ground warms in spring. Moths, butterflies, hoverflies, and bumblebees search the flowers for nectar and pollen; blowflies breed on carcasses; damselflies, dragonflies, and caddisflies hover above the ponds; and swarms of midges, mosquitoes, and botflies plague the grazing caribou.

Beautiful demoiselle

Damselflies spend years as larvae in ponds, feeding on other insects and growing slowly. When mature they climb out and fly for only a few days, long enough to mate and lay eggs.

THE ARCTIC
SUMMER BLOOM

Arctic land plants survive winter under tightly packed snow, blanketed from winds and extremely low temperatures. So do many insects, mice, lemmings, and other small animals. In spring, as the snow melts, the sun's rays stimulate plant growth. Ponds and lakes thaw; algae, pondweeds, mosses, grasses, and flowering plants grow rapidly. As the air warms, insects by the million emerge, and birds and mammals that have wintered over begin to fatten. Thousands of migrant birds fly north, some from as far as Africa and South America, to breed among the spring and summer abundance. Caribou, or reindeer, also move north, and porcupines, foxes, and brown and black bears emerge.

Cottongrass (above)
During the summer, cottongrass seed heads are a common sight across tundra regions. The fluffy seed heads keep the plant's reproductive organs warm by trapping heat.

Willow ptarmigan
This hen willow ptarmigan is in cryptic summer plumage. Known as willow ptarmigans because they feed almost entirely on leaves and buds of dwarf willows, these birds need year-round camouflage to protect them from predators. Mottled brown in summer and white in winter, they simply disappear into their background.

**Willow ptarmigan
winter plumage**

**Willow ptarmigan
summer plumage**

Cranberries and reindeer moss (right)

The tundra turns brilliant red in fall as the dwarf shrubs prepare to shed their leaves. Red berries appear, too, rich in nutrients for bears and other animals. Among them grow lacy reindeer moss—a lichen that is half fungus, half alga, which caribou, or reindeer, like to eat.

Reindeer (left)

Reindeer are the wild and domesticated herds of Europe and Asia; caribou are wild deer of Arctic North America. This reindeer is nibbling on the spring grasses of Svalbard, an archipelago in the Arctic Ocean. Reindeer migrate north in spring, south in fall across the tundra. Calves are born during the spring migration.

Daylight hours (below)

As spring advances, hours of daylight increase rapidly; the farther north, the longer the days. After the fall equinox, days grow shorter than nights. For every extra hour of summer daylight, there is an extra hour of darkness in winter.

	JAN	FEB	MAR	APR	MAY	JUN	JUL	AUG	SEPT	OCT	NOV	DEC
80°N	0	2.3	13.6	24	24	24	24	24	13.1	0.8	0	0
70°N	2.5	8.3	12.5	17.1	24	24	24	17.2	12.6	8.2	2.4	0
60°N	7.1	9.8	12.3	15.1	17.6	18.9	17.7	15.1	12.4	9.7	7.1	5.9

Geese migration

Millions of ducks, geese, and shorebirds that could not survive Arctic winters spend winter in temperate regions. In early spring they fly north, reaching the tundra just as the snow is disappearing, the ponds are thawing, and the grass is beginning to grow. The summers here are short, so these seasonal migrants are always in a hurry to start nesting and laying their clutches of eggs.

Barnacle geese (right and above)

Barnacle geese that nest in Svalbard winter in Britain; those that breed in the eastern Siberian Arctic spend their winters in the Netherlands. If spring comes late and the snow stays on the ground, they may not be able to breed at all.

THE ARCTIC
HUNTERS AND HUNTED

On the tundra, plant-eating mammals, birds, and insects are preyed on by foxes, wolves, weasels, owls, falcons, ravens, and skuas. Birds and small mammals fall prey to smaller hunters; wolves take the big musk oxen and caribou, leaving skin and bones to be picked over by foxes and scavenging birds. Summer-visiting shorebirds feed mainly on ground-living insects. In streams, ponds, and lakes, ducks dabble for weeds and aquatic insects or dive deeper for fish. Grizzly and polar bears feed on anything from berries to dead caribou, and polar bears and Arctic foxes go out onto the sea ice to feed on seals.

Great gray owl (above)
Great gray owls live in the northern forests and along the forest–tundra edge. Like snowy owls they hunt for voles, mice, and small lemmings, watching and listening for movement, then swooping and pouncing to carry off their catch. Males bring most of the food to the nests.

Feeding at sea

The basic sea food is plankton—tiny plant cells and shrimplike crustaceans that proliferate when the sea ice melts in spring. Animals from small fish to big whales feed on plankton, and the fish in turn are eaten by most seals, dolphins, small whales, and seabirds. Bearded seals and walrus eat clams, which live on the seabed and feed on debris that falls from above.

Orca (above)
Also called killer whales, orcas are found all over the world including the Arctic. They hunt in packs for seals and other whales. An orca can eat seven seals in one meal.

Harp seal mother and pup (below)
Harp seals live out on the sea ice, feeding on capelin, cod, and other shoaling fish. Pups are silky white for their first 12 days, then molt into harsher gray fur for swimming.

Char (left)
Some char live in lakes, others in streams and rivers, where they feed mainly on insects and smaller fish. Despite spending part of their lives in the sea, river char can also be found far up mountain streams, where they feast on salmon eggs.

Arctic wolf (right)
Arctic wolves hunt in packs of a dozen or more, often following migrating caribou or musk oxen and killing the calves and older animals that cannot keep up with the herds. They feed also on birds and small mammals.

Walrus (above)
Walruses look and swim like seals. They live on coastal sea ice and along Arctic shores, feeding by diving to the seabed, which they rake with their tusks for clams.

THE ARCTIC
THE POLAR BEAR

Polar bears live around the Arctic Ocean and neighboring seas. Males weigh up to 1,322 pounds (600 kg); females up to 550 pounds (250 kg). Polar bears spend much of their lives on sea ice that, in winter, spreads along the coasts and covers the ocean. As year-round residents in the Arctic, polar bears have to survive subzero temperatures. Their dense white fur, up to 12 inches (30 cm) thick, protects them from the cold. The fur is waterproof too, so bears can swim for hours in icy seas. In early spring, breeding seals are their main food. In summer, when the ice melts, they forage on land, eating grasses, berries, birds' eggs, and nestlings. In fall, they fatten on fish from freshwater streams.

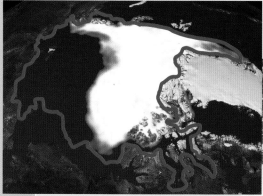

Sea ice changes (left)
Areas of both permanent and annually renewed Arctic sea ice grow smaller year by year and have lost 38 percent of their area over the past 30 years. Numbers of both seals and polar bears are likely to fall; they may disappear altogether from some areas.

Defending their ground (right)
Living where food is seldom plentiful, polar bears usually walk on their own. Two or three together are most likely to be a mother with cubs. When lone males meet, they growl, roar, and even wrestle until one is driven away.

Hunting on sea ice (left)
Despite their weight and bulk, polar bears are agile. They leap from floe to floe and wander many miles every day in search of food.

Family group (below)
Cubs stay with their mother for up to two years, until almost fully grown. It is a hard life, especially in winter, and one or more in each family may die. Those cubs that survive wander off independently, then the mother is ready to find another mate.

Winter in the den (above)
Polar bears mate in summer. In fall, the pregnant females dig dens for themselves in snowbanks, where they sleep throughout winter. Around December each gives birth to one, two, or sometimes three rabbit-sized cubs, which feed on the mother's rich milk. Between feeds, mothers and cubs save energy by sleeping. By March or April the cubs are large enough to leave the den.

Hunting to survive

Polar bears spend part of their time on land, but more on sea ice in coastal channels and bays. Females give birth on land, but take their cubs onto the sea ice where food is easier to find. Food is never plentiful so, after mating, males and females go their separate ways. Mothers hunt and bring up the cubs on their own.

Seal meat (below)
On the sea ice, bears hunt for seals, which in spring are raising pups among the floes. The adult female knows how to find and kill the seals, providing a meal for herself and her cubs.

Whale carcass (above)
Polar bears are always ready to eat whatever they can find. Here, a mother and her grown cubs have followed the scent to a dead whale, washed up on a Svalbard shore.

ANTARCTIC DESERT

Antarctica is truly a desert, the largest and driest on Earth, yet it contains 70 percent of the world's fresh water and 90 percent of its ice. Life is rare on the ice sheet and restricted to the margins near the "warm" ocean. Water temperatures drop to a minimum of 28.7°F (−1.8°C) in winter beneath sea ice. At the margins of the continent, dark rocks absorb sunlight and heat, leading to the growth of algae and lichens on their warm surface.

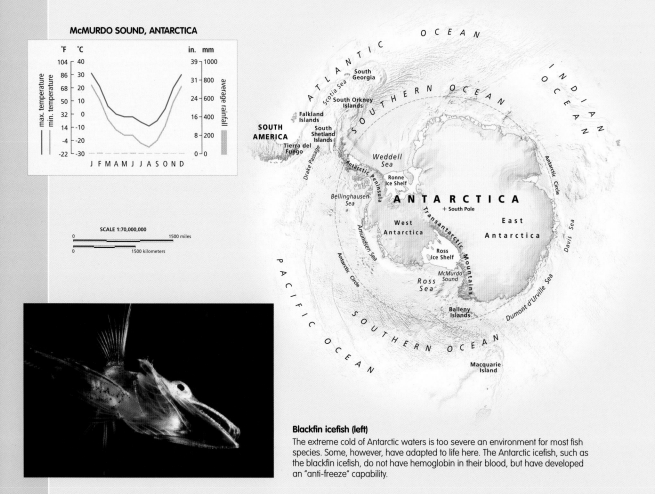

McMURDO SOUND, ANTARCTICA

SCALE 1:70,000,000

0   1500 miles

0   1500 kilometers

Blackfin icefish (left)

The extreme cold of Antarctic waters is too severe an environment for most fish species. Some, however, have adapted to life here. The Antarctic icefish, such as the blackfin icefish, do not have hemoglobin in their blood, but have developed an "anti-freeze" capability.

Leopard seal (above)

Leopard seals have a disproportionately large head and wide-opening, strong jaws. Their varied diet includes large catches such as penguins and young crabeater seals, but they also filter seawater for krill. They are occasionally seen ashore on subantarctic islands.

Antarctic fur seal (below left)

These seals, which belong to the group known as eared seals, occur on islands close to the Antarctic continent but they do not breed on the ice. They spend most of the winter at sea, pursuing their diet of fish, krill, rock lobsters, and penguins.

Chinstrap penguins (below)

A colony of chinstrap penguins is climbing an iceberg off the Antarctic Peninsula. Leopard seals prey on adult chinstraps, while eggs and chicks are at risk from birds such as the brown skua and sheathbill.

Crabeater seal (right)

The crabeater seal is the most abundant seal species on Earth. It inhabits Antarctic pack ice and its population is estimated at 11 to 12 million. This seal has characteristic tri-lobed teeth, allowing it to filter krill-rich water. Krill are its major food.

THE ANTARCTIC
LONG-DISTANCE MIGRANTS

Migration from the severe climatic conditions of polar regions is vital for many animals: food is plentiful in summer but in winter few animal species can survive. The emperor penguin is the only animal that is a year-round resident on the Antarctic ice. Baleen whales, such as the humpback, migrate in both hemispheres along well-marked routes to the tropics during the polar winters. The northern and southern right whales, which have more restricted distributions and migration paths, also spend winter in warmer waters. Many bird and seal species also make long seasonal migrations from the high-latitude regions in winter.

Migration paths (below)
Most aquatic migrating animals remain in their home hemisphere, even though they may travel long distances, but birds have no such limits and may migrate from one pole to the other. Whales migrate from polar regions, where they feed in summer, to the tropics where they mate and have their young. Seals migrate to bear their young on islands or other coasts in lower, subpolar latitudes.

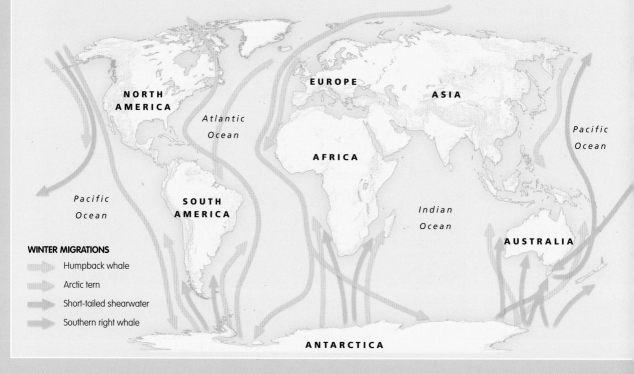

WINTER MIGRATIONS

- Humpback whale
- Arctic tern
- Short-tailed shearwater
- Southern right whale

Humpback whale (above)
Humpback whales feed on swarms of krill in Antarctic waters. They gulp massive mouthfuls of krill and water, which are then filtered through their baleen "sieve," allowing them to retain and eat the krill. In the Arctic, humpback pods work cooperatively to form curtains of bubbles that concentrate krill in a restricted area. The humpback ends its migration in tropical waters. Breaching may be a signal to others in the pod or elsewhere.

⚡ Conservation watch: fin whale

The Antarctic fin whale is second only to the blue whale in size. It is the fastest of the rorquals and cruises at 15 to 20 miles per hour (24–32 km/h). Its large size made it a desirable catch during the 20th-century whaling period and numbers have suffered.

Southern right whale (left)
A southern right whale displays the unique callosities on its head and back. The species was named "the right whale" by whalers because it is slow, and therefore easier to catch, has a high oil content, and floats when dead.

Migratory birds

Birds that remain in the south polar regions year-round experience the maximum contrast between polar winters and summers. The Antarctic tern and several penguin species remain in the region; others, such as the albatross and the Arctic tern, travel vast distances.

Arctic tern (right)
Arctic terns are renowned as great migrators—from their Arctic breeding grounds to the Antarctic. They can hover while observing small fish near the water's surface, then dive on their catch.

Arctic tern chick (right)
Arctic tern chicks bred in the Arctic weigh only a few ounces. They migrate to the Antarctic for the southern summer.

Short-tailed shearwater (left)
Short-tailed shearwaters breed in southeastern Australia and have two forms of migration. During the southern hemisphere's winter, they fly to the Aleutian Islands and Kamchatka Peninsula in the north Pacific, before returning in spring. In spring–summer, they make a round trip to Antarctic waters, gathering food for their young.

THE ANTARCTIC
ANTARCTIC BIRDS

Early sailors dubbed the Southern Ocean winds the "Roaring '40s," the "Furious '50s," and the "Screaming '60s." These winds provide excellent flying conditions for albatrosses and petrels that use the energy from the wind for flight. Small oceanic islands in the Southern Ocean serve as nesting sites for millions of seabirds, which seek prey in the surrounding seas. Their aerodynamically streamlined bodies reduce the energy required for flight, and enable them to forage far from land. Seabirds use a variety of methods to capture prey, including surface seizing and diving.

Snow petrel nest (left)
Year-round residents of the Antarctic, snow petrels feed in open water among the ice. They are agile fliers and can survive winter storms. Snow petrels nest on the ground, laying one egg on bare rock in early summer.

Snowy sheathbill (above)
Snowy sheathbills are found on the Antarctic Peninsula and on islands in the South Atlantic Ocean. Their breeding distribution is closely associated with penguins, other species of seabirds, and fur seal colonies. During the summer months they scavenge from these colonies, taking eggs, chicks, and carrion. They winter in Patagonia, Tierra del Fuego, and the Falkland Islands. Flights may exceed 2,000 miles (3,200 km) in each direction.

Wandering albatross

Albatrosses are perhaps the most efficient fliers on the planet. The wandering albatross has the largest wingspan of any bird, up to 11 feet 6 inches (3.5 m). These long wings generate enormous lift but prevent them from flapping too rapidly. As a result, they are gliders, flying for long periods without flapping their wings.

Male display (left)
Breeding takes place on subantarctic and Antarctic islands. A breeding male advertises himself by bringing his wings to full stretch, raising his head, and calling to prospective partners.

Aerodynamic design (right and below)
A bird's wing is shaped so that air passes more quickly across the top, curved, surface than the bottom, providing essential lift.

Air flow

Uplift

Courtship rituals (left)
Wandering albatrosses breed only every second year. Albatrosses use various courtship behaviors and vocalizations to establish the pair bond for the first time and, like many species of seabirds, they mate for life.

South polar skua (left)
A gentoo penguin is defending its territory against a south polar skua. These skuas are predatory scavengers which will take eggs and small penguin chicks for food, but are aggressive in defense of their own breeding territories. The hook at the tip of their bill is used to rip flesh.

THE ANTARCTIC
PENGUIN PARADE

Of the 17 species of penguins, only five species breed on or near the Antarctic continent: emperor, Adélie, chinstrap, macaroni, and gentoo penguins. The remaining species breed on subantarctic and temperate islands as far north as the Galápagos Islands at the equator, but all are confined to the southern hemisphere. Despite evolving from flighted ancestors, penguins are flightless but they "fly" through the water in order to feed on krill and fish. Their feathers are denser than those of any other bird, providing a streamlined and well-insulated body, and they have a thick layer of fat under the skin, providing further insulation and energy reserves for periods when they cannot feed.

Penguin distribution (above)
Penguins are found along the coasts of all southern hemisphere continents, the Antarctic Peninsula, and on the small oceanic islands in the Southern Ocean. All five species of Antarctic penguins breed around the Antarctic continent, but the Adélie, chinstrap, gentoo, and macaroni penguins choose only the coastal ice-free areas. Only emperor penguin colonies are found on the winter sea ice.

Chinstrap penguins (left)
Chinstrap penguins are so named because of the distinctive thin black line under their bills and on their cheeks. Their breeding colonies are found throughout the Antarctic Peninsula and on islands in the South Atlantic Ocean. A small breeding population is also found on the Balleny Islands, south of New Zealand.

Emperor penguin
Aptenodytes forsteri

King penguin
Aptenodytes patagonicus

Chinstrap penguin
Pygoscelis antarctica

Adélie penguin
Pygoscelis adeliae

Yellow-eyed penguin
Megadyptes antipodes

Magellanic penguin
Spheniscus magellanicus

Fiordland penguin
Eudyptes pachyrhynchus

Little penguin
Eudyptula minor

Penguin variety (below)
Penguins are not just black and white: they are adorned with colorful crests, washes of rich oranges and yellows, and unique feather spots. Each species has a different shaped bill.

King penguin colony (below)
King penguin colonies can number more than 100,000 pairs—so large the colonies are visible in satellite images. They are found on many of the subantarctic islands in the Southern Ocean, where the maritime climate contrasts with the cold and dry climate of the Antarctic.

Adélie penguins (above)
Adélie penguins are among the iconic species of penguin in the Antarctic and are the most widely distributed. Their diet is primarily crustaceans and fish, and they are capable of diving to 660 feet (200 m) to search for prey. Between dives, they rest on the surface or on ice floes to avoid predators such as leopard seals.

Rearing offspring

Penguin chicks in the Antarctic face numerous threats from the moment they hatch. Temperatures can be extreme: as low as -40°F (-40°C) in midwinter when emperor penguin eggs hatch.

Protection (left)
Until the chicks are almost half grown, they need their parents to protect them from the elements as their own downy feathers are insufficient.

Bringing food (right)
King penguins take more than a year to raise their chicks and, during winter months, a chick may wait weeks for its next meal. The parents forage over vast distances to provide their large chick with enough food.

Gentoo nest (above)
A rocky nest, built by the male, provides a home for gentoo penguin eggs and chicks. It is elevated above the surrounding terrain so that when the snow melts during the summer it will not be flooded.

CHAPTER NINE

THE
OCEANS

Spinner dolphins

Spinner dolphins live in the warm waters of the world. These social, active, and intelligent creatures are among the most acrobatic of dolphins, being named for their spinning as they leap through the air. They can travel at speeds of over 20 miles an hour (32 km/h). All dolphins are cetaceans—a group of mammals that includes whales and porpoises.

THE OCEANS

Some 70 percent of Earth's surface is covered by water, and life could not exist without it. The oceans comprise a vast three-dimensional space, where conditions at one spot on Earth can vary from bright, tropical warmth at the surface to perpetually dark, polar cold only a couple of miles below. Marine ecosystems can range from highly productive, brackish marshes, rocky coasts, and coral reefs to sterile mid-ocean regions bereft of nutrients. In this cornucopia of habitats, an extraordinary diversity of organisms has evolved with a wide array of adaptations to life in the sea.

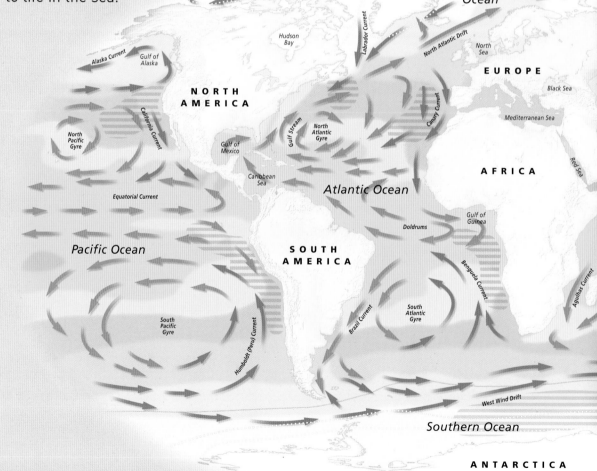

Arctic Ocean

Hudson Bay

Labrador Current

North Atlantic Drift

North Sea

EUROPE

Black Sea

Alaska Current

Gulf of Alaska

NORTH AMERICA

Canary Current

Mediterranean Sea

North Pacific Gyre

California Current

Gulf of Mexico

Gulf Stream

North Atlantic Gyre

AFRICA

Red Sea

Caribbean Sea

Atlantic Ocean

Equatorial Current

Gulf of Guinea

Doldrums

Pacific Ocean

SOUTH AMERICA

Benguela Current

Agulhas Current

South Pacific Gyre

Humboldt (Peru) Current

Brazil Current

South Atlantic Gyre

West Wind Drift

Southern Ocean

ANTARCTICA

Above 86°F (30°C)	··· Summer pack ice limit
77-86°F (25-30°C)	··· Winter pack ice limit
68-77°F (20-25°C)	→ Warm current
59-68°F (15-20°C)	→ Cool current
50-59°F (19-15°C)	— Antarctic polar frontal zone
41-50°F (5-10°C)	
Under 41°F (5°C)	
Upwelling	**SCALE 1:109,000,000**
	Robinson Projection

Currents and temperature (below left)

The oceans are dominated by current gyres driven by wind and Earth's rotation. These rotate clockwise in the northern hemisphere and counterclockwise in the southern hemisphere, bringing warm, tropical water to higher latitudes on the western sides of oceans, and cooler, temperate water to lower latitudes on the eastern sides. Thus, within an ocean basin, tropical plants and animals are found over a wider area in the west than in the east.

Pacific Ocean

The Pacific is the oldest and largest ocean. The coral reefs, stretching from Indonesia to the Great Barrier Reef off eastern Australia, harbor the most diverse marine fauna on Earth.

Atlantic Ocean

The Atlantic formed 150 million years ago when the continents of Europe and North America broke apart, and Africa and South America separated along a submarine seam.

Indian Ocean

The Indian Ocean shares much of its tropical marine fauna with the western Pacific, with which it is connected. Currents move freely around the Indonesian islands and Australia.

Arctic Ocean

The Arctic Ocean is essentially landlocked, and typified for aeons by permanent sea ice. Recent global warming is causing summer melting and threatens Arctic ecosystems.

Southern Ocean

The nutrient-rich Southern Ocean, which flows around Antarctica, supports high plankton production. Great whales gather there in summer to gorge on shrimplike krill.

ASIA

Sea of Okhotsk

Bering Sea

Oyashio (Kamchatka) Current

North Pacific Current

Sea of Japan

Yellow Sea

Kuroshio (Japan) Current

China

India

Pacific Ocean

Arabian Sea

Bay of Bengal

South China Sea

Celebes Sea

Equatorial Current

Doldrums

Java Sea

Indian Ocean

Arafura Sea

Coral Sea

AUSTRALIA

Indian Ocean Gyre

West Australian Current

Great Australian Bight

East Australian Current

Tasman Sea

New Zealand

THE PACIFIC OCEAN

The sea's richest biodiversity and biological productivity occurs in the Pacific Ocean. Because the size of the Pacific has moderated its marine climate, complex ecosystems have evolved. Coral reef communities of the Indo-Australian archipelago have the greatest diversity of tropical marine species, while the rocky coasts and kelp forests of the eastern North Pacific are home to the greatest temperate biodiversity. The Pacific has some of the highest oceanic nutrient levels and heaviest marine plankton blooms, supporting some of the most productive fisheries on Earth.

The dynamic Pacific (below)

The central Pacific is marked by a long mountain ridge system from which Earth's crust arises and creeps west and east to collide with the continents. This violent tectonic activity—announced by earthquakes—causes mountain ranges and volcanoes to rise. Thus the perimeter of the Pacific is called the Ring of Fire.

THE FACTS	
Area	60.1 million square miles (155.6 million km²)
Average depth	13,125 feet (4,000 m)
Maximum depth	35,840 feet (10,924 m)
Maximum width	11,200 miles (18,000 km)
Maximum length	8,600 miles (13,900 km)
Coastline length	84,297 miles (135,663 km)

SCALE 1:115,000,000

Hawaiian turkeyfish (above)

The chain of volcanic islands in the Hawaiian archipelago formed over the same hot spot and were carried northwest on the Pacific Plate. This allowed shallow-water species to island-hop along the chain and unique species had time to evolve. Of the 600 or so species of shorefish in Hawaii, 25 percent are endemic. They include the Hawaiian turkeyfish, a reef fish with venomous spines.

Brown booby (left)

Boobies are the avian torpedoes of the sea, folding their wings and dropping like darts out of the sky to skewer their anchovy prey in a trail of bubbles. Boobies congregate in rich ocean areas, where plankton abounds to support productive ocean food webs and large shoals of forage fish, such as anchovies.

Ocean zones (below)

Living space in the sea is divided into two major realms: pelagic, up in the water column; and benthic, on the seafloor. The majority of marine creatures are benthic. Sunlight, temperature, pressure, and animal life change dramatically with depth.

Sunlight zone
Surface to 660 feet (200 m)

With enough light for plants to perform photosynthesis, this zone contains most of the ocean's life.

Plankton

Floating or drifting species are made up of zooplankton (animals such as krill and the Portuguese man-of-war) and phytoplankton (plants such as algae).

Nekton

Nekton are species that swim on their own, such as fish and dolphins.

Benthos

Marine bottom-dwellers include creepers such as crabs, immobile species such as mussels, and burrowers such as bristleworms.

Shore, low tide and high tide zones

Continental shelf

Continental slope

Abyssal plain

Continental rise

Midnight zone
3,300 feet (1,000 m) to bottom

This deep zone is pitch-black apart from occasional bioluminescence from deep-sea species.

Twilight zone
660–3,300 feet (200–1,000 m)

Some sunlight filters through to the twilight zone, but not enough to sustain plants.

Kelp forest (left)

Kelp are giant brown algae that may grow to 160 feet (50 m) or more in length. They require cool coastal temperatures and a rocky bottom upon which to attach. Kelp forests in the eastern Pacific provide a complex ecosystem that supports a wide variety of marine fish, such as this calico bass.

⚡ Conservation watch: leatherback turtle

The warm-blooded leatherback turtle can reach 1 ton (910 kg) in weight, and can dive more than 3,000 feet (914 m) to feast on jellyfish. Tens of thousands of leatherbacks once nested on the Pacific beaches of Central America, but no longer. Pacific leatherback populations have been decimated by capture in high-seas fisheries.

THE ATLANTIC OCEAN

Climatic variations in the Atlantic Ocean have been more extreme than in the Pacific, and species diversity is much lower because of periodic extinctions. Both the Mediterranean and the Caribbean seas were once tropical arms of the Atlantic. When glaciers covered much of Europe and North America 10,000 years ago, only the tropical species in the Caribbean survived. Even so, the Caribbean today has only about half as many species of reef fish as we see in the western Pacific.

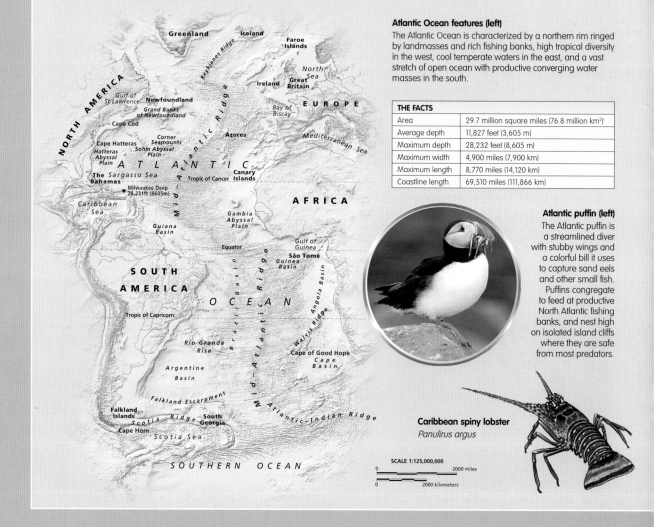

Atlantic Ocean features (left)

The Atlantic Ocean is characterized by a northern rim ringed by landmasses and rich fishing banks, high tropical diversity in the west, cool temperate waters in the east, and a vast stretch of open ocean with productive converging water masses in the south.

THE FACTS	
Area	29.7 million square miles (76.8 million km²)
Average depth	11,827 feet (3,605 m)
Maximum depth	28,232 feet (8,605 m)
Maximum width	4,900 miles (7,900 km)
Maximum length	8,770 miles (14,120 km)
Coastline length	69,510 miles (111,866 km)

Atlantic puffin (left)

The Atlantic puffin is a streamlined diver with stubby wings and a colorful bill it uses to capture sand eels and other small fish. Puffins congregate to feed at productive North Atlantic fishing banks, and nest high on isolated island cliffs where they are safe from most predators.

Caribbean spiny lobster
Panulirus argus

SCALE 1:125,000,000

0   2000 miles

0   2000 kilometers

Loggerhead turtle (left)
Loggerhead turtles hatched on Florida beaches are carried northeast in the Gulf Stream around the North Atlantic gyre before returning to the United States. The Gulf Stream, a powerful ocean current, is a part of the massive gyre that moves water clockwise around the North Atlantic.

Deep-sea fish (below)

Some of the strangest-looking fish live in the deep ocean below 3,300 feet (1,000 m). Adapted to life with little food and no daylight, they have watery muscles and soft bones that require less food to build and sustain. Some deep-sea fish, like the anglers, sport bioluminescent lures to attract their prey.

Black swallower (left)
This species can swallow prey larger than itself by extending its huge stomach.

Sperm whale and giant squid (right)
Sperm whales roam the seas from Arctic ice to clear tropical waters. Using their own sonar system, sperm whales may dive more than a mile (1.6 km) deep and stay submerged for two hours in search of giant squid and other prey.

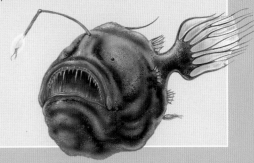

Gelatinous blindfish (right)
This small fish has a white, jellylike body and, like many deep-sea species, a tiny eye. It lives on the seafloor in deep waters.

Gulper eel (below)
The enormous mouth of this eel-like fish is loosely hinged, allowing it to consume large prey. The whiplike tail ends in a glowing light-organ.

Stoplight loosejaw (right)
One of the few fish that can produce red light, this species has a light-organ beneath each eye. Its large lower jaw can extend far in front of its skull.

Krøyer's deep-sea anglerfish (below)
This female anglerfish has a lure with a light-organ to attract prey. The tiny parasitic male attached to her hind body supplies sperm when needed.

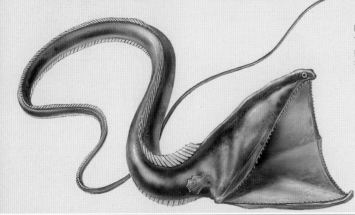

THE INDIAN OCEAN

The Indian Ocean has a rich tropical shore fauna that stretches from South Africa, north to the Red Sea, east around the Indian subcontinent, and south through the Indo-Malayan archipelago to Western Australia. Coral reefs abound in the east and west, and sandy and muddy mangrove habitats dominate the Indian coast.

Animal life of the Indian Ocean is closely related to that of the western Pacific, with many tropical shorefish species ranging from South Africa to the islands of the South Pacific. The Indian Ocean is home to a particularly wide variety of sharks, from small, bottom-grubbing catsharks to large, camouflaged wobbegongs.

Indian Ocean features below)

More than 100 million years ago, India, Australia, Antarctica, Africa, and South America were joined in a supercontinent called Gondwana. India and Australia broke away to open the Indian Ocean basin.

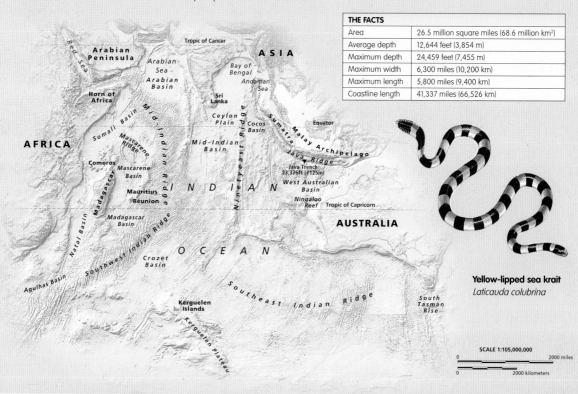

THE FACTS	
Area	26.5 million square miles (68.6 million km²)
Average depth	12,644 feet (3,854 m)
Maximum depth	24,459 feet (7,455 m)
Maximum width	6,300 miles (10,200 km)
Maximum length	5,800 miles (9,400 km)
Coastline length	41,337 miles (66,526 km)

Yellow-lipped sea krait
Laticauda colubrina

SCALE 1:105,000,000

0 — 2000 miles

0 — 2000 kilometers

⚡ The coelacanth

Coelacanths, primitive cousins of early fish that evolved into land vertebrates, were thought to have become extinct 65 million years ago. Then, in 1938, a trawler fishing off Mozambique dragged up a dark, bulky, rough-scaled monster of the deep. The creature was a coelacanth, in effect a living fossil. Today, remnant coelacanth populations have been found off East and South Africa, the Comoros Islands, Madagascar, and the Indonesian island of Sulawesi. Coelacanths frequent undersea volcanic slopes, hiding in caves by day and foraging at night as they drift with the currents.

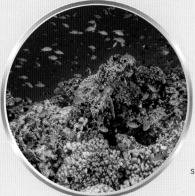

Coral communities (left)

The Indian Ocean hosts a cornucopia of corals. Regions with little freshwater input and very clear water, such as the Red Sea (pictured), have particularly rich coral communities. Reef corals can occur deeper there because enough sunlight penetrates to allow photosynthesis by the algae that help nourish corals. Global warming and high sea temperatures cause potentially fatal coral bleaching.

Great white shark (above)

Great white sharks were thought to be coastal denizens until recent satellite tracking experiments showed that they can migrate thousands of miles across the open ocean. A mature female great white tagged off South Africa swam all the way across the Indian Ocean to Western Australia, then returned within the year. The reasons for such sojourns remain obscure, but breeding is a prime candidate.

Dolphins and baitball (below)

Dolphins and several species of sharks follow migrating shoals of sardines, traveling south along the South African coast in summer and north in winter. Sardines and other schooling fish often form tight, spherical schools, called baitballs, when threatened by predators.

Giant manta ray (above)

Manta rays fly through tropical seas with flapping wings and mouths agape, filtering plankton as they go. The largest of all rays, the giant manta may reach 22 feet (6.5 m) in width. Mantas sometimes propel their huge bodies completely out of the water, landing with a thunderous splash.

THE ARCTIC OCEAN

Relatively few species inhabit the Arctic, a result of fluctuating climate during recent geological time. Sea ice has been a potent force in shaping the evolution of the creatures that do live there. The edges of the ice pack melt and shrink in spring and summer, providing a rich transition zone that supports lush phytoplankton growth. This primary production is the basis for most Arctic marine food webs.

Arctic Ocean features (below)
Surrounded by land, the Arctic Ocean has been subject to extreme climatic fluctuations and species extinctions over time. Today, most families of animals in the Arctic Ocean have evolved from North Pacific groups that entered through periodic openings of the Bering Strait.

THE FACTS	
Area	5.4 million square miles (14.1 million km²)
Average depth	4,690 feet (1,430 m)
Maximum depth	18,455 feet (5,625 m)
Maximum width	2,000 miles (3,200 km)
Maximum length	3,100 miles (5,000 km)
Coastline length	28,203 miles (45,389 km)

Common feather star
Florometra serratissima

Whale species

There are two major types of whales: toothed species that feed on active fish and squid, and baleen whales that use long sheets of hairlike baleen to sieve out zooplankton and small fish from the water. Arctic residents include two toothed whales—the beluga and narwhal—and one baleen whale—the bowhead. Other baleen whales, such as the fin, minke, and North Atlantic right, arrive in summer to graze on zooplankton.

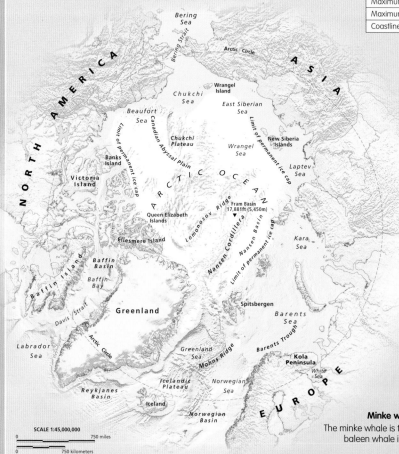

Minke whale (right)
The minke whale is the smallest baleen whale in the Arctic.

Arctic jellyfish

Jelly animals are important predators in pelagic Arctic ecosystems. They include the 150 or so species of true jellyfish, or hydromedusae, and the eight species of colonial siphonophores. Both groups paralyze their prey with long, sticky, stinging tentacles, and eat fish, squid, shrimps, and even other jellyfish. A small number of harmless comb jellies have also been found in the Arctic Ocean.

Hula skirt siphonophore (right)
This siphonophore grows to about 16 inches (41 cm) and, despite its small size, packs a powerful sting like its tropical cousin, the Portuguese man-of-war.

Arctic lion's mane (left)
This is the largest jellyfish in the world, with a bell-shaped body up to 7.5 feet (2.3 m) wide and tentacles 120 feet (36.5 m) long. Its venomous sting could kill a human.

Habitat zones (below)

The Arctic summer brings birds to nest on the tundra and feed in the rich ocean waters. Explosive blooms of phytoplankton called diatoms support tiny grazing copepods and amphipods, both in the water and the pores of the ice. These in turn are consumed by small fish, such as capelin and herring, as well as by large whales. On the bottom, bristleworms, brittle stars, and clams abound.

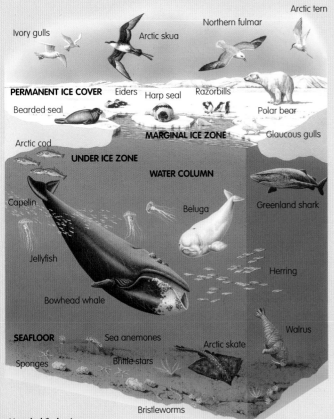

Arctic tern

Northern fulmar

Ivory gulls

Arctic skua

PERMANENT ICE COVER

Eiders

Harp seal

Razorbills

Bearded seal

Polar bear

MARGINAL ICE ZONE

Glaucous gulls

Arctic cod

UNDER ICE ZONE

WATER COLUMN

Capelin

Beluga

Greenland shark

Jellyfish

Herring

Bowhead whale

SEAFLOOR

Sea anemones

Walrus

Arctic skate

Sponges

Brittle stars

Bristleworms

Narwhal (below)

The male narwhal has a single spiral tusk, like a unicorn's horn.

Beluga (above)

Belugas are gray at birth but turn white by the time they are five years old.

Fin whale (right)

Fin whales often lunge-feed through clouds of krill.

Bowhead whale (left)

The bowhead is hunted by Inuit people and is an important part of their culture.

North Atlantic right whale (right)

With fewer than 350 individuals left, this species is near extinction.

THE SOUTHERN OCEAN

The Southern Ocean flows around the frigid continent of Antarctica. This ocean has provided a stable polar climate where cold-water animals have had time to evolve and diversify. Among the most remarkable creatures are the 90 species of notothenioid fish, which fill many ecological niches. Among them is the crocodile icefish. They have special molecules in their blood called glycoproteins that act like antifreeze.

Southern Ocean features (below)

The Southern Ocean is bounded on the north by the Antarctic polar frontal zone, where cold, dense Antarctic water meets the much warmer, lighter waters of the Pacific, Atlantic, and Indian oceans. Here, little mixing occurs because of differences in seawater density.

THE FACTS

Area	7.8 million square miles (20.3 million km²)
Average depth	14,750 feet (4,500 m)
Maximum depth	24,032 feet (7,235 m)
Maximum width	1,700 miles (2,700 km)
Maximum length	13,400 miles (21,500 km)
Coastline length	11,165 miles (17,968 km)

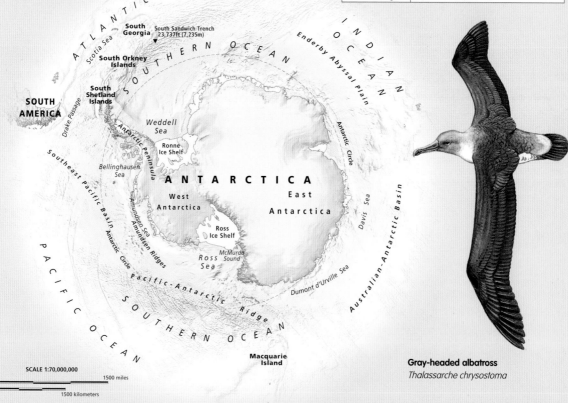

Gray-headed albatross
Thalassarche chrysostoma

SCALE 1:70,000,000

0 — 1500 miles

0 — 1500 kilometers

⚡ Conservation watch: blue whale

The blue whale is the largest creature that ever lived on Earth, measuring up to 108 feet (33 m) in length, and weighing as much as 176 tons (160 t). Blue whales congregate in the Southern Ocean in summer to gorge on clouds of krill. In winter they head to more hospitable tropical climes to rest and have their calves.

Bottom-dwellers

Antarctic bottom communities are much more diverse than those of the Arctic. More than 90 percent of the invertebrates on the continental shelf originated in the Antarctic and occur nowhere else. Southern Ocean currents bring suspended zooplankton, phytoplankton, bacteria, and other microorganisms to bottom communities dominated by sponges, sea squirts, feather stars, and other filter feeders. In the deep Southern Ocean, hundreds of new species of worms and other tiny bottom creatures have recently been discovered.

Starfish (right)
The *Odontaster validus* starfish is a common member of Antarctic bottom communities. It is an omnivorous scavenger, consuming anything it finds.

Anemone (right)
Anemones are closely related to jellyfish. They prey on fish and other creatures that venture too close to their stinging tentacles.

McMurdo Sound ocean floor (right)
In this photo of McMurdo Sound, several red Antarctic sea urchins can be seen, as well as Antarctic scallops and a brittlestar. The Antarctic sea urchin grazes on algae, and camouflages itself with bits of shell and other debris to avoid predators.

Crocodile icefish (right)
The crocodile icefish, a common Antarctic bottom-dweller, sits quietly waiting to ambush passing prey. This sit-and-wait strategy has reached its apex among the icefishes, which lack hemoglobin and take up all the oxygen they need from the frigid, oxygen-rich Antarctic water.

Keystone krill

Krill are small—1½ to 2½ inches (4–6 cm) long—shrimplike creatures that swim in the Southern Ocean in swarms as dense as 13,000 per cubic yard (10,000 per m³). Living as long as five years, these small animals are the keystone food source upon which many species of fish, squid, penguins, seals, and whales depend for survival.

Krill (right)
A ready source of protein, krill have attracted the interest of industrial fisheries. Large-scale harvest of krill has prompted concern that Antarctic food webs could be disrupted.

Southern distribution (right)
Krill live in cold, productive seas at both ends of Earth, but reach their greatest concentrations in the Southern Ocean, where their phytoplankton food is at its most abundant.

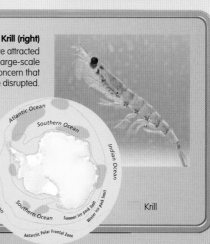

Atlantic Ocean
Southern Ocean
Indian Ocean
Pacific Ocean
Southern Ocean
Summer ice pack limit
Winter ice pack limit
Antarctic Polar Frontal Zone

Krill

ANIMAL FACTFILE

Scientists have described and named at least 1.7 million species of plants, animals, and microorganisms, but new species are discovered almost every day and the total number of lifeforms is estimated at between 10 million and 30 million. The discipline of taxonomy provides a unique name for each organism and sorts organisms into hierarchies of increasingly exclusive groups, or taxa, based on their evolutionary relationships. The basic category is the species. Species are populations of organisms that share one or more similarities not found in related organisms, and can usually reproduce sexually only with each other. Each species is assigned a two-part scientific name. The first part, the generic name, gives the genus, the group of closely related organisms to which the species belongs. The second part, the specific name, is unique to that species within the genus. Animals are known by various common names around the world, so the scientific name is Latinized to avoid confusion. All taxa above the species level are meant to comprise an ancestral species and all its descendants. Recent genetic techniques have allowed comparison of organisms' DNA, forcing scientists to rethink the classification of many animals.

SPECIES
Lynx rufus
Bobcat

GENUS
Lynx
Bobcat, Eurasian lynx, Canadian lynx

FAMILY
Felidae
Bobcat, domestic cat, lion, leopard, jaguar

ORDER
Carnivora
Bobcat, seal, wolf, bear, skunk, meerkat

CLASS
Mammalia
Bobcat, kangaroo, human, dolphin, woolly mammoth

PHYLUM
Chordata
Bobcat, shark, salamander, dinosaur, albatross

KINGDOM
Animalia
Bobcat, stick insect, sea urchin, parrot, crocodile

Animal classification

All lifeforms can be classified according to the Linnaean system. Each nested category contains organisms with progressively similar characteristics. This bobcat belongs to kingdom Animalia (all animals); phylum Chordata (animals with a centralized nerve cord); class Mammalia (all mammals); order Carnivora (with specialized teeth for eating meat); family Felidae (all cats); and genus *Lynx* (all lynxes). Finally, no other organism shares the scientific name of this species, *Lynx rufus*.

MAMMALS

Mammals occupy all continents and almost all habitats. They nurse their young with milk from mammary glands, usually have body hair, and have a lower jaw bone that attaches directly to the skull. The 29 orders of the class Mammalia are divided into three major groups based on the structure of the reproductive tract. The most primitive are the egg-laying mammals, classified in a single order, the monotremes. Marsupials, which give birth to young in a very early stage of development, are now considered to consist of seven orders. The other 21 orders are made up of placental mammals. Recent DNA evidence indicates that there have been three major radiations of placentals in Africa, South America, and the northern hemisphere. The following is a comprehensive listing of mammal orders.

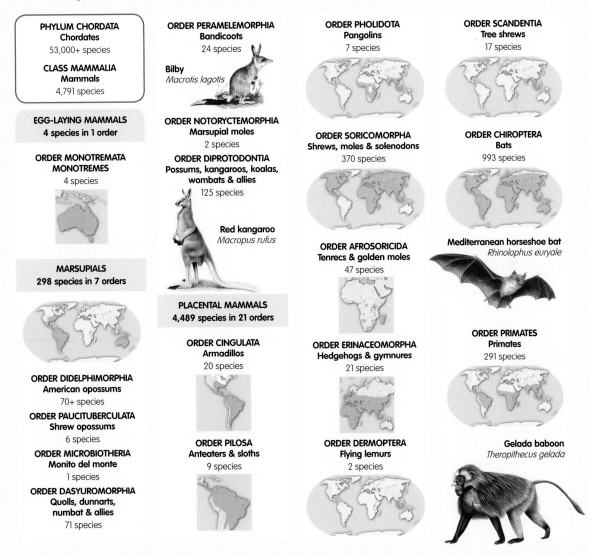

PHYLUM CHORDATA
Chordates
53,000+ species

CLASS MAMMALIA
Mammals
4,791 species

EGG-LAYING MAMMALS
4 species in 1 order

ORDER MONOTREMATA
MONOTREMES
4 species

MARSUPIALS
298 species in 7 orders

ORDER DIDELPHIMORPHIA
American opossums
70+ species

ORDER PAUCITUBERCULATA
Shrew opossums
6 species

ORDER MICROBIOTHERIA
Monito del monte
1 species

ORDER DASYUROMORPHIA
Quolls, dunnarts, numbat & allies
71 species

ORDER PERAMELEMORPHIA
Bandicoots
24 species

Bilby
Macrotis lagotis

ORDER NOTORYCTEMORPHIA
Marsupial moles
2 species

ORDER DIPROTODONTIA
Possums, kangaroos, koalas, wombats & allies
125 species

Red kangaroo
Macropus rufus

PLACENTAL MAMMALS
4,489 species in 21 orders

ORDER CINGULATA
Armadillos
20 species

ORDER PILOSA
Anteaters & sloths
9 species

ORDER PHOLIDOTA
Pangolins
7 species

ORDER SORICOMORPHA
Shrews, moles & solenodons
370 species

ORDER AFROSORICIDA
Tenrecs & golden moles
47 species

ORDER ERINACEOMORPHA
Hedgehogs & gymnures
21 species

ORDER DERMOPTERA
Flying lemurs
2 species

ORDER SCANDENTIA
Tree shrews
17 species

ORDER CHIROPTERA
Bats
993 species

Mediterranean horseshoe bat
Rhinolophus euryale

ORDER PRIMATES
Primates
291 species

Gelada baboon
Theropithecus gelada

ORDER CARNIVORA
Carnivores
275 species

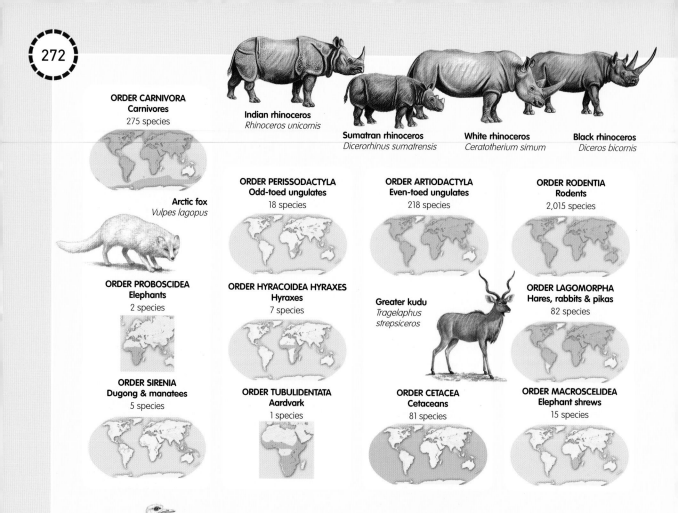

Indian rhinoceros
Rhinoceros unicornis

Sumatran rhinoceros
Dicerorhinus sumatrensis

White rhinoceros
Ceratotherium simum

Black rhinoceros
Diceros bicornis

Arctic fox
Vulpes lagopus

ORDER PERISSODACTYLA
Odd-toed ungulates
18 species

ORDER ARTIODACTYLA
Even-toed ungulates
218 species

ORDER RODENTIA
Rodents
2,015 species

ORDER PROBOSCIDEA
Elephants
2 species

ORDER HYRACOIDEA HYRAXES
Hyraxes
7 species

Greater kudu
Tragelaphus strepsiceros

ORDER LAGOMORPHA
Hares, rabbits & pikas
82 species

ORDER SIRENIA
Dugong & manatees
5 species

ORDER TUBULIDENTATA
Aardvark
1 species

ORDER CETACEA
Cetaceans
81 species

ORDER MACROSCELIDEA
Elephant shrews
15 species

BIRDS

Birds may be the most mobile of all the animals. They descended from reptiles that developed the ability to fly, and although some bird species have lost their flying ability, they all retain feathers. The American ornithologist Alexander Wetmore devised a classification of the orders and families of birds in the 1930s, basing it on structural similarities in limbs, skeletons, and feathers. Since then, DNA and other molecular studies have shown that many structural traits traditionally used for classifying birds are unreliable because of convergent evolution. The bird classification used here takes account of many of these changes. The following is a comprehensive list of bird orders.

PHYLUM CHORDATA
Chordates
53,000+ species

CLASS AVES
Birds
9,743 species

ORDER TINAMIFORMES
Tinamous
74 species

ORDER STRUTHIONIFORMES
Ostrich
1 species

ORDER RHEIFORMES
Rheas
2 species

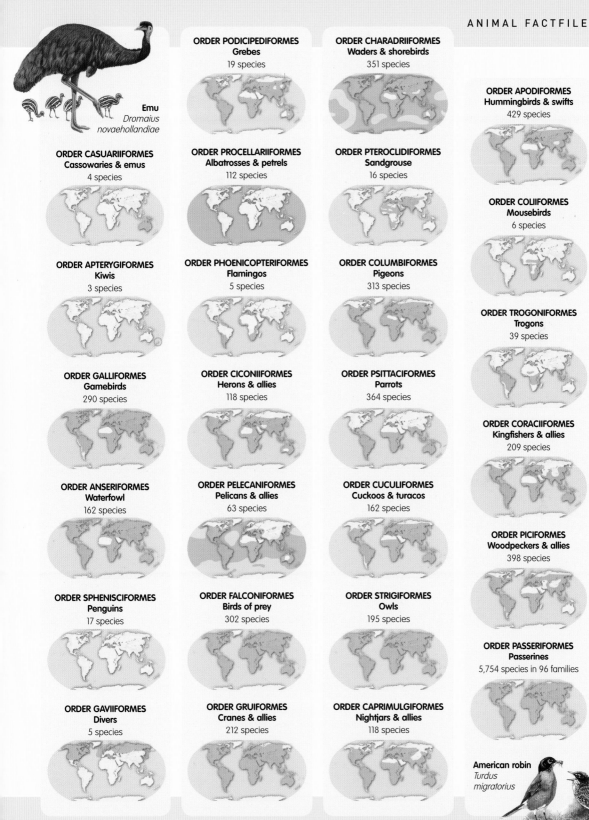

Emu
Dromaius novaehollandiae

ORDER PODICIPEDIFORMES
Grebes
19 species

ORDER CHARADRIIFORMES
Waders & shorebirds
351 species

ORDER APODIFORMES
Hummingbirds & swifts
429 species

ORDER CASUARIIFORMES
Cassowaries & emus
4 species

ORDER PROCELLARIIFORMES
Albatrosses & petrels
112 species

ORDER PTEROCLIDIFORMES
Sandgrouse
16 species

ORDER COLIIFORMES
Mousebirds
6 species

ORDER APTERYGIFORMES
Kiwis
3 species

ORDER PHOENICOPTERIFORMES
Flamingos
5 species

ORDER COLUMBIFORMES
Pigeons
313 species

ORDER TROGONIFORMES
Trogons
39 species

ORDER GALLIFORMES
Gamebirds
290 species

ORDER CICONIIFORMES
Herons & allies
118 species

ORDER PSITTACIFORMES
Parrots
364 species

ORDER CORACIIFORMES
Kingfishers & allies
209 species

ORDER ANSERIFORMES
Waterfowl
162 species

ORDER PELECANIFORMES
Pelicans & allies
63 species

ORDER CUCULIFORMES
Cuckoos & turacos
162 species

ORDER PICIFORMES
Woodpeckers & allies
398 species

ORDER SPHENISCIFORMES
Penguins
17 species

ORDER FALCONIFORMES
Birds of prey
302 species

ORDER STRIGIFORMES
Owls
195 species

ORDER PASSERIFORMES
Passerines
5,754 species in 96 families

ORDER GAVIIFORMES
Divers
5 species

ORDER GRUIFORMES
Cranes & allies
212 species

ORDER CAPRIMULGIFORMES
Nightjars & allies
118 species

American robin
Turdus migratorius

REPTILES

Reptiles were the first animals to conquer land. With their impermeable scaly skin, internal fertilization, and closed eggs, they were able to live independently of water. The class Reptilia—living reptiles—traditionally includes the four orders of turtles, crocodilians, tuatara, and squamates (which contains suborders of lizards, snakes, and worm lizards). With DNA evidence, many relationships in this class have become controversial. The traditional reptile groupings have been used here, but most are currently under revision. Crocodilians are in fact most closely related to birds, and turtles may belong in a separate class altogether. The suborders within Squamata are artificial, as limbless lizards, snakes, and worm lizards all evolved from lizards that lost their limbs. Only the status of the tuatara as an ancient order by itself is agreed upon. The following is a comprehensive listing of reptile orders.

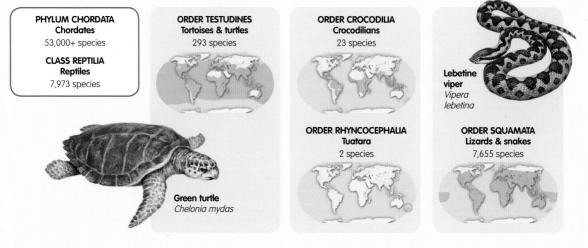

PHYLUM CHORDATA
Chordates
53,000+ species

CLASS REPTILIA
Reptiles
7,973 species

ORDER TESTUDINES
Tortoises & turtles
293 species

ORDER CROCODILIA
Crocodilians
23 species

Lebetine viper
Vipera lebetina

ORDER RHYNCOCEPHALIA
Tuatara
2 species

ORDER SQUAMATA
Lizards & snakes
7,655 species

Green turtle
Chelonia mydas

AMPHIBIANS

Amphibians have smooth skin without scales. They lay eggs in water and metamorphose from a water-breathing juvenile to an air-breathing adult. The living amphibians evolved from the same common ancestor and are grouped into three orders: the frogs and toads (Anura), the salamanders and newts (Caudata), and the caecilians (Gymnophiona).

Corroboree frog
Pseudophryne corroboree

PHYLUM CHORDATA
Chordates
53,000+ species

CLASS AMPHIBIA
Amphibians
5,558 species

ORDER CAUDATA
Salamanders & newts
472 species

ORDER GYMNOPHIONA
Caecilians
149 species

ORDER ANURA
Frogs & toads
4,937 species

Mudpuppy
Necturus maculosus

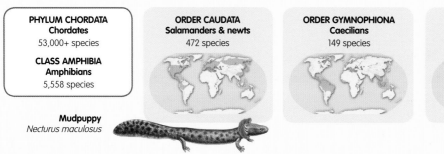

FISH

Fish are an immensely diverse array of animals, and most biologists regard the term "fish" as a convenient name, rather than a closely defined taxonomic entity, that describes aquatic vertebrates with gills and fins. There are various classification schemes for the fish but one of the most widely accepted recognizes five classes of living species grouped into two superclasses: the jawless fish of Agnatha, comprising hagfish and lampreys, and the jawed fish of Gnathostoma, comprising cartilaginous fish (sharks and rays), lobe-finned fish (lungfish and allies), and ray-finned fish (most bony fish).

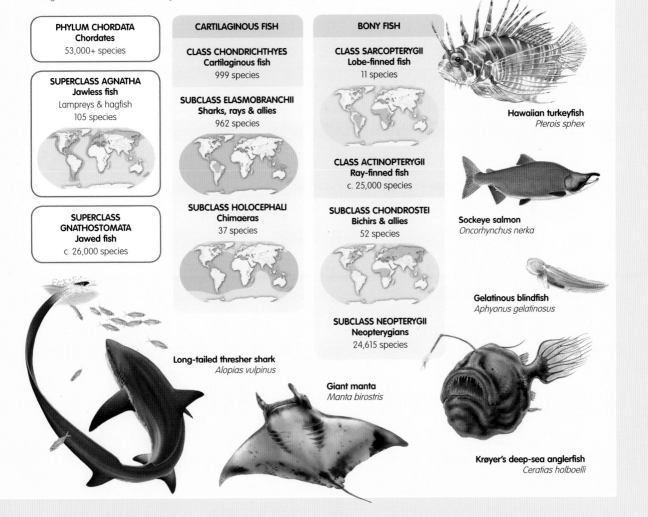

PHYLUM CHORDATA
Chordates
53,000+ species

SUPERCLASS AGNATHA
Jawless fish
Lampreys & hagfish
105 species

SUPERCLASS GNATHOSTOMATA
Jawed fish
c. 26,000 species

CARTILAGINOUS FISH

CLASS CHONDRICHTHYES
Cartilaginous fish
999 species

SUBCLASS ELASMOBRANCHII
Sharks, rays & allies
962 species

SUBCLASS HOLOCEPHALI
Chimaeras
37 species

BONY FISH

CLASS SARCOPTERYGII
Lobe-finned fish
11 species

CLASS ACTINOPTERYGII
Ray-finned fish
c. 25,000 species

SUBCLASS CHONDROSTEI
Bichirs & allies
52 species

SUBCLASS NEOPTERYGII
Neopterygians
24,615 species

Hawaiian turkeyfish
Pterois sphex

Sockeye salmon
Oncorhynchus nerka

Gelatinous blindfish
Aphyonus gelatinosus

Long-tailed thresher shark
Alopias vulpinus

Giant manta
Manta birostris

Krøyer's deep-sea anglerfish
Ceratias holboelli

INVERTEBRATES

Monarch butterfly
Danaus plexippus

More than 95 percent of animals are invertebrates. They are characterized by a structure that they all lack: a backbone or vertebral column. Invertebrates are divided into about 30 phyla, each displaying a distinct body form. Their evolutionary relationships can be inferred from their anatomy, their early development, and more recently from molecular analyses, particularly DNA. Features that define phyla include the organization of the body from a loose association of cells (Porifera), through tissue formation (Cnidaria), to the development of organs (Platyhelminthes). The acquisition of a fluid-filled body cavity was a defining point in evolution that allowed animals, such as Nematoda, Annelida, and many other phyla of worms, to move about by a hydraulic system driven by fluid pressure. While these phyla are soft-bodied, others are protected and supported by various types of skeletons, such as shells in Mollusca and a jointed exoskeleton in Arthropoda. The way in which embryos develop divide many advanced phyla into two lineages, one leading through the Echinodermata to the Chordata, the phylum to which vertebrates belong, the other containing the bulk of animal phyla. The continual identification of new invertebrate species indicates that the 1.3 million or so known invertebrates are nowhere near the full inventory.

CORAL REEF

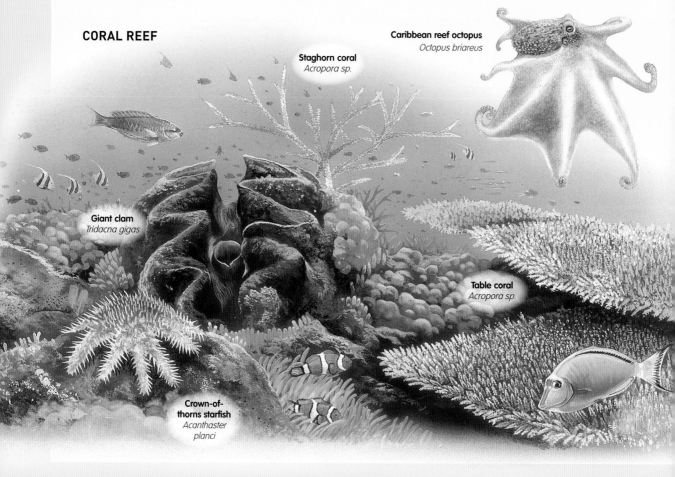

Caribbean reef octopus
Octopus briareus

Staghorn coral
Acropora sp.

Giant clam
Tridacna gigas

Table coral
Acropora sp.

Crown-of-thorns starfish
Acanthaster planci

PHYLUM CHORDATA
Chordates
53,000+ species

Azure
damselfly
*Coenagrion
puella*

SUBPHYLUM UROCHORDATA
Sea squirts
2,000 + species
**SUBPHYLUM
CEPHALOCHORDATA**
Lancelets
30 species

PHYLUM PORIFERA
Sponges
9,000 species

PHYLUM CNIDARIA
Cnidarians
Sea anemones, corals,
jellyfish & allies
9,000 species

PHYLUM PLATYHELMINTHES
Flatworms
13,000 species

PHYLUM NEMATODA
Roundworms
20,000+ species

PHYLUM MOLLUSCA
Mollusks
Bivalves, snails, squid & allies
75,000 species

PHYLUM ANNELIDA
Segmented worms
12,000 species

PHYLUM ARTHROPODA
Arthropods
1.1 million+ species

SUBPHYLUM CHELICERATA
Chelicerates
81,000+ species
CLASS ARACHNIDA
Arachnids
80,000 species
CLASS MEROSTOMATA
Horseshoe crabs
4 species

CLASS PYCNOGONIDA
Sea spiders
1,000 species
SUBPHYLUM MYRIAPODA
Myriapods
Centipedes & allies
13,500 species
SUBPHYLUM CRUSTACEA
Crustaceans
42,000 species
SUBPHYLUM HEXAPODA
Hexapods
1 million+ species
CLASS INSECTA
Insects
1 million+ species
CLASS COLLEMBOLA
Springtails
7,900 species
CLASS PROTURA
Proturans
500 species
CLASS DIPLURA
Diplurans
800 species

PHYLUM ECHINODERMATA
Echinoderms
Sea stars, sea urchins & allies
6,000 species

PHYLUM NEMERTEA
Ribbon worms
900 species

PHYLUM ENTROPROCTA
Goblet worms
650 species

PHYLUM TARDIGRADA
Water bears
600 species

Horseshoe
crab
*Limulus
polyphemus*

PHYLUM CTENOPHORA
Comb jellies
100 species

PHYLUM ROTIFERA
Rotifers
Wheel animals
1,800 species

PHYLUM HEMICHORDATA
Hemichordates
Acorn worms
90 species

PHYLUM CHAETOGNATHA
Arrow worms
90 species

Camberwell
beauty
*Nymphalis
antiopa*

PHYLUM GASTROTRICHA
Gastrotrichs
700 species

PHYLUM KINORHYNCHA
Spiny-crown worms
150 species

PHYLUM PHORONIDA
Horseshoe worms
20 species

PHYLUM ONYCHOPHORA
Velvet worms
100+ species

PHYLUM BRACHIOPODA
Brachiopods
Lamp shells
350 species

PHYLUM BRYOZOA
Bryozoans
Lace animals
5,000 species

PHYLUM SIPUNCULA
Peanut worms
150 species

Map butterfly
*Araschnia
levana*

PHYLUM ECHIURA
Spoon worms
160 species

PHYLUM PRIAPULIDA
Phallus worms
17 species

PHYLUM NEMATOMORPHA
Horsehair worms
240 species

PHYLUM ACANTHOCEPHALA
Spiny-headed worms
1,000 species

PHYLUM POGONOPHORA
Beard worms
80 species

PHYLUM GNATHOSTOMULIDA
Sand worms
80 species

PHYLUM CYCLIOPHORA
Cycliophorans
3 species

PHYLUM PLACOZOA
Placozoans
2 species

PHYLUM ORTHONECTIDA
Orthonectids
20 species

PHYLUM RHOMBOZOA
Rhombozoans
150 species

Lesser purple
emperor
Apaturailia

GLOSSARY

Adaptation
A change in an animal's behavior or body that allows it to survive and breed in new conditions.

Amphibian
A vertebrate animal that lays its eggs in water and that spends its early life in water and its adult life on land.

Aquatic
Living all or most of the time in water.

Arboreal
Living all or most of the time in trees.

Arthropod
An animal with jointed legs and a hard exoskeleton; includes insects, spiders, crustaceans, centipedes, and millipedes.

Bacteria
Microscopic lifeforms that are usually just a single cell.

Baleen
The comblike, fibrous plates found in some whales.

Benthic
Relating to or occurring at the bottom of a body of water or the depths of the ocean.

Biodiversity
The total number of species of plants and animals in a particular location.

Biodiversity hotspot
An area where the diversity of species is under threat.

Biogeography
The study of the way plants and animals are distributed.

Bioluminescence
Light produced by living organisms.

Biome
Major habitat type that is generally identified with its dominant vegetation. Biomes include grasslands, coniferous forests, deserts, and tundra.

Biosphere
The part of the world that can support life.

Bivalve
A mollusk, such as an oyster or a mussel, that has two shells that are joined at a hinge.

Braided watercourse
Part of a stream or river that has interlacing channels.

Breach
The action of a whale as it springs upward from the water.

Browser
A plant-eating mammal that uses its hands or lips to pick leaves from trees and bushes.

Caecilian
A tropical, wormlike, burrowing amphibian.

Canopy
Of a forest, the upper layer composed entirely of trees.

Captive breeding
The breeding by humans of endangered animal species under controlled conditions.

Carapace
A hard outer covering, such as a turtle's shell.

Carnivore
An animal that eats mainly meat.

Carrion
The rotting flesh and other remains of dead animals.

Cartilaginous fish
A fish with a skeleton made of cartilage, such as a shark, ray, or chimaera.

Casque
A bony or horny protrusion on the head of some birds.

Cays
Small, sandy islands that form on coral reefs.

Cerebral cortex
The thin, outer layer of gray matter in the hemispheres in the brains of humans and upper mammals.

Colonial species
Species of animals that breed together in large groups.

Continental drift
The theory that the present distribution of continents is the result of the fragmentation of one or more pre-existing super-continents that have drifted apart.

Copepod
One of a number of tiny freshwater and marine crustaceans.

Coral bleaching
The loss of color affecting coral reefs when the algae that live in them are killed or forced out.

Coverts
Small feathers that cover the base of a bird's wing and tail feathers.

Cranium
The skull of a vertebrate animal.

Crepuscular
Becoming active around dusk or in the early evening.

Crop
A thin-walled, saclike pocket of the gullet, used by birds to store food before digestion or to feed chicks by regurgitation.

Cryptic
Hard to detect as a result of color, shape, or behavioral patterns.

Deciduous forest
An area dominated by woody perennial plants that shed their leaves at a particular time, season, or growth stage.

Decomposer
An organism, such as a bacterium or a fungus, that consumes dead organisms and returns them to ecological cycles.

Deep-sea hydrothermal vent
A spring of superheated, mineral-rich water found on some ridges deep in the ocean.

Deforestation
The cutting down of forest trees for timber, or to clear land for farming or building.

Dermal
To do with the skin, especially the dermis, the second layer of an animal's skin.

Diatom
One of many kinds of tiny algae in oceans and freshwater.

Dimorphic
Having two distinct forms within a species. Sexual dimorphism is the situation in which the male and female of a species differ in size and/or appearance.

Display
Behavior used by an animal to communicate with its own species, or with other animals.

Diurnal
Active during the day. Most reptiles are diurnal because they rely on the Sun's heat to provide energy.

Diversity
The variety of plant and animal species in the natural world.

Dormant
To be in a sleeplike state, often because of environmental conditions; the body's activity slows for this period.

Echolocation
A system of navigation that relies on sound rather than sight or touch.

Ecology
The interrelationship between organisms and the environment in which they exist.

Ecosystem
A community of plants and animals and the environment to which they are adapted.

Electroreceptors
Specialized organs found in some fish and mammals that detect electrical activity from the bodies of other animals.

Embryo
An unborn animal in the earliest stages of development. An embryo may grow inside its mother's body, or in an egg outside her body.

Emergent
A forest tree that is taller than those around it.

Endemic
A species, or other taxon, found only in one habitat or region.

Ephemeral wetlands
Areas that become flooded in spring and early summer or after heavy rain.

Epiphyte
A plant that grows on a tree or other plant, but does not feed on or damage its host.

Estivate
To spend a period of time in a state of inactivity to avoid unfavorable conditions.

Evolution
Gradual change in plants and animals, over many generations, in response to their environment.

Exotic
A foreign or non-native species of animal or plant.

Extinction
The death of a species.

Filter feeder
An animal that obtains food by straining small prey from seawater.

Flyway
A route regularly taken by birds when they migrate.

Food chain
A system in which one organism forms food for another, which in turn is eaten by another.

Forage
To search for and eat food.

Fossil
A remnant or trace of a plant or animal from a past geological age, usually found in rock.

Fry
Young or small fish.

Functionally extinct
Reduced to a point where extinction is inevitable.

Fungi
Lifeforms, such as mushrooms, molds, mildews, and yeasts, that contain no chlorophyll and that live parasitically on living and dead organisms.

Gastroliths
Stones swallowed by such animals as crocodilians, that stay in the stomach to help crush food.

Genera
The plural of "genus," which is the second lowest group in the scientific classification of living things.

Genetic material
The substance that stores the genetic information of a lifeform. The genetic material of almost all lifeforms is deoxyribonucleic acid (DNA).

Gestation period
The period of time during which a female animal is pregnant.

Gills
Organs that collect oxygen from water and are used for breathing.

Gizzard
In birds, the equivalent of the stomach in mammals. Grit and stones inside the gizzard help to grind up food.

Global warming
The increase in the temperature of Earth and its lower atmosphere due to activities such as burning fossil fuels and deforestation.

Gullet
Found in birds, the gullet is the equivalent of the esophagus in mammals. This tube passes food from the bill to the gizzard.

Gyre
A circular motion in a body of water.

Habitat
The area in which an animal naturally lives. Many different kinds of animals live in the same environment, but each kind lives in a different habitat within that environment.

Harem
A group of female animals that mate and live with one male.

Herbivore
An animal that eats only plant material, such as leaves, bark, roots, and seeds.

Hibernate
To remain completely inactive during the cold winter months.

Hierarchy
The different levels in the scientific classification of living things. "Phylum," "class," "order," "family," and "genus" are ranks in the zoological hierarchy.

Incisors
The front teeth of an animal, used for cutting food.

Incubate
To keep eggs in an environment, outside the female's body, in which they can develop and hatch.

Insectivore
An animal that eats only or mainly insects or invertebrates. Some insectivores also eat small vertebrates.

Intertidal zone
The area of a seashore that is covered by water at high tide and exposed to the air at low tide.

Invasive species
Animal or plant species introduced by humans into areas where they do not occur naturally and which threaten native species.

Invertebrate
An animal with no backbone. Many invertebrates are soft-bodied, such as worms or octopuses, but most have an exoskeleton, or hard external skeleton.

Keratin
A protein found in horns, hair, scales, and feathers.

Keystone species
Animal or plant species that are so abundant in their environment that they make a strong impact on it.

Larva (pl. larvae)
A young animal that looks completely different from its parents. An insect larva, sometimes called a grub, maggot, or caterpillar, changes into an adult by either complete or incomplete metamorphosis.

Mammal
A warm-blooded vertebrate that suckles its young with milk and has a single bone in its lower jaw. Although most mammals have hair and give birth to live young, some, such as whales and dolphins, have little or no hair; others, the monotremes, lay eggs.

Mandible
Biting jaw of an insect.

Mangroves
Flowering shrubs and trees tolerant of saltwater, found on low-lying tropical coasts and estuaries.

Marsupial
A mammal that gives birth to young that are not fully developed. These young are usually protected in a pouch (where they feed on milk) before they can move around independently.

Mass extinction
The simultaneous extinction of an entire species or of a number of species, often as the result of a catastrophic event.

Microbial fermentation
The decomposition of foodstuffs by the action of microbes in an animal's large intestine.

Microhabitat
A very limited environment—such as a tree stump—in which an organism lives.

Microorganisms
Microscopic lifeforms, such as bacteria.

Migration
A usually seasonal journey from one habitat to another, to find food, or to mate and lay eggs or give birth.

Mollusk
An animal, such as a snail or squid, with no backbone and a soft body that is often partly or fully enclosed by a shell.

Molt
To shed an outer layer of the body, such as hair, skin, scales, feathers, or the exoskeleton.

Monoculture
The use of agricultural or forest land for the cultivation of a single crop or organism.

Monotreme
A primitive mammal with many features in common with reptiles. Monotremes lay eggs.

Montane forest
A forest that grows on the middle slopes of a mountain.

Mutualism
An alliance between two species that is beneficial to both.

Natal burrow
The underground place where a burrowing animal gives birth to its young.

Natural selection
The process by which organisms adapt to their environment by reproducing in ways most favorable to their survival.

Nekton
Animals that swim freely in the sea and are not dependent on the action of waves or currents.

Niche
The ecological role played by a species within an animal community.

Nocturnal
Active at night.

Omnivore
An animal that eats both plant and animal food.

Opportunistic
Feeding on whatever food is available, rather than on a specific diet.

Opposable
Describing a thumb that can reach and touch all the fingers on the same hand, or a toe that can touch all the other toes on the same foot.

Order
A major group used in taxonomic classification. An order forms part of a class, and is further divided into one or more families.

Organism
Any form of animal or plant life. An organism consists of separate parts that work together to support its existence.

Oviparous
Reproducing by laying eggs. Little or no development occurs within the mother's body; instead, the embryos develop inside the egg.

Ovipositor
A tubelike organ through which female insects lay their eggs.

Ovoviviparous
Reproducing by giving birth to live young that have developed from eggs within the mother's body. The eggs may hatch as they are laid or soon after.

Pair bond
A partnership maintained between a male and a female animal through several breeding attempts.

Pampas
Extensive grassy plains in South America, east of the Andes.

Parallel evolution
The situation in which related groups living in isolation develop similar structures to cope with similar evolutionary pressures.

Passerine
Any species of bird belonging to the order Passeriformes, often described as a songbird or a perching bird.

Pelagic
Swimming freely in the open ocean.

Permafrost
Ground that has remained frozen for at least two successive winters and the intervening summer.

Pheromone
A chemical released by an animal that affects the behavior of others of the same species.

Placental mammal
A mammal that nourishes its developing young inside its body with a blood-rich organ called a placenta.

Plankton
The plant (phytoplankton) or animal (zooplankton) organisms that float or drift in the open sea.

Pollen
A dustlike substance produced by male flowers, or by the male organs in a flower, and used in the plant's reproduction.

Prairie
An extensive plain or undulating land, covered mainly by grass.

Predator
An animal that lives mainly by killing and eating other animals.

Prehensile
Grasping or gripping.

Prey
Animals that are hunted, killed, and eaten by other animals.

Pride
A group of lions.

Primate
A member of the mammalian order Primates. This order includes humans, apes, and lemurs.

Proboscis
In insects, a long, tubular mouthpart used for feeding. In some mammals, a proboscis is an elongated nose, snout, or trunk.

Progeny
The offspring or descendants of animals or plants.

Prokaryote
An organism, usually single-celled, in which the cell has no nucleus or membrane-bound organelles.

Pupa (pl. pupae)
The stage during which an insect transforms from a larva to an adult.

Rain forest
A tropical forest that receives at least 100 inches (250 cm) of rain each year.

Range
The entire geographic area across which a species is regularly found.

Raptor
A diurnal bird of prey, such as a hawk or falcon.

Ratites
Flightless birds, such as emus and cassowaries, that lack a keel on their breastbone.

Receptors
Nerve endings through which animals receive sensory stimuli.

Red List of Threatened Species
A list of endangered animal and plant species compiled regularly by the International Union for the Conservation of Nature and Natural Resources (IUCN), which was established in 1963.

Remnant population
A small number of surviving plants or animals in an area where they were previously abundant.

Reptile
Animals that breathe air, are cold-blooded and have scaly bodies.

Rodent
A member of the order Rodentia. Rodents are relatively small gnawing mammals.

Ruminants
Hoofed animals, such as cattle, antelopes, goats, and other members of the family *Bovidae*—with a four-chambered stomach.

Salt marsh
An area of soft, wet land periodically covered by saltwater.

Scavenger
An animal that eats carrion, often the remains of animals killed by predators.

Seagrass
Long-leaved, grasslike plants that grow in temperate coastal waters.

Sea ice
Ocean water that has frozen and formed ice.

Siphonophore
One of various kinds of pelagic floating or free-swimming bell-like or disklike gelatinous invertebrates.

Speciation
The formation of a new species by means of evolution.

Species
A group of animals with similar features that are able to breed together and produce fertile young.

Spermatophore
A container or package of sperm that is passed from male to female during mating.

Sphagnum bogs
Damp, spongy areas where decomposing mossy sphagnum plants combine with other plant materials to form peat.

Stridulate
To make a sound by scraping objects together. Many insects communicate in this way.

Subtropical
The region that lies approximately between latitudes 35° and 40° in both hemispheres.

Symbiosis
An alliance between two species that is usually beneficial to both.

Taxonomy
The system of classifying living things into various groups and subgroups according to similarities in features and adaptations.

Temperate
Describes a region that has a warm summer and a cool winter. Most of the world's temperate regions are located between the tropics and the polar regions.

Terrestrial
Living all or most of the time on land.

Territory
An area inhabited by an animal and defended against intruders.

Thermal
A column of rising air.

Thermoregulation
The capacity of an organism to keep its temperature within a certain range.

Toothed whale
A whale that has slicing teeth and a throat that is able to swallow large pieces of prey.

Torpor
A sleeplike state in which bodily processes are greatly slowed.

Tundra
A cold, barren area where much of the soil is frozen and the vegetation consists mainly of mosses, lichens, and other small plants.

Understory
The forest trees that form a canopy below the main canopy.

Vascular plant
A plant that has an internal system of cells that transport water, sugars, and other substances throughout the plant body.

Venom
Poison injected by animals into a predator or prey through fangs, stingers, spines, or similar structures.

Vertebrate
An animal with a backbone. All vertebrates have an internal skeleton of cartilage or bone.

Viviparous
Reproducing by means of young that develop inside the mother's body and are born live.

Vocalization
Vocal sounds that animals use for communication.

Water column
The conceptual model of a body of water from the surface to the bottom.

Wetlands
Land that is covered for a part of the year with fresh or salt water. It has vegetation adapted to life in saturated soils.

INDEX

Page numbers in *italics* refer to illustrations and photographs.

ACKNOWLEDGMENTS

Key t=top; l=left; r=right; tl=top left; tcl=top center left; tc=top center; tcr=top center right; tr=top right; cl=center left; c=center; cr=center right; b=bottom; bl=bottom left; bcl=bottom center left; bc=bottom center; bcr=bottom center right; br=bottom right

Photo credits

GI = Getty Images; iS = iStock; SH = Shutterstock

2–3 SH/Andrzej Kubik; **6** bl, br iS; cl SH/Levent Konuk; cr, tr SH; **10–11** iS/1001slide; **13** t–b iS, SH/bikeriderlondon, SH/Artur Janichev, iS, iS, iS, SH/Galina Savina, iS; **15** iS; **18** t, c, br iS; br SH/Kathryn Wilmott; **21** iS/Angelika Stern; **22** SH/Houshmand Rabbani; **23** SH/Oleg Znamenskiy; **24** SH/sergyiway; **25** bl, br iS; **27** l–r iS; SH/Gerald A. DeBoer, SH/Zhukova Valentyna, SH/Edmund Lowe Photography, SH/ kanta_kulat; **28** NASA; **29** c, b iS; **30** t SH/Anatoliy Lukich; c iS; bl SH/Nagel Photography; br SH/Manu M Nair; **31** tl SH/Grobler du Preez; tcl SH/Arno Dietz; ct iS; cr SH/kongsak sumano; bl, br iS; **33** tl SH/Dr. Alan Lipkin; tr SH/Peter van Dam; cr, br iS; **35** tl SH/Brian Lasenby; cl SH/Tania Thomson; bl SH; tr SH/Arto Hakola; cr iS; br NOAA Okeanos Explorer Program; **36** iS/Frank Hildebrand; **37** t iS; r SH/jennyt; **39** SH/ Natalia D; **40** USFWS Mountain-Prairie; **41** SH/Erni; ct SH/dannybregman; cb SH/Bildagentur Zoonar GmbH; b iS; **43** tl, c iS; tr SH/Patrick Rolands; br SH/Nimit Virdi; **44–45** SH/Kuttelvaserova Stuchelova; **46** tl, tr, lct, bl iS; cr SH; bcl SH/Wolfgang Kruck; br SH/Delizar; **49** l SH/David Havel; r iS; **50** t SH/Ondrej Prosicky; bl SH/Oleksandr Katrusha; bc, br iS; **51** SH/Sue Robinson; **52** SH/Pesat Jaroslav; **53** tl iS; tr SH/Karel Bartik; bl SH/Rudmer Zwerver; **54** SH; **55** l SH; r SH/Martin Mecnarowski; **57** tl, c SH; cl, tr SH/Bildagentur Zoonar GmbH; br SH/MLorenz; bl Martin Pelanek; **58** SH; **59** tl iS; tr SH; bl SH/Mark Caunt; cl SH/scattoselvaggio; br SH/Michael Roeder; **60** t SH/burnel1; b iS; **62** l SH/Tony Brindley; c SH; **63** tl SH; c iS; r SH/Galyna Andrushko; **65** SH/Ana Gram; **66** SH/withGod; **67** tl SH/Tony Brindley; tr SH/Ian Duffield; cr SH; bl SH/StockPhotoAstur; br SH/Mark Kaunt; **69** tl, tr, c iS; br SH; **70** SH/Tony Millls; **71** tl SH/BMJ; tr SH/ David Dohnal; b SH/Lynsey Allan; **72** SH/Erni; **73** c SH; br SH/Rudmer Zwerver; **74–5** SH/Kevin Le; **76** tl, tr, ctl, ctr, cbl iS; cbr SH/Ricardo Reitmeyer; bl SH/Elle1; br SH/Robert Crow; **78** bl SH/Richard Seeley; br SH/Nick Fox; **79** t SH/Dennis W. Donohue; bl iS/SeventhDay Photography; **80** t SH/Howard Sandler; c iS; b SH/Nadezhda Bolotina; **82** SH/visceralimage; **83** tl SH/Michal Ninger; tr SH/FotoRequest; c SH/Stephan Morris; b SH/Kris Wiktor; **84** SH; **85** tl SH/AndreAnita; tr, cr SH; bl SH/Vasik Olga; **86** SH/Brian Lasenby; **87** t SH/John Navajo; c SH/Robert Bohrer; b SH/C Gara; **88** t SH/Daniel Korzeniewski; b SH/Vibe Images; **89** t–b iS; **91** t SH/Robert Cicchetti; c SH/Matt Jeppson; b iS/tunart; **92** t SH/Rusty Dodson; bl SH/outdoorsman; br SH/Ro Francis; **93** t SH/Peter Kirillov; b SH/Henk Benklage; **94** iS; **95** t SH/ wildpix645; c SH/Dennis W. Donohue; bl SH/Lorraine Logan; br SH/creative; **96** c iS; b SH/Tom Reichner; **97** SH/Martha Marks; **99** tl SH/ Martha Marks; cl iS/win247; cr iS; br SH/Don Mammoser; **100** l, r SH; **101** t, b iS; **102** iS; **103** tl SH/Debbie Steinhausser; cl, cr, b iS; **104** SH/ Martha Marks; **105** tl, tr iS; cl SH/Ronsmith; **106** bl–r iS; t SH/Jason Patrick Ross; **107** t SH/Matt Jeppsom; **109** tl SH; tr SH/Jo Crebbin; cl SH/Steve Bower; **110** t SH/Wei Lian; cl, cr iS; bc SH/Stubblefield Photography; **112** r SH/JHVEPhoto; l iS; **113** tl SH; tr, bl, br iS; **114–15** SH/ Dynamicfoto; **116** t, bcl, bcr, bl, br SH; tcl, tcr iS; **119** SH/Ostill; tr SH/Sergey Uryadnikov; cr SH/Naaman Abreu; bl SH/Leonardo Mercon; **120** r iS; **121** tr US Fish and Wildlife Service; cl SH/Tilo G; bl SH/Eduardo Rivero; bc SH/Kevin Wells Photography; **122** t SH/ milosk50; b SH/Kris Wiktor; **124** l SH/ Christian Musat; r SH/Christian Vinces; **125** t SH; c iS; bl SH/Ammit Jack; **126** t SH/Salparadis; r SH/ Berendje Photography; cl SH; bl SH/Sylvia Adams; **127** l SH/MarcusVDT; r SH/perlphoto; **128** iS; **129** t SH/Bildagentur Zoonar GmbH; cl SH/ Andrea Izzotti; cr SH/Martin Mecnarowski; br iS; **130** t SH/Iakov Filimonov; b iS; **131** SH/Iakov Filimonov; **132** iS; **134** SH/Kjersti Joergensen; **135** t iS; c SH; b SH/BlueOrange Studio; **136** SH/Andrew M. Allport; **137** l SH/Steffen Foerster; r SH/Andre Dib; **139** tl SH/JeremyRichards; tr SH/Ekaterina Pokrovsky; cl SH/Eduardo Rivero; bl SH/Andrea Izzotti; **140** l SH/Jose Marques Lopes; tr SH/Luis César Tejo; br SH/Luciano Queiroz; **141** t SH/Andrew M. Allport; b SH/NH; **142** tl SH/Sergey Uryadnikov; br SH/belizediversity; **143** tr SH/Andrea Izzotti; cr SH/ Vilainecrevette; **144–5** SH/Vibe Images; **146** tl SH/oflo69; tcl SH/Conny Sjostrom; tcr, br SH; tr, cr, cl, bcl, bcr, bl iS; **148** t SH/Gudkov Andrey; c SH/kongsak sumano; b SH/davemhuntphotography; **149** t SH/Guenter Albers; c SH/Vikas Garg; b SH/Scott E Read; **150** SH/Gabor Nedecky; **151** t SH/Huangdi; c SH/Allocricetulus; b SH/Anita Huszti; **152** SH/Maksimilian; **153** tr SH/Jarry; tl SH/Sergey Krasnoshchokov; bl SH/Eduard Kyslynskyy; br SH/Fufachew Ivan Andreevich; **154** t SH/Aleksandr Hunta; b SH/Geo-Zlat; **155** SH/TheNatureWeb.Net; **156** SH/Bahadir Yeniceri; **157** tr SH/SIHASAKPRACHUM; bl SH/IfSea; br SH/Perfect Lazybones; **159** tl SH/Mogens Trolle; c SH/Travel Stock; cr SH/neelsky; br SH/Eric Isselee; **160** SH/Brian Kinney; **161** tl SH/Hung Chung Chih; tc SH/Ondrej Prosicky; cr iS; br SH/Brad Thompson; **162** SH; **163** tl, tr SH; c SH/Surrphoto; bl–r iS; **164** GI/Stephen Dalton/Minden Pictures; bl AS Kono; **165** iS/thawats; **166** tr SH/Kate Capture; bl SH/Matej Hudovernik; **167** tl SH/Kjersti Joergensen; bl SH/Berendje Photography; cr SH/warmer; **168** SH/Panu Ruangjan; **169** tr, bc, br iS; bl SH/ AndreAnita; **170** SH/Heiko Kiera; **171** tl SH/taruntulaz; tr SH/Yatra; **172** SH/Gregg Yan; bl SH; **173** cl SH/Joe McDonald; cr SH; **174–5** SH/ Johan Swanepoel; **176** tl, cr, bcl, bcr, bl SH; tr, tcl, tcr, cl iS; br Mark Harris; **178** SH/JMx Images; bl iS; br SH/Jessica Bethke; **179** t SH/ Dennis W. Donohue; c iS; b SH/Artush; **180** cr SH/Nico Traut; bc SH/Wolf Avni; **181** l SH/Cat Downie; c SH/Sergei25; r iS; **183** t SH/Sergey Uryadnikov; cl iS; cr SH/MaZiKab; **185** tr SH/Matthias G. Ziegler; bl SH/Gudkov Andrey; **187** tl SH/NaturesMomentsuk; cr SH/Tomas Kotouc; bl SH/ArCaLu; br Kris Maes; **189** tl, bl, br iS; tc Bartolucci; tcr SH/Oleg Znamenskiy; cl SH/Darren Foard; **190** cr SH/Herbert Kratky; b SH/ Volodymyr Burdiak; **191** t SH/Robin Nieuwenkamp; tr SH/Volt Collection; cr SH/lumen-digital; **192** cl SH/Peter Schwarz; bl iS; **193** tr SH/ JonathanC Photography; tl SH/mario.bono; cl SH/PHOTOCREO Michal Bednarek; br SH/Graham Needham; bl SH/Dave Pusey; **194** SH/ Naturegraphica Stock; **195** tr SH/Angela N Perryman; cl SH/Ecoprint; bl SH/reptiles4all; **196** iS; **197** tc iS/Andy Schar; tr SH/MyImages, Micha; cr SH/Erwin Niemand; b iS; **198** t SH/Steve Brigman; b SH/Jiri Cvrk; **199** tc, tr iS; **201** tl, cr, bl iS; tr SH/Kelsey Green; cl SH/ anetapics; br SH/Ecoprint; **202** bl SH/Dudarev Mikhail; br SH/javarman; **203** tl, cr, bl, bc iS; br SH/Vladimir Wrangel; **204** Mark Harris; **205** tl Silke Baron; tr, c, br Mark Harris; cl SH/Krzysztof Odziomek; cr Christian Krause/www.flickr.com/alienx; **206–7** SH/kkaplin; **208** tl, tr, tcl, bcl, bl, br iS; tcr iS/John Carnemolla; bcr SH/Lidian Neeleman; **210** iS/John Carnemolla; **211** t SH/PomInOz; cr Vassil; bl SH/reptiles4all; br SH; **212** cl iS; cr GI/Gerry Ellis/Minden Pictures; **213** SH/John Carnemolla; **214** c SH/Paul Looyen; cr SH/Serguei Levykin; **215** tr SH/jurra8; cl Catzatsea; **216** iS; **217** tr SH/Birdiegal; c iS; **218** b Justin Welbergen; **219** tr SH/Rosa Jay; **220** SH/Gypsytwitcher; **221** SH/Dmitri Gomon; **222** SH/underworld; **223** tl SH/Steven J Taylor; cr iS; **224** cr SH/FiledIMAGE; bl SH/Eric Middelkoop; **225** tl SH/FiledIMAGE; tr Elias Neideck; **227** l SH/Katarina Christenson; c SH/Manon van Os; r SH/ChameleonsEye; **229** tl SH/Katarina Christenson; cr SH/Dennis Jacobsen; cl Fir0002; br iS/Mastamak; **231** tl SH/Kim Howell; cl SH/Eldad Yitzhak; bl SH/Lakeview Images; br Mnolf; **233** t SH/Ashley Whitworth; ct GraniteThighs; cl Mickaël T., cr SH/Gypsytwitcher; **234** SH/nexus 7; **235** SH/Edwin Butter; **236-7** iS/Keith Szafranski; **238** iS; **239** iS; **241** t SH/alla; tcr SH/Stanislav Duben; tcl, bcl SH; bcr SH/saraporn; b SH/Jaco Visser; **242** t SH/gdefilip; b iS; **243** tl, b SH/Incredible Arctic; tr SH/Marina Khlybova; **244** t SH/outdoorsman; bl SH/Catmando; br SH/Vladimir Melnik; **245** t SH/Dan Bach Kristensen; r SH/Pictureguy; cl SH/tryton2011; **246** l NASA; r SH; **247** t SH/Ondrej Prosicky; c SH; bl, br iS; **248** WikiCommons; **249** tl SH/Marcos Amend; tr SH/Mogens Trolle; cl SH/MZPHOTO.CZ; br SH/Mariusz Potocki; **251** tl SH/Gudkov Andrey; bl SH/ivandon; cl SH/Eduardo Rivero; cr SH/Juan Garcia; br SH; **252** l, r SH/Dmytro Pylypenko; **253** tl SH/Volt Collection; cl SH/MZPHOTO.CZ; b SH/Stephen Lew; **254** iS; **255** cl SH/Volt Collection; cr SH/Rich Lindie; bl, br iS; bc SH; **256-7** SH/timsimages; **259** t–b SH/Benedikt Juerges, SH/Tory Kallman, SH/Andrey Armyagov, SH/DonLand, SH/hecke61; **260** SH/Mick Rush; **261** bl SH/Darren J. Bradley; br SH/ACEgan; **262** SH/Francesco de Marco; **263** SH/Wollertz; **265** t SH/bluehand; c SH/simak; b SH/Andrea Izzotti; **267** t iS/Vebjarn Karlsen; b SH/maikbrand; **269** tr, tcr SH/Andrea Izzotti; cl NSF/USAP, photo by Steve Clabuesc; cr Marrabbio2; br SH/Dmytro Pylypenko.

Illustration credits

Andrew Beckett 22l; **Andre Boos** 159br; **Martin Camm** 185t, 263tr; **Robin Carter/The Art Agency** 40, 79, 81, 109, 133br, 260, 263bcr, bl, br, cl, cr, 265bl, cr; **Dan Cole/The Art Agency** 55, 64, 65, 78, 111, 183r, 186, 210, 235b, c, cl, cr, bl, 219c, b, 227tr, 214, 215; **Fiammetta Dogi/The Art Agency** 21, 103; **Mike Donnelly/The Art Agency** 24, 25, 125; **Sandra Doyle/The Art Agency** 63br, 97, 212r, 213, 223br, c, cl, tc, 225br; **Jane Durston/The Art Agency** 95tr, 101, 103br, bcr, 121br, 129, 143br, 165b, 173b, 181, 195t; **Brin Edwards/The Art Agency** 19t, c, 99tr, 107b, 108, 119b, 131, 143l, 233b; **Christer Eriksson** 15tl, 29t, 197r; **John Francis** 223tl, 224bl; **Jon Gittoes** 71c, 121cl; **Ray Grinaway** 36tl; **Tim Hayward** 51cl, 53bc, br, 62l, 188; **Steve Hobbs** 112l; **Bob Hynes** 169tc; **Ian Jackson/The Art Agency** 51tr, 73t, 87b, 91, 105, 195b; **Stuart Jackson-Carter/The Art Agency** 53c, 58, 93, 127tl, tr, 171b, 199, 216–17, 220–1, 226, 227b; **David Kirshner** 14tr, tr, 26, 29r, 34tl, br, l, cl, 49cr, 60, 68, 69, 85b, 98, 107t, 121tc, 127cl, 135, 137t, tr, b, 139, 159tr, 161bl, 169tl, 170, 172, 182, 184bl, c, 187, 191, 197tl, l, 203l, 215cr, r, tr, 218, 220l, 222, 225l, 230, 231, 232l, r, 235r, 243, 265t; **Frank Knight** 91, 120bl, 123tr, 171tr; **Iain McKellar** 48b, 66, 113tl, 221tr; **James McKinnon** 123b, 163b, 231tr; **Magic Group** 87tr, 203c; **Rob Mancini** 14cr; **Robert Morton** 253tr; **Peter Bull Art Studio** 71cl, 151, 154, 155, 157, 159l, 242, 247tr; **Sandra Pond/The Art Agency** 82, 104; **Mick Posen/The Art Agency** 263tr; **Tony Pyrzakowski** 29t, 63; **Edwina Riddell** 164, 165t; **Trevor Ruth** 262br; **Peter Schouten** 22b, 183bc, cr; **Peter Scott/The Art Agency** 125cl; **Mario Sparaciari** 34t; **Kevin Stead** 36b, 211tr; **Roger Swainston** 15tr; **Myke Taylor/The Art Agency** 61, 71cr, 73br, 123c, cr, tl; **Sharif Taraby** 14bl; **Claude Thivierge/Contact Jupiter** 38cr, 39b, c; **Guy Troughton** 19b, 40, 54cl, cr, 133tl, tc, tr, bl, 184bc, br, 185cr, 200, 205bl, 212bl, 213l, 216ct, 223tr, 228, 229tr; **Trevor Weekes** 36c.

Map and graph credits

Maps by Will Pringle and Laurie Whiddon/Map Illustrations, with additional graphic information by Andrew Davies/Creative Communication.

Infographics by Andrew Davies/Creative Communication.